THE 1,2,3- AND 1,2,4-TRIAZINES, TETRAZINES AND PENTAZINES

This is the tenth volume published in the series

THE CHEMISTRY OF HETEROCYCLIC COMPOUNDS

THE CHEMISTRY OF HETEROCYCLIC COMPOUNDS

A SERIES OF MONOGRAPHS

ARNOLD WEISSBERGER, *Consulting Editor*

THE 1,2,3- AND 1,2,4-TRIAZINES, TETRAZINES AND PENTAZINES

JOHN G. ERICKSON

Central Research Department, Minnesota Mining & Manufacturing Company,
St. Paul, Minnesota

PAUL F. WILEY

Lilly Research Laboratories, Eli Lilly and Company,
Indianapolis, Indiana

V. P. WYSTRACH

Stamford Research Laboratories, American Cyanamid Company,
Stamford, Connecticut

1956

INTERSCIENCE PUBLISHERS, INC., NEW YORK

INTERSCIENCE PUBLISHERS LTD., LONDON

Library of Congress Catalog Card Number 56–10821

INTERSCIENCE PUBLISHERS, INC., 250 Fifth Avenue, New York 1, N.Y.

For Great Britain and Northern Ireland:

Interscience Publishers Ltd., 88/90 Chancery Lane, London, W.C. 2

PRINTED IN THE NETHERLANDS

The Chemistry of Heterocyclic Compounds

The chemistry of heterocyclic compounds is one of the most complex branches of organic chemistry. It is equally interesting for its theoretical implications, for the diversity of its synthetic procedures, and for the physiological and industrial significance of heterocyclic compounds.

A field of such importance and intrinsic difficulty should be made as readily accessible as possible, and the lack of a modern detailed and comprehensive presentation of heterocyclic chemistry is therefore keenly felt. It is the intention of the present series to fill this gap by expert presentations of the various branches of heterocyclic chemistry. The subdivisions have been designed to cover the field in its entirety by monographs which reflect the importance and the interrelations of the various compounds, and accommodate the specific interests of the authors.

Research Laboratories   ARNOLD WEISSBERGER
Eastman Kodak Company
Rochester, New York

Preface

This volume presents, with the exception of 1,3,5-triazines, the chemistry of all six-membered nitrogen heterocycles containing more than two nitrogen atoms in the ring. It also covers all condensed systems containing the rings. We have tried to make a complete survey of the literature covered by *Chemical Abstracts* through 1950. A few later references of special interest are also included.

The structures assigned to many of these compounds rest only upon their modes of formation and upon elemental analyses. We have accepted these structures without comment, except where equally likely or more plausible structures may be written. In many cases, keto-enol tautomerism is possible. Here we have usually assumed enolization if it makes the heterocyclic ring fully aromatic, This principle cannot be followed completely because chemical evidence, in some cases, favors the keto tautomers. Future research in these fields should include use of physical methods, such as studies of absorption spectra, in determining the structures of some of these compounds.

The Ring Index and *Chemical Abstracts* systems of nomenclature and numbering are usually employed in this book. Ring systems are given the orientations used by the compilers of *The Ring Index* when developing methods of numbering positions. The numbers assigned by *The Ring Index* to fundamental ring systems are given throughout the volume (thus *R.I.* 159).

In arranging the material, we have considered first the types of ring system involved. The Table of Contents shows the method of classification. Then, in handling the compounds possessing any given ring system, we have used substantially the same treatment as Meyer and Jacobson. That is, compounds are taken up in the following order:

parent heterocycles, their homologs and aryl derivatives,
halogen derivatives,
amines,
hydroxy and oxo derivatives,
mercapto and thioxo derivatives,
ketones, and
carboxylic acids.

Further, under each of the categories listed above, the more nearly aromatic compounds are considered first, followed by successive degrees of hydrogenation. Methods of preparation are described first, followed by discussions of chemical and physical properties. In a few places, particularly in Chapter III, we found that the material was more efficiently organized by deviating somewhat from this order of treatment. To a considerable extent, the system of classification just described is also a classification by methods of ring closure. We have used tables as liberally as possible.

We wish to acknowledge the contribution of Dr. D. W. Kaiser, who was one of the original authors of this monograph, and who did part of the literature search but was unable to continue for reasons of health. We also wish to thank the following persons for their kindness in reading portions of the manuscript and for valuable criticisms and suggestions: Drs. Kendrick R. Eilar, Owen A. Moe, Scott Searles, George L. Sutherland, D. Stanley Tarbell, and Donald T. Warner. Thanks are also due Miss Margaret Carlson, formerly of the American Cyanamid Research Library, for much appreciated help in acquiring some of the literature used.

We want especially to thank our wives for their assistance in the preparation of the manuscript.

St. Paul, Minnesota	J. G. E.
Indianapolis, Indiana	P. F. W.
Stamford, Connecticut	V. P. W.

Contents

CHAPTER I

The 1,2,3-Triazines

Introduction

Three systems of triazine compounds are known. Two of these, the 1,2,3,- and the 1,2,4-triazines, are discussed in this volume. In this chapter we have taken up the 1,2,3-triazines, certainly the least studied but perhaps the most interesting of the triazines

The systematic designation, *1,2,3-triazine*, is still widely used for compound I. However, both *Chemical Abstracts* and *The Ring Index*[58] prefer the name, *v-triazine*, where *v-* denotes vicinal nitrogen atoms. *The Ring Index* uses both *v-* and 1,2,3-prefixes in the naming of con-

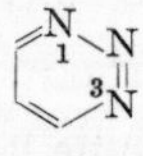

(I)

1,2,3-Triazine
v-Triazine
β-Triazine

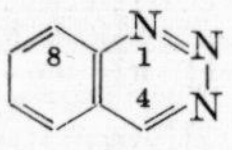

(II)

1,2,3-Benzotriazine
β-Phentriazine

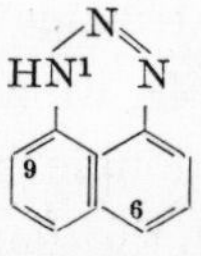

(III)

1-Naphtho[1,8]triazine
The azimide of 1,8-diaminonaphthalene

densed systems. A much less satisfactory name—fortunately seldom used—is *β-triazine*. The origin of the β-designation is not clear. It seems to have arisen, though, from a suggestion by Widman[79] that 1,2,3-benzotriazine (II) be called *β-phentriazine*, apparently because two of its nitrogen atoms are in positions beta to the benzene ring. Some condensed systems containing 1,2,3-triazine rings are named as *azimide* or *azoimide* derivatives of the diamino compounds from which they are obtained. Thus, III, which is formed by the action of nitrous acid upon 1,8-diaminonaphthalene, is sometimes called the *azimide* of that compound. The *azimide* nomenclature is not often used in the more recent literature. Besides the names mentioned here, others, usually trivial or misleading, have been applied to some of the 1,2,3-triazines; they will be mentioned as the corresponding compounds are discussed.

No naturally occurring compounds containing 1,2,3-triazine rings have been reported. This is not surprising, in view of the great reactivity of this type of ring. Although the first synthesis of a 1,2,3-triazine was reported in 1874, we still know little about this group of compounds. A few systematic studies of these compounds were made in the last decade or so of the nineteenth century and the first part of the present century. In more recent times, most of the contributions to our knowledge of 1,2,3-triazines have been by-products of work in other directions. Our knowledge falls short in three respects. First, many types of 1,2,3-triazines have never been prepared, possibly because no one has yet attempted their syntheses. Secondly, virtually the only preparative method so far discovered for 1,2,3-triazines involves the cyclization of diazonium derivatives of *o*-aminobenzylamines and certain amino amides. These diazonium derivatives can be prepared by the action of nitrous acid upon the diamines or the aminoamides, or they can be regarded as being formed as intermediates in other reactions. Obviously, some types of triazine derivatives can not be prepared in such a manner. As an example, we might mention triazines wherein there is no nitrogen-nitrogen double bond. The monocyclic triazines constitute another case in which the diazonium method would probably fail. Other synthetic methods must be developed before we can acquire a well-rounded knowledge of the 1,2,3-triazines. Finally, the reactions of 1,2,3-triazines have not been very thoroughly studied. Many types of reactions apparently have not yet been applied to this group of compounds. Some challenging problems will arise when the chemical properties of 1,2,3-triazines are explored more completely. We already know enough about these compounds to see that further work will turn up many more compounds that are unstable to the point of explosiveness.

As will be seen in the following pages, the 1,2,3-triazine ring is easily opened. Refined techniques will indeed be necessary to carry out reactions and keep the triazine ring intact. The reader will easily see that many opportunities still exist for significant contributions in this field.

1. UNCONDENSED 1,2,3-TRIAZINES

A. Unbridged 1,2,3-Triazine Rings

v-Triazine (I) ($R.I.$ 158) is an unknown compound. Apparently, no attempts have been made to prepare it. Reasonably plausible syntheses can be written for it but their success would depend upon, among other factors, the stability of the ring in such a compound. Since condensed systems containing the v-triazine ring are known to be relatively unstable, it is not clear whether v-triazine could survive under the conditions of reactions which might yield it. Maccoll[42] has computed values for the long wave length electronic absorption spectrum (first band at 4330 A.) and resonance energy (25 kcal./mole).

Only one unbridged, uncondensed 1,2,3-triazine has been reported. Ruhemann and Morrell[64] heated the ethyl ester of benzyldicarboxyglutaconic acid with phenylhydrazine (eq. 1). They isolated several products. One of these, obtained in very low yield, was a solid, m.p. 259°, soluble in alkali. On the basis of its nitrogen analysis (14.97% N), they

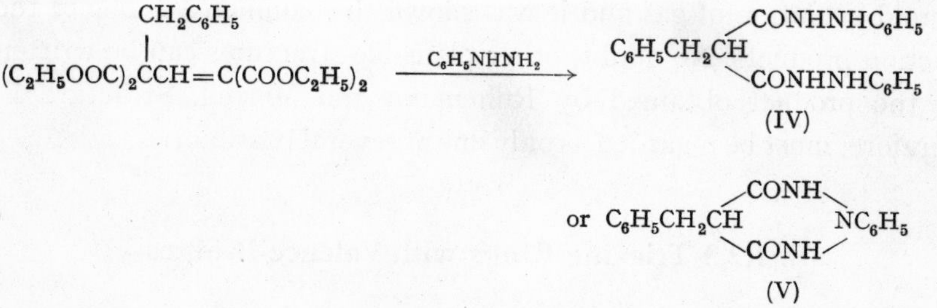

$$\underset{\substack{|\\ (C_2H_5OOC)_2CCH=C(COOC_2H_5)_2}}{\overset{CH_2C_6H_5}{}} \xrightarrow{C_6H_5NHNH_2} \underset{(IV)}{C_6H_5CH_2CH\overset{CONHNHC_6H_5}{\underset{CONHNHC_6H_5}{<}}}$$

$$\text{or } C_6H_5CH_2CH\overset{CONH}{\underset{CONH}{<}}NC_6H_5 \quad (1)$$

$$(V)$$

decided that this compound was either IV (14.96% N) or V (14.94% N). Structures of this sort are plausible at first glance because another of the reaction products is benzylmalonic ester, apparently formed by cleavage of the starting material. Compound IV was prepared in a different manner and was found to have a different melting point and to be insoluble in alkali. Accordingly, they assigned structure V to this product. The evidence for structure V is hardly conclusive and several arguments can be advanced against it. In the first place, it seems that, if IV is insoluble in alkali, V should also be insoluble. Certainly, the two structures both should contain the active hydrogen characteristic of malonic acid derivatives. Second, V would presumably be formed from IV by the loss of aniline. One would scarcely expect rupture of the nitrogen-nitrogen bond in a phenylhydrazinyl group of IV, followed by formation of a new nitrogen-nitrogen bond through cyclization to V, under the conditions of the experiment (heating on the steam bath). We wish to suggest that structure VI, despite a difference in nitrogen content (15.55% N), is at least as likely a possibility as V. Structure VI

$$C_6H_5CH_2CH \begin{array}{c} \diagup CONH_2 \\ \diagdown CONHNHC_6H_5 \end{array}$$

(VI)

also accounts for the nitrogen analysis observed and is free from objections based on the difficulties of cyclization under these mild experimental conditions. The objection based on the alkali insolubility of IV can still be raised against VI. Compound VI could be formed from IV by reduction with phenylhydrazine. An oxidation-reduction reaction of some sort is known to have occurred during the experiment; there was a rapid evolution of gas and it was shown that ammonia is one of the reaction products. No doubt, other plausible structures can be written for the product obtained by Ruhemann and Morrell. Structure V, therefore, must be regarded as only one of several possibilities.

B. 1,2,3-Triazine Rings with Valence Bridges

Almost certainly, no compounds of this class have been prepared. The class is discussed here only because it has been recognized by Beilstein[7] and *The Ring Index*. Stolz[69] heated the methochloride of 1-phenyl-3-chloro-5-methylpyrazole with aqueous ammonia (eq. 2) and isolated a product to which he assigned structure VII. However, the

editors of Beilstein have put forth structure VIII as an alternative
possibility. We believe that structure VIII is out of the question. In the
first place, such a ring system would probably be too strained to exist.

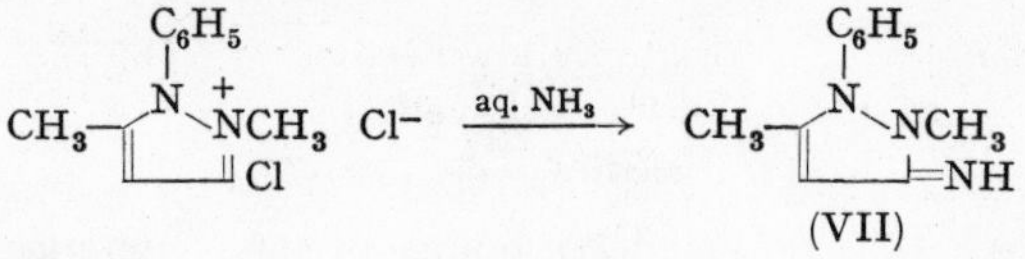

$$
\underset{(VII)}{CH_3 \text{-}} \overset{\overset{C_6H_5}{\underset{|}{N^+}}}{\underset{Cl}{\diagup}} NCH_3 \quad Cl^- \xrightarrow{\text{aq. NH}_3} \quad CH_3\text{-} \overset{\overset{C_6H_5}{\underset{|}{N}}}{\diagup} \underset{=NH}{NCH_3}
$$

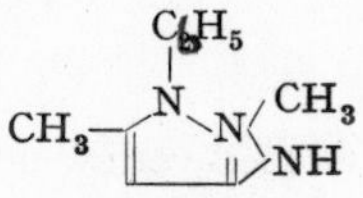

(2)

$$
\underset{(VIII)}{CH_3\text{-}} \overset{\overset{C_6H_5}{\underset{|}{N}}}{\diagup} \text{-}N \overset{CH_3}{\underset{NH}{\diagdown}}
$$

Second, structure VIII, as written, possesses a penta-covalent nitrogen
atom.

The ring system of VIII is named as a derivative of *1,2,6-triaza-
bicyclo[3.1.0]hexane* by *The Ring Index (R.I.* 446). Another name that
has been used is *pyrazole-2(2),3-imine.*

2. 1,2,3-TRIAZINE RINGS CONDENSED
WITH CARBOCYCLES

A. Condensed with Benzene

(1) 1,2,3-Benzotriazine

This ring system (II) is No. 933 in *The Ring Index.* 1,2,3-Benzo-
triazine has never been prepared. As with many other triazines, no one
seems to have attempted its synthesis. Many substituted 1,2,3-benzo-
triazines are known, however, and a number of these are listed in
Table I-1. This table contains those 1,2,3-benzotriazines that are fully
aromatic in structure. We have also included those 1,2,3-benzo-
triazines the structures of which are not certain and which may or may
not be fully aromatic. In the following discussion we have summarized
the evidence for each of these questionable structures.

The closest approach to the synthesis of 1,2,3-benzotriazine is

TABLE I-1. 1,2,3-Benzotriazines

Substituents	Color, crystal habit	M.p., °C.	Ref.
4-Acetoxy[a]	Bright yellow needles	165	29
4-Acetylmercapto	Silky golden-yellow needles	144	63
4-Benzoylmercapto	Quadratic orange prisms	163 (dec.)	63
4-Benzoyloxy[a]		132–133	29
6-Cyano-4,8-dihydroxy-5,7-dinitro[a]		Explodes very violently	51, 24
6-Cyano-4,8-dihydroxy-5,7-dinitro, potassium salt	Golden-yellow needles	Explodes very violently at about 210	51
?,?-Dibromo-3-oxide[a]		182 (dec.)	4
5,8-Dichloro-3-oxide[a]		168.5 (dec.)	4
6,8-Dimethyl-4-hydroxy[a]	Colorless needles	219–220 (dec.)	2, 5
6,8-Dimethyl-3-oxide[a]	Lemon yellow needles	181.5–182.5	6
4-Hydroxy[a]	Weakly rose-colored needles	211–212 (dec.)	80
	Gleaming leaves	213 (dec.)	77
	Small white needles	212–213 (dec.)	63
	Snow-white gleaming needles	213 (dec.)	2, 3
		207	35
7-Hydroxy-8-methoxy-3-oxide[a]			70
4-Hydroxy-6-methyl[a]		228	3, 5
4-Hydroxy-7-methyl[a]	White needles	226 (dec.)	72
4-Hydroxy-6-nitro[a]	Yellowish leaves	185 (dec.)	41
4-Hydroxylamino[a]		181	60
4-Hydroxylamino, hydrochloride[a]		151	60
4-Mercapto	Gleaming golden-yellow needles	187.5 (dec.)	63
4-Methyl-3-oxide[a]	Orange-red leaves	185–188 (dec.)	45
4-Methylmercapto	Yellow	101–102	63
3-Oxide[a]		158–159	45
		160–160.5	4
3-Oxide-4-phenyl[a]	Canary-yellow leaves	154 (dec.)	45

[a] Not the only possible structure. See the text.

found in the work of Bamberger and Weiler,[6] Bamberger and Demuth,[4] Sumuleanu,[70] and Meisenheimer, Senn, and Zimmermann.[45] By treating oximes of *o*-aminobenzaldehyde and substituted *o*-aminobenzaldehydes with nitrous acid, Bamberger and colleagues obtained products they regarded as oximes of 3-ketoindiazoles (eq. 3). Meisenheimer and co-workers obtained products of closely similar chemical and physical properties from the reactions of nitrous acid with the *syn* oximes of *o*-aminoacetophenone and *o*-aminobenzophenone (eq. 4). Meisenheimer believed that his products were the 3-oxides of 4-substituted 1,2,3-benzotriazines (X). Since structures similar to IX are hardly possible

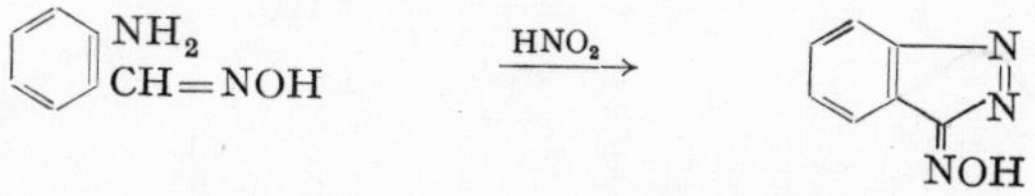

(3)

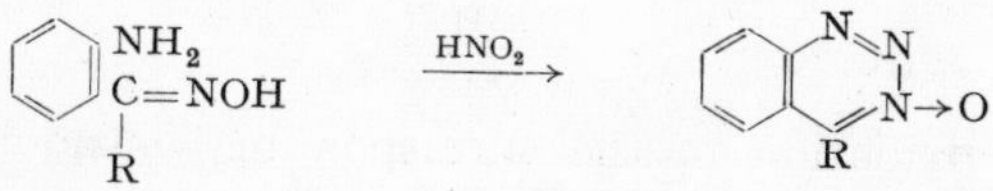

(IX)

(4)

(X)

for his products, he suggested that Bamberger's compounds also contained triazine rings. The yields of these cyclized products are excellent (90%) with the ketoximes, but poor (15%) with the aldoximes.

The presence of triazine rings in the products obtained by Bamberger and by Meisenheimer has not been rigorously proved. However, the following considerations strongly indicate that these compounds are indeed benzotriazines. In the first place, as is shown below, the products from *o*-aminobenzaldehyde oximes and from *o*-aminophenyl ketoximes are quite similar in chemical properties and this fact suggests similarity of structure. They agree closely also in such physical properties as solubility, crystallization and color. Second, for the compounds prepared from *o*-aminophenyl ketoximes, there appears to be only one plausible type of structure (X) that agrees with their analyses and chemical behavior. Finally, it is conceivable that the action of nitrous acid upon *o*-aminobenzaldehyde oxime may first give an indiazole (IX); further action of nitrous acid upon this may convert it to a benzotriazine (X). Bamberger has shown that oxidizing agents convert 3-aminoindiazole to 4-hydroxy-1,2,3-benzotriazine.

All of these oxime-nitrous acid products undergo ring opening to yield *o*-azidobenzaldehydes and *o*-azidophenyl ketones. Thus, Bamberger and Demuth obtained 2-azido-3,5-dimethylbenzaldehyde by treating one of their reaction products (written here with a triazine oxide structure) with alkali (eq. 5). The structure of this azido compound

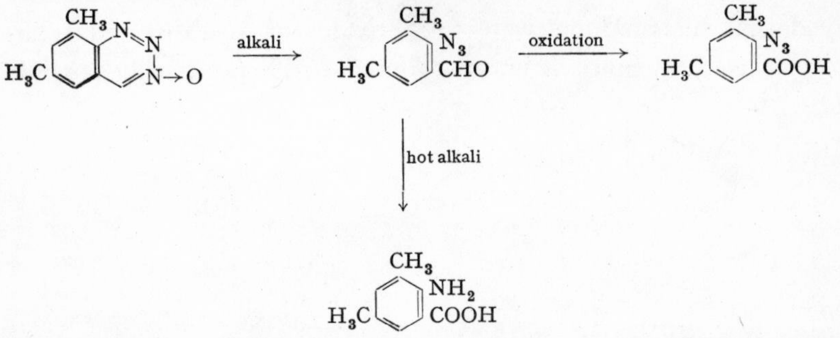

$$(5)$$

was proved by oxidation to the corresponding *o*-azidobenzoic acid (eq. 5); this was identical with a sample prepared in another manner. The azidobenzaldehyde was also converted to an anthranilic acid by treatment with alkali. Other reagents may be used to open these (presumed) triazine rings. With hydroxylamine, the starting *o*-aminoacetophenone oximes are formed.[45] Meisenheimer and colleagues found that either cold dilute sulfuric acid or a mixture of phosphorus trichloride and phosphorus pentachloride would convert their *o*-aminoacetophenone oxime-nitrous acid product to *o*-azidoacetophenone (eq. 6); this could be isolated as its dinitrophenylhydrazone or further cyclized to 3-methylanthranil. Dilute hydrochloric acid opens the

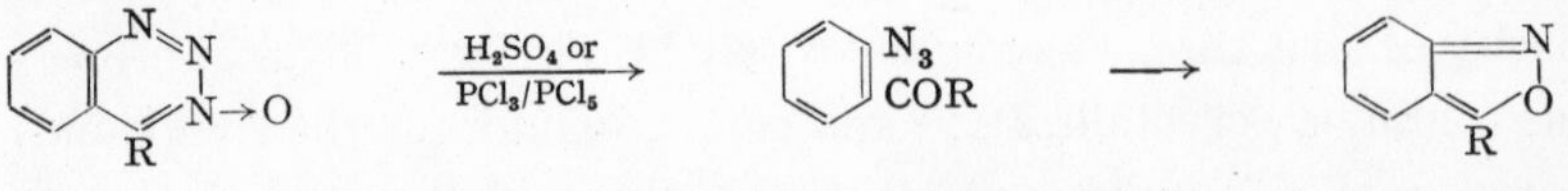

$$(6)$$

ring of the *o*-aminobenzophenone oxime-nitrous acid product but the intermediate *o*-azidobenzophenone could not be isolated since it cyclizes too rapidly, forming 3-phenylanthranil. The compound prepared from nitrous acid and the oxime of 2-amino-3,5-dimethylbenzaldehyde, when heated with dilute sulfuric acid, is converted to 2-amino-3,5-dimethylbenzaldehyde and 2-hydroxy-3,5-dimethyl-benz-aldehyde. If we exclude the possibility of rearrangements occurring during ring opening, it appears that the isolation of these azido compounds shows the presence of a chain of three connected nitrogen atoms in these nitrous acid-o-aminophenyl carboxime products. This, of course, is good evidence for the 1,2,3-benzotriazine 3-oxide structures. An attempt to prove the 1,2,3-triazine structure by reduction of the o-aminoacetophenone oxime-nitrous acid compound with zinc dust and acetic acid yielded only 3-methylindiazole (eq. 7). We shall shortly

$$\text{(image)} \quad \xrightarrow[\text{HOAc}]{\text{Zn}} \quad \text{(image)} \quad (7)$$

discuss the reactions of 1,2,3-benzotriazines with such compounds as β-naphthol, whereby azo dyestuffs are formed. For the present we shall say only that, while the product obtained from nitrous acid and the oxime of 2-amino-3,5-dimethylbenzaldehyde gives an intense red color with α-naphthylamine in hot acetic acid solution, it fails to show any color with alkaline α-naphthol and with β-naphthol in acetic acid.[6] The exact significance of these results is not clear.

It seems likely that the action of nitrous acid upon the oximes of o-aminobenzaldehydes and o-aminophenyl ketones does indeed yield compounds containing the 1,2,3-triazine 3-oxide grouping. If this is true, it probably represents the most promising method of obtaining 1,2,3-benzotriazine itself. A very gentle reduction of compound X (R = H), whose only effect would be to remove the oxide oxygen, would give the desired result. Unfortunately, the molecule presumably also contains the very easily cleaved –N=N–N– grouping; this makes the danger of ring opening perhaps too great. However, the problem seems worthy of some study.

3,4-Dihydro-1,2,3-benzotriazine has not been prepared, although a few of its 3-substitution products are known (Table I-2). All have been prepared by the action of nitrous acid on substituted o-amino-benzylamines. Busch[10] treated o-aminobenzylamine itself with nitrous acid (eq. 8) but failed to get the desired product. Instead he obtained

TABLE 1-2. 3,4-Dihydro-1,2,3-benzotriazines

Substituents	Color, crystal habit	M.p., °C.	Derivatives with m.p., °C.	Ref.
3-Acetyl	Flesh-colored tablets	138 (dec.)	H_2PtCl_6 deriv., 90 (dec.).	11
3-p-Anisyl	Yellow crystals	139 (dec.)	Hydrochloride, 91 (dec.). H_2PtCl_6 deriv., starts to dec. at 100. Picrate, 125 (dec.).	12
3-Benzenesulfonyl	Minute colorless leaflets	130 (violent dec.)		48, 49
3-Benzoyl	Needles	114–115 (dec.)	H_2PtCl_6 deriv., 85 (dec.).	11
3-Benzyl	Gleaming white needles	91 (dec.)	H_2PtCl_6 deriv., 101 (dec.). Picrate, 167 (dec.).	11
3-p-Bromophenyl	Bright yellow leaves	164	Hydrochloride, 105–106. H_2PtCl_6 deriv., 191 (dec.). $HAuCl_4$ deriv., 109 (dec.). Picrate, 106 (dec.).	12
3-o-Chloroazobenzyl				13
3-m-Chlorophenyl	Yellow needles	146–147 (dec.)		12
3-p-Chlorophenyl	Yellow leaves	134	Hydrochloride, 103 (dec.). H_2PtCl_6 deriv., 130 (dec.). $HAuCl_4$ deriv., 105 (dec.). Picrate, 109 (dec.).	12
3-Ethyl	Yellowish oil		Hydrochloride, needles, 141. Hydrobromide, 151. Sulfate, 150. H_2PtCl_6 deriv., 70 (dec.). Picrate, 150 (dec.).	10
3-o-(2-Hydroxy-1-naphthylazo)-benzyl		185 (dec.)		13
3-Methyl		72–73. Dec. over 120	Hydrochloride, 146–147 (dec.). H_2PtCl_6 deriv., 163 (dec.).[2] Picrate, 172 (dec.).	10
6-Methyl-3-p-tolyl	Yellowish needles	173 (dec.)	Picrate, 138 (dec.). H_2PtCl_6 deriv., 180 (dec.).	75
5-Nitro-3-phenyl	Brownish-yellow	153–154 (dec.)		62
3-p-Phenetyl	Golden leaves	144 (dec.)	Hydrochloride, 115 (dec.). H_2PtCl_6 deriv., 100 (dec.). Hydrobromide, 104. Picrate, 120 (dec.).	12
3-Phenyl	Gleaming, almost colorless leaves	128 (dec.)	H_2PtCl_6 deriv., 130 (dec.). Picrate, 111 (dec.).	9
3-p-Tolyl	Gleaming crystals	151 (dec.)	H_2PtCl_6 deriv., 190 (dec.). Picrate, 132 (dec.).	9

an amorphous powder, m.p. 140–150° (dec.), which, it was suggested, may have been 3,1,2,4-benzoxadiazine (XI). There was much nitrogen

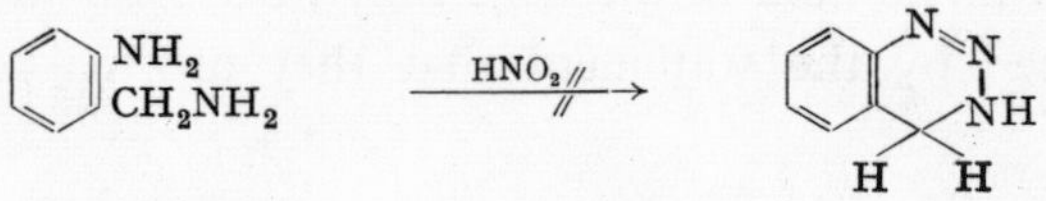

$$\text{(8)}$$

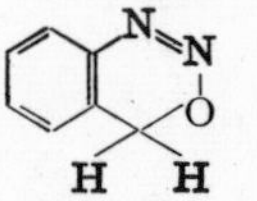

(XI)

evolved during this reaction. 3-Acyl derivatives of 3,4-dihydro-1,2,3-benzotriazine are known. Busch[11] prepared the 3-acetyl and 3-benzoyl derivatives by the reaction of nitrous acid with N-o-aminobenzyl-acetamide and the corresponding benzamide (eq. 9). Morgan and Micklethwait[48] obtained the 3-benzenesulfonyl derivative by a similar reaction.

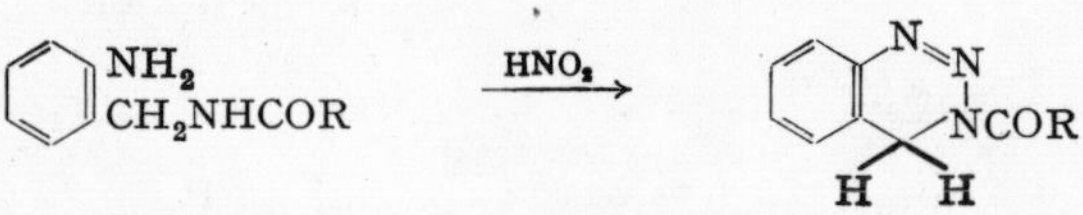

$$\text{(9)}$$

The 3-methyl and 3-ethyl derivatives of 3,4-dihydro-1,2,3-benzo-triazine were prepared by Busch,[10] using the same type of reaction—the action of nitrous acid upon substituted o-aminobenzylamines. Busch,[9–13] von Walther and Bamberg,[75] and Reich and Ghazarian[62] have prepared a number of 3-aryl analogs in the same way. All are listed in Table I-2. The use of amyl nitrite in these preparations may give better results than nitrous acid.[12] These cyclizations fail when the proposed 3-aryl group has a substituent in the ortho position. A less satisfactory method of obtaining these 3-aryl derivatives is by the reaction of nitrous acid with 1-(o-aminobenzyl)-1-arylhydrazines[9]

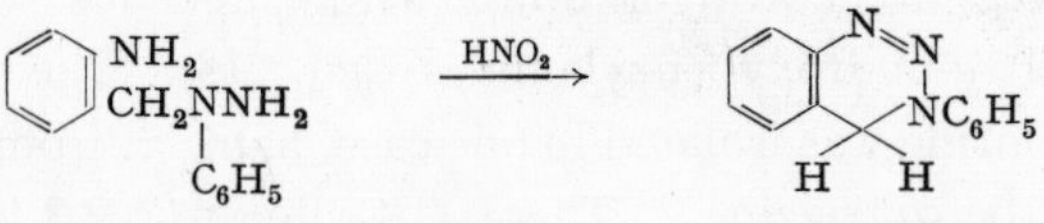

$$\text{(10)}$$

(eq. 10). Attempts to prepare 3-phenyl-3,4-dihydro-1,2,3-benzotriazine by the action of oxidizing agents upon 1-(o-aminobenzyl)-1-phenylhydrazine or by the action of reducing agents upon N-(o-nitrobenzyl)-N-nitrosoaniline failed.[9]

The known reactions of these 3,4-dihydro-1,2,3-benzotriazines can be summarized by the statement that they are masked diazonium

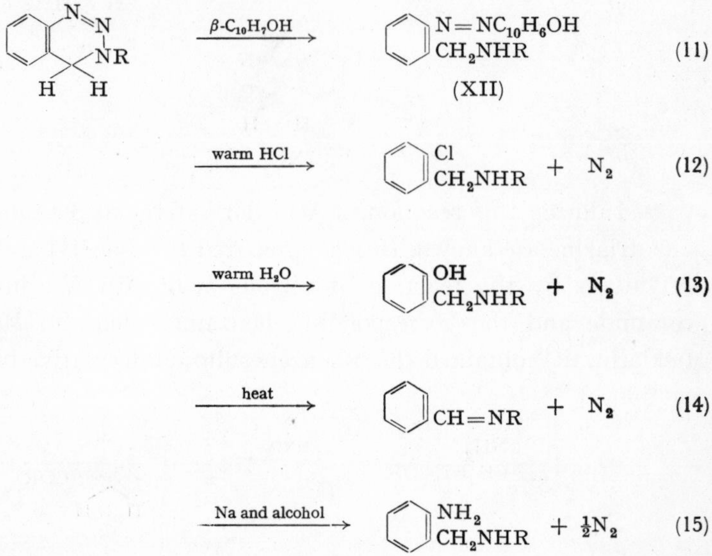

$$\text{(benzotriazine structure)} \xrightarrow{\beta\text{-}C_{10}H_7OH} \begin{array}{l} N = NC_{10}H_6OH \\ CH_2NHR \end{array} \quad (11)$$

$$\text{(XII)}$$

$$\xrightarrow{\text{warm HCl}} \begin{array}{l} Cl \\ CH_2NHR \end{array} + N_2 \quad (12)$$

$$\xrightarrow{\text{warm } H_2O} \begin{array}{l} OH \\ CH_2NHR \end{array} + N_2 \quad (13)$$

$$\xrightarrow{\text{heat}} CH = NR + N_2 \quad (14)$$

$$\xrightarrow{\text{Na and alcohol}} \begin{array}{l} NH_2 \\ CH_2NHR \end{array} + \tfrac{1}{2}N_2 \quad (15)$$

compounds. Thus, the ring opens between the 2 and 3 positions upon treatment with compounds that ordinarily react with diazonium compounds. For example, reaction with β-naphthol gives an azo dyestuff (XII, R = acyl, alkyl or aryl) (eq. 11).[10, 11, 48] Other reactions proceed just as with true diazonium compounds.[10, 11] The dihydrobenzotriazines are weakly basic and their hydrochlorides may be obtained with cold concentrated hydrochloric acid but dilution with water or addition of alkali liberates the free dihydrobenzotriazines. Warm concentrated hydrochloric acid gives N-substituted o-chlorobenzylamines (eq. 12); gentle warming in neutral or dilute acidic aqueous solution yields N-substituted o-hydroxybenzylamines (eq. 13). The intermediate diazonium chloride was isolated in one case, namely, from 3-acetyl-3,4-dihydro-1,2,3-benzotriazine.[11] These 3,4-dihydro-1,2,3-benzotriazines are unstable and decompose on melting, splitting out nitrogen and forming imines (eq. 14). Attempted reduction of the triazine ring with sodium and alcohol leads to ring opening and the formation of *o*-amino-benzylamines (eq. 15).[11]

The 3-substituted 3,4-dihydro-1,2,3-benzotriazines are colorless or yellow solids, easily soluble in most organic solvents except ligroin. Their melting points are listed in Table I–2. Other physical properties have not been determined, with the exception of the absorption spectrum of 3-phenyl-3,4-dihydro-1,2,3-benzotriazine, studied by Ramart-Lucas, Hoch, and Grumez.[61]

Hydroxylamino Derivatives. Pinnow and Sämann[60] treated *o*-amino-benzamide oxime with nitrous acid and thereby obtained a product (eq. 16) that might have either of the two structures XIIIa or XIIIb,

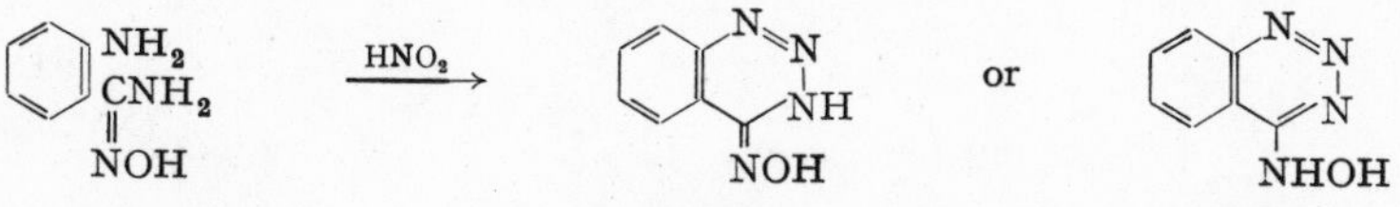

$$\text{(16)}$$

(XIIIa)   (XIIIb)

$$\text{(17)}$$

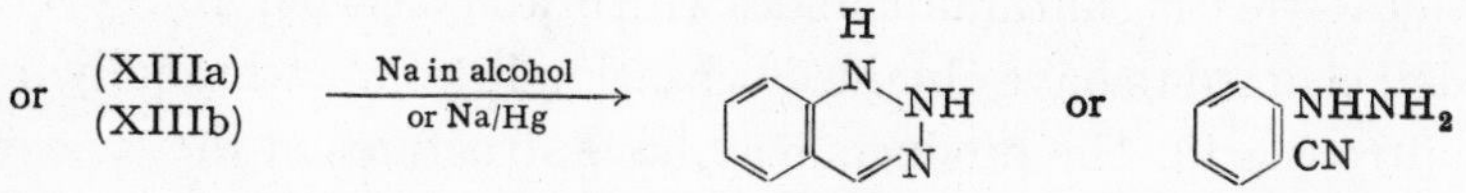

(XIV)   (XV)

although they wrote only XIIIa. It was observed to be both weakly basic and weakly acidic. Because of this amphoteric nature, the compound may well react, under some conditions, as 4-hydroxylamino-1,2,3-benzotriazine (XIIIb). When reduced with sodium in alcohol or with sodium amalgam (eq. 17), it yields a basic material, $C_7H_7N_3$, which, they said, was 1,2-dihydro-1,2,3-benzotriazine (XIV). Gabriel,[28] however, believed that this $C_7H_7N_3$ is actually *o*-cyanophenylhydrazine (XV). In support of his contention, he showed that the melting points of various derivatives of authentic *o*-cyanophenylhydrazine agree quite closely with those reported by Pinnow and Sämann for derivatives of their reduction product.

Hydroxy and Oxo Derivatives. It is not possible to decide between structures XIIIa and XIIIb in the absence of further experimental work. The problem of distinguishing between keto and enolic tautomeric forms will recur many times in this book. In general, we recognize that such a tautomerism is a mobile system and that either form may be favored under certain conditions. The use of infrared absorption spectra would be of great value in assigning preferred structures to these compounds. We find tautomerism again with the *benzazimides*.

Finger[25] was apparently the first to employ the name *benzazimide*. It suggests that the compound is an *azimide* of an *o*-aminobenzamide but it is really not descriptive and is little more than a trivial name. We have chosen to use it here because it is short and because more systematic names commit one to definite structures. As we shall see, we do not yet know which is the better structure to write for the

$$\underset{\text{(XVIa)}}{\text{[structure]}} \quad \xrightarrow{\text{HNO}_2} \quad \underset{\text{(XVIa)}}{\text{[structure]}} \quad \text{or} \quad \underset{\text{(XVIb)}}{\text{[structure]}} \quad (18)$$

benzazimides. The most commonly used method of preparing benzazimides is treating anthranilamides with nitrous acid (eq. 18).[25, 35, 41, 50, 77] Thode[71] claimed to have obtained benzazimide from anthranilhydrazide and nitrous acid. The products may have structures of the type either of XVIa or XVIb. As well as benzazimide itself (XVIa or XVIb), several substituted benzazimides, bearing groups on the benzene ring, have been prepared. All are listed in Table I-1, where the fully aromatic structure (XVIb) has been assumed for purposes of naming and tabulation.

A benzazimide of special interest is that derived from isopurpuric acid. Potassium isopurpurate can be prepared from picric acid and potassium cyanide. Nietzki and Petri[51] showed that, when it is alternately treated with dilute hydrochloric acid and redissolved in potassium hydroxide solution, it is converted to a compound, $C_8HKN_6O_6$, isolated as golden-yellow needles that could be dried at 100° but that exploded with extraordinary violence at about 210°. This product was still acidic and would form a dipotassium salt which was less explosive. Nietzki and Petri believed that isopurpuric acid is an aniline (XVII) and thought their explosive compound was a potassium diazotate (XVIII) (eq. 19). Since the nitrogen content of XVIII is greater than that of XVII, it was suggested that some isopurpurate decomposed to yield nitrous acid, which diazotized the remainder of the isopurpurate. The yield of explosive compound was only 25%. It could be raised

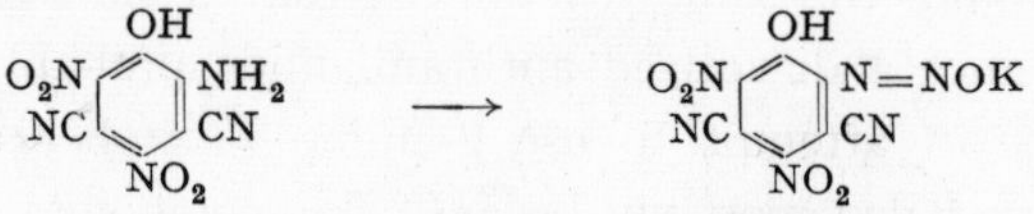

$$
\begin{array}{ccc}
\text{(XVII)} & \longrightarrow & \text{(XVIII)}
\end{array}
\tag{19}
$$

considerably by the addition of nitrous acid; this also gave a purer product. In later work, Fierz and Brütsch[24] also obtained this explosive compound. They treated potassium isopurpurate with nitrous acid or amyl nitrite to obtain an intermediate diazonium compound, wherein a cyano group has been hydrolyzed to an amide group. This diazonium compound possesses the ability to couple with α-naphthol. When dissolved in alkali, it rapidly loses the ability to couple and needles of the explosive compound precipitate out. Fierz and Brütsch also referred to this material as "extraordinarily explosive". Accepting the view of Borsche[8] that isopurpuric acid is a hydroxylamine (XIX), they

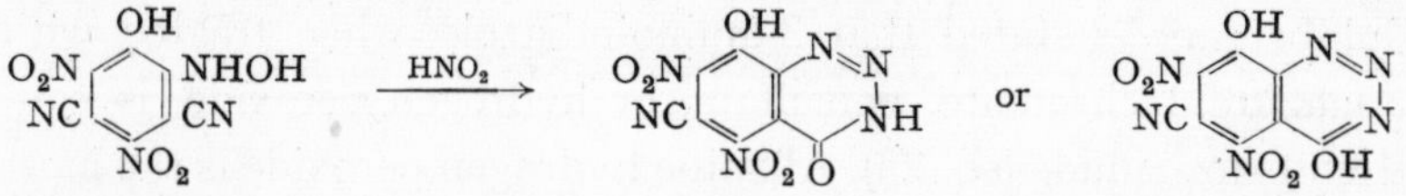

$$
\begin{array}{ccccc}
\text{(XIX)} & \xrightarrow{\text{HNO}_2} & \text{(XXa)} & \text{or} & \text{(XXb)}
\end{array}
\tag{20}
$$

wrote XXa as the structure of the acid from which this explosive salt was derived. The tautomeric structure, XXb, is not excluded. We believe that, were it not for the unstable nature of the compound, it too might be made to couple with α-naphthol. As will be shown shortly, most benzazimides couple with molten α-naphthol.

Some other syntheses of benzazimide remain to be mentioned. Jacini[35] prepared benzazimide by treating isatoic diamide with nitrous

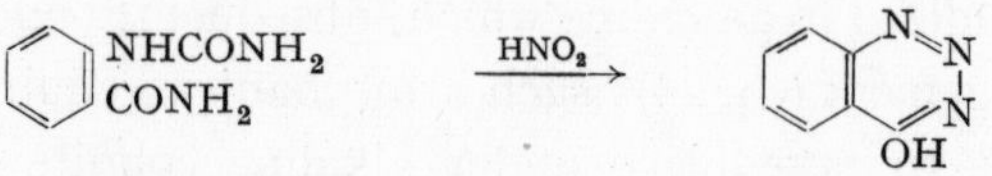

$$
\tag{21}
$$

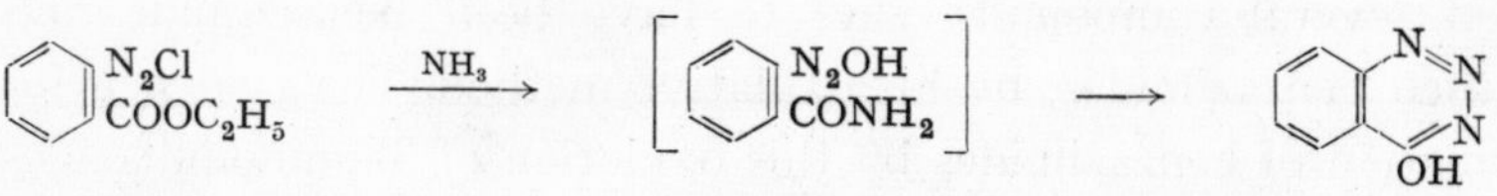

$$
\tag{22}
$$

acid (eq. 21). Zacharias[80] treated the diazonium chloride from ethyl anthranilate with ammonia to get benzazimide (eq. 22). This is, of course, essentially the same reaction as that discussed in preceding paragraphs, since a diazotized anthranilamide probably occurs as an intermediate. An attempt to use 2-amino-3-nitrobenzoic acid in a similar fashion failed, possibly because this compound is too weakly basic. Thode[71] treated anthranilhydrazide with nitrous acid to obtain benzazimide. An unexpected synthesis of benzazimides involves the action of oxidizing agents upon 3-aminoindiazoles. Thus, Bamberger and

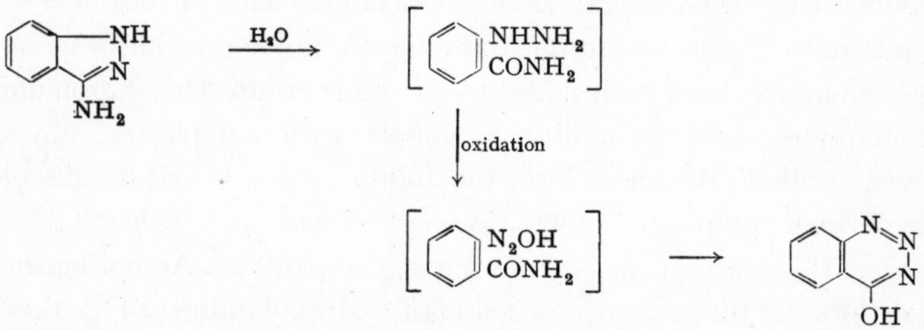

von Goldberger[2, 3, 5] stated that 3-aminoindiazole, when treated with permanganate, bichromate, persulfate, or hydrogen peroxide, is converted to benzazimide (eq. 23). Alkaline hydrogen peroxide is the most satisfactory reagent for this purpose.[2] (With potassium ferricyanide, the reaction takes a different course.) A mechanism involving hydrolytic opening of the indiazole ring to o-hydrazinobenzamide was proposed; this intermediate was supposed to be oxidized to a diazonium compound which then cyclized to benzazimide.[5] Support for this mechanism is found in the fact that during and after the oxidation the reaction mixture forms intense colors when treated with alkaline β-naphthol and resorcinol. It is possible, of course, that these colors were formed by coupling reactions involving benzazimides. Perhaps the aminoindiazole is oxidized to an oxime which subsequently undergoes a Beckmann rearrangement (eq. 24); such a mechanism requires a Beckmann rearrangement to take place under alkaline conditions. Bamberger prepared several compounds, said to have been benzazimide and substituted benzazimides, by his oxidative method. The evidence for the formation of benzazimides by this oxidation of 3-aminoindiazoles

is good, although not extensive. It consists of the isolation of benzazimide itself, with the theoretical carbon, hydrogen, and nitrogen
analyses and possessing the same melting point as benzazimide pre-

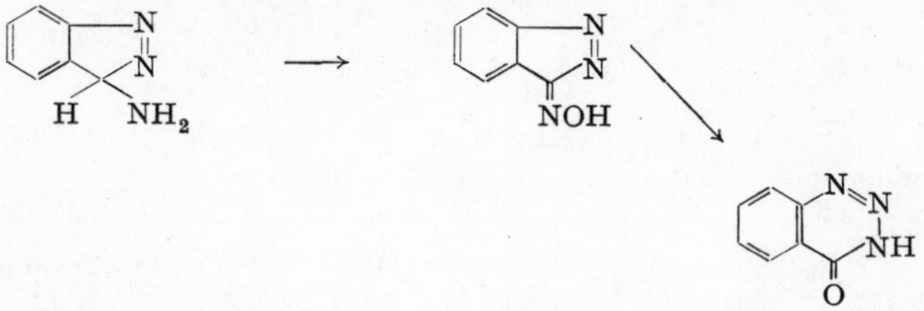

(24)

pared in other ways. Furthermore, the benzazimide prepared by
oxidation of 3-aminoindiazole gave colored coupling products with
α-naphthylamine and resorcinol. Accordingly, the compounds prepared by oxidation of 3-aminoindiazoles are listed in Table I-1 as
benzotriazine derivatives.

The reactions of benzazimide do not definitely indicate whether
structure XVIa or XVIb is correct; in fact, benzazimide no doubt
constitutes a mobile tautomeric system. It is acidic and easily soluble
in alkali or ammonia; addition of acid to such solution reprecipitates
it unchanged. It is also soluble in concentrated hydrochloric acid and
is reprecipitated by the addition of water. Although it is soluble in
ammonium hydroxide solution, it is not a sufficiently strong acid to
permit isolation of the ammonium salt. The explosive silver salt was
prepared by addition of silver nitrate to an ammoniacal solution of
benzazimide.[41] The sodium salt, which was also isolated, was prepared
by reaction of benzazimide with sodium ethoxide. The sodium and
silver salts, when treated with benzoyl chloride or acetyl chloride,
yield the same acyl derivatives,[29] which may have either structure XXI
or XXII (eq. 25). Structure XXI was used in listing these compounds
in Table I-1. Heller preferred XXII but XXI is also possible since it
was observed that these acyl derivatives are very easily cleaved by
dilute alkali. Such easy hydrolysis is characteristic of both enol esters
(XXI) and N-acyl amides (XXII). Kratz[41] prepared the acyl derivatives of 6-nitrobenzazimide in a similar manner. The sodium or
silver salts of benzazimide, when treated with ethyl chloroformate,
yield a carbethoxy derivative; here the product seems quite certainly

---

3-carbethoxy-4-oxo-3,4-dihydro-1,2,3-benzotriazine because hot dilute hydrochloric acid converts it to a dioxobenzoxazine, wherein the

carbonyl-nitrogen link has been retained (eq. 26).[29] Alkylation of these metal salts of benzazimide with methyl iodide yields N-methyl derivatives (eq. 27).[25, 29, 41, 77]

Heller[29] stated that reduction of benzazimide with zinc dust and ammonium hydroxide yields 3-oxo-dihydroindiazole (eq. 28).

Each of the benzazimide syntheses given above involves the formation of diazonium groupings and subsequent cyclization involving these groupings. The characteristic properties of the diazonium group do not disappear with this cyclization, for these 1,2,3-benzotriazines act as masked diazonium compounds. Thus, benzazimide, when heated with resorcinol, forms a colored azo compound (eq. 29).

Bamberger[5] regarded this as evidence that benzazimide possesses structure XVIa but this reasoning is not convincing. More examples

TABLE I-3. 4-Oxo-3,4-dihydro-1,2,3-benzotriazines

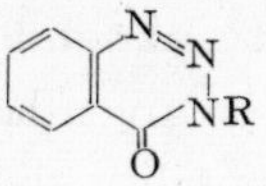

Substituents besides the 4-oxo group	Color, crystal habit	M.p., °C.	Ref.
3-Acetamido	Fine needles .	206 (dec.)	30
3-Amino	Large gray leaves	152–153 (dec.)	30
3-Anilino	Yellow needles	135 (dec.)	40
3-p-Arsonophenyl	Microcrystalline leaflets		37
3-Benzamido	Rhombohedra	205–206 (dec.)	30
3-Benzylideneamino	Needles	174–175	34
3-p-Bromophenyl	Colorless plates	196	20
3-Carbethoxy		65–66	29
3-Carbethoxyamino		147	31
3-Carbomethoxyamino	Needles	149	31
3-o-Carboxyphenyl	Colorless thick crystals	192 (vigorous dec.)	46
3-o-(N-o-Carboxyphenyl-carbamyl)phenyl	Colorless crystals	201 (vigorous dec.)	46
7-Chloro-3-(7-chloro-4-oxo-3,4-dihydro-1,2,3-benzotriazin-3-yl)	Colorless needles	245	33
3-o,p-Dibromophenyl	Compact prisms	136	20
3-o,p-Dimethylphenyl	White needles	132 (no dec.)	44
6,6'-Dinitro-3,3'-ethylenebis	Brown leaves	>290	41
3-Ethyl		70	25
3-Ethyl-6-nitro	Yellowish tablets	105	41
3,3'-Ethylenebis	Light yellow needles	216	26
3-Methyl	Needles or tablets	123	25, 29, 77
3-Methyl-6-nitro	Yellow leaves	199	41
6-Nitro-3-phenyl	Yellowish leaves	190	41
3-m-Nitrophenyl	White needles	238 (no dec.)	44
3-p-Nitrophenyl	Fine needles	252–254 (no dec.)	44
3-(4-Oxo-3,4-dihydro-1,2,3-benzotriazin-3-yl)	Prisms	249 (dec.)	32
3-Phenyl	Almost white needles	150–151	59
		151	44
3-(1-Phenylethylidene-amino)	Yellow prisms	168.5	30
3-m-Tolyl	White needles	150 (no dec.)	44
3-o-Tolyl		166 (no dec.)	44
3-p-Tolyl	White needles	143 (no dec.)	44

of this ability of condensed 1,2,3-triazines to act as diazonium compounds will be given later.

The possibility that benzazimide may be 4-oxo-3,4-dihydro-1,2,3-benzotriazine (XVIa) has been recognized. Some 3-alkyl- and 3-aryl-4-oxo-3,4-dihydro-1,2,3-benzotriazines have been prepared and are listed in Table I-3. The 3-alkyl derivatives (XXIII, R = alkyl) have

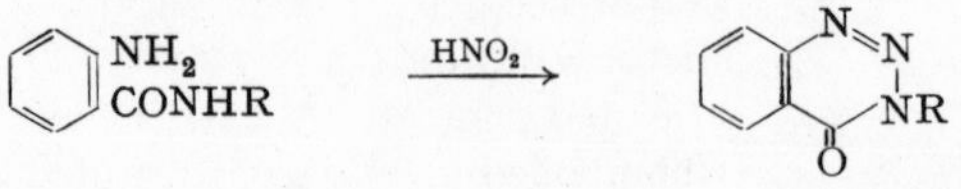

(30)

(XXIII)

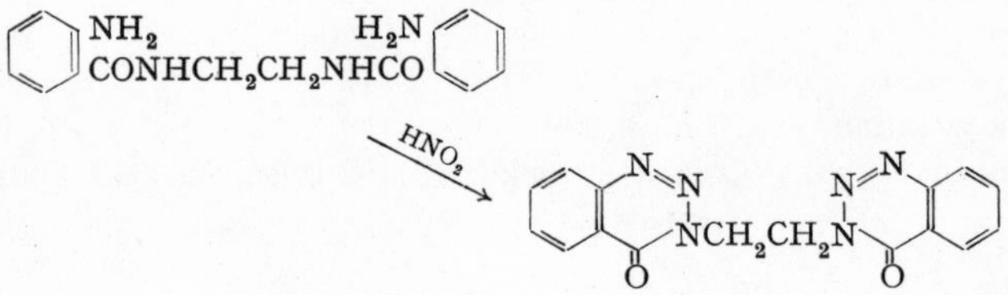

(31)

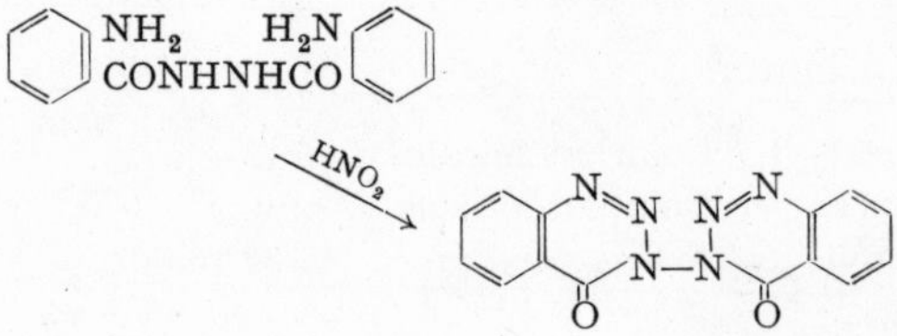

(32)

been made in two ways. The method involving alkylation of benzazimides has already been discussed. By a second method, these 3-alkyl derivatives are obtained in the reaction of substituted anthranilamides with nitrous acid (eq. 30).[41, 77] Similar reactions produce 1,2-bis(4-oxo-3,4-dihydro-1,2,3-benzotriazin-3-yl)ethane (eq. 31)[26,41] and 3,3'-bi-(4-oxo-3,4-dihydro-1,2,3-benzotriazinyl) (eq. 32).[32,33] 3-Aryl derivatives also can be prepared by the action of nitrous acid upon the proper anthranilamide.[37,46,59] Meyer[46] remarked that there are two possible

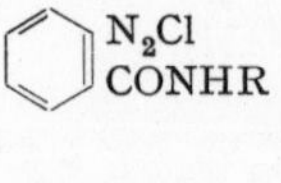

(XXIV)

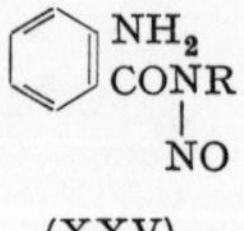

(XXV)

intermediates in this reaction. A diazonium chloride (XXIV) or a nitroso compound (XXV) may be the first compound formed and may then cyclize to the triazone. While the reaction is being carried out, the solution develops an intense yellow color, which disappears after a short time. Meyer felt that this indicated **XXV** is the intermediate form, since nitroso compounds are colored while diazonium salts are colorless.

Another method of preparing 3-aryl derivatives was employed by Mehner,[44] who found that certain diazoamino esters are cyclized in boiling alcohol (eq. 33). By this means, he obtained several 3-aryl deri-

$$\text{C}_6\text{H}_4\begin{array}{l}\text{N}=\text{NNHC}_6\text{H}_5\\ \text{COOCH}_3\end{array} \xrightarrow[\text{alcohol}]{\text{boiling}} \quad + \quad \text{CH}_3\text{OH} \qquad (33)$$

vatives. The presence of water in the alcohol is said to be essential for this cyclization. This method failed for 3-*o*-carboxyphenyl-4-oxo-3,4-dihydro-1,2,3-benzotriazine because its precursor decomposed gradually in boiling alcohol. Chattaway and Walker[20] also used this method; they treated methyl anthranilate with diazonium salts, then heated the resulting diazoamino esters with water to obtain cyclization.

The reactions of the 3-substituted-4-oxo-3,4-dihydro-1,2,3-benzotriazines are analogous to those described for other benzotriazines; they behave as masked diazonium compounds and undergo ring opening. Although none of these compounds has been studied very thoroughly, a number of reactions have been carried out involving some member or other of this group of compounds. We have generalized the results of these studies to cover the entire group. When heated with α-naphthylamine or β-naphthol in strongly acidic solution, they form colored dyestuffs, resulting from the formation of azo compounds (eq. 34).[46] Excess cold aqueous potassium hydroxide converts these 3-

$$\xrightarrow{\beta\text{-napthol}} \quad \text{C}_6\text{H}_4\begin{array}{l}\text{N}=\text{NC}_{10}\text{H}_6\text{OH}\\ \text{CONHR}\end{array} \qquad (34)$$

substituted 4-oxo-3,4-dihydro-1,2,3-benzotriazines to anthranilic acid.[25] Hot aqueous alkali or warm alcoholic alkali also opens their rings and

$$\xrightarrow[\text{alcoholic NaOH}]{\text{aqueous or}} \quad \text{C}_6\text{H}_4\begin{array}{l}\text{N}=\text{NNHR}\\ \text{COONa}\end{array} \qquad (35)$$

diazoamino compounds are formed when R is aryl (eq. 35).[44] If they are heated with alkali until no more nitrogen is evolved, one can isolate anthranilic acids.[41] 3,3'-Bi-(4-oxo-3,4-dihydro-1,2,3-benzotriazinyl), heated with alcoholic potassium hydroxide on the steam bath, yields nitrogen and an unknown compound which was not analyzed. Regarding the identity of this unknown product, we can say only that it is not salicylhydrazide or disalicylhydrazide.[32]

The effects of acids upon 3-substituted 4-oxo-3,4-dihydro-1,2,3-benzotriazines depend upon the nature and the concentration of the acids. With hot dilute sulfuric acid, upon short heating, one obtains anthranilic acids; upon longer heating, salicylic acids are formed (eq. 36).[41] On the other hand, dilute sulfuric acid in acetic acid converts

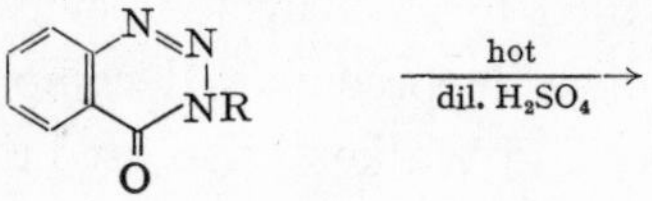

$$\text{hot dil. } H_2SO_4 \quad (36)$$

$$\text{dil. } H_2SO_4 \text{ in HOAc} \quad (37)$$

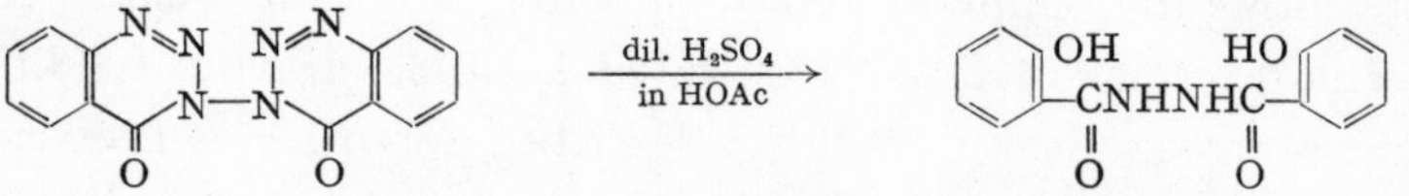

$$\text{hot dil. HCl} \quad (38)$$

$$\text{hot conc. HCl} \quad (39)$$

a bi-1,2,3-benzotriazinyl to disalicylhydrazide (eq. 37).[32] With boiling dilute hydrochloric acid, it appears possible first to isolate an intermediate diazonium compound; continued heating produces a salicylamide (eq. 38).[46] Concentrated hydrochloric acid replaces the potential diazonium group with chlorine and hydrolyzes the amide group, yielding o-chlorobenzoic acids (eq. 39).[25, 26, 41, 44]

Sodium amalgam does not appear to be effective in opening the ring in 3-substituted 4-oxo-3,4-dihydro-1,2,3-benzotriazines.[44] Stannous chloride with hydrochloric acid converts these compounds to anthranilic acids.[44] Boiling titanous chloride solution reduces these triazines to benzamides (eq. 40).[46]

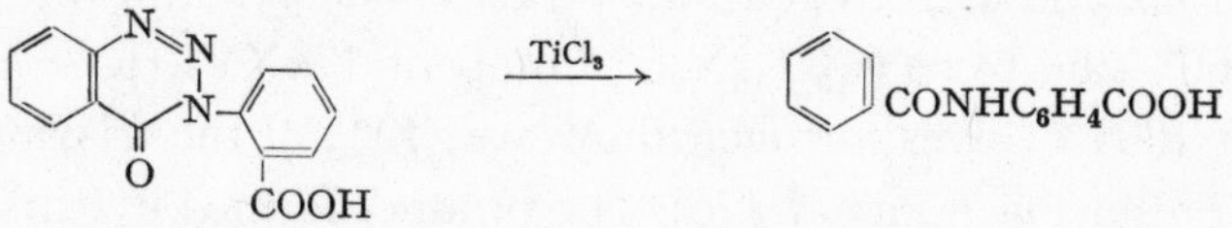

$$\xrightarrow{\text{TiCl}_3}$$ (40)

$$CONHC_6H_4COOH$$

An attempt to prepare 1-methyl-4-oxo-1,4-dihydro-1,2,3-benzo-triazine by the reaction of ethyl N-methyl-N-nitrosoanthranilate with ammonia failed (eq 41).[80] The products isolated were N-methyl-

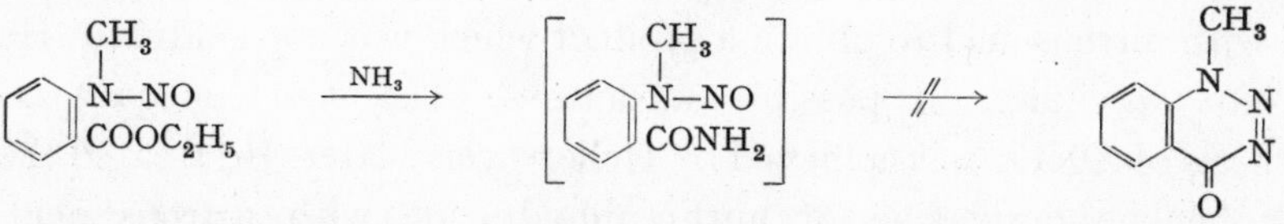

$$\xrightarrow{\text{NH}_3} \qquad \xrightarrow{\quad//\quad} \qquad (41)$$

anthranilic acid and its amide. Finger prepared o-(methylnitrosoamino)-benzamide; it would not cyclize to 1-methyl-4-oxo-1,4-dihydro-1,2,3-benzotriazine.

Shah[68] has reported the preparation of several arylimines of 4-oxo-3,4-dihydro-1,2,3-benzotriazines. Primary aromatic amines, heated with carbon tetrachloride in the presence of copper bronze, yield N,N'-diaryl-o-aminobenzamidines. These react with nitrous acid. The products, on the basis of their nitrogen analyses, were said to be 3-aryl-4-arylimino-3,4-dihydro-1,2,3-benzotriazines (eq. 42). The prod-

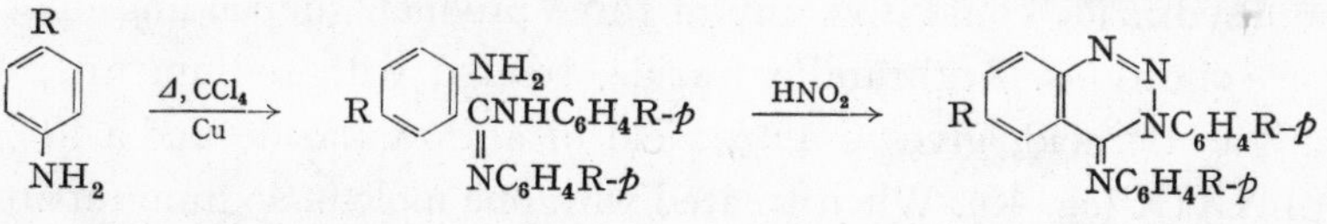

$$\xrightarrow[\text{Cu}]{\Delta,\,CCl_4} \qquad \xrightarrow{\text{HNO}_2} \qquad (42)$$

(XXVI)

$$\xrightarrow{\Delta} \qquad \text{or} \qquad (43)$$

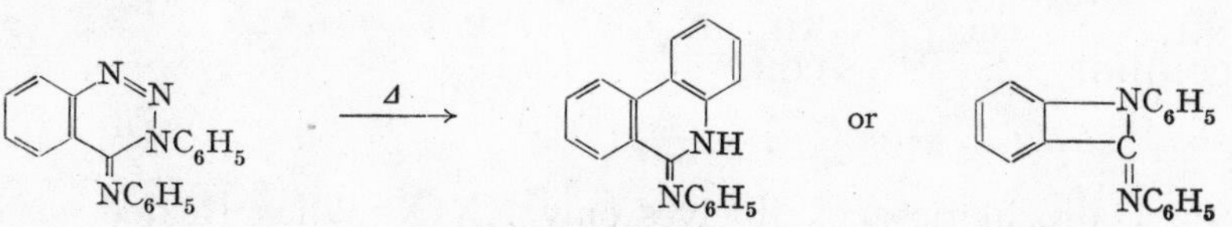

(XXVII)   (XXVIII)

uct from aniline (XXVI, R = H) is obtained in 90% yield as yellow rhombohedra, m.p. 139–140°; the product from p-toluidine (XXVI,

$R = CH_3$) as rectangular laminae, m.p. 145°; that from p-anisidine (XXVI, $R = CH_3O$) melts at 122–123°. Compound XXVI ($R = H$), with dilute hydrochloric acid at room temperature in the presence of copper bronze, loses nitrogen and yields an uncrystallizable powder, m.p. 55–60°, said to be $C_{19}H_{15}N_2Cl$. Compound XXVI ($R = H$), when heated at 180°, evolves nitrogen; however, 40% of the triazine can be recovered after ten hours at 175°. The product formed by this thermal decomposition, according to Shah, can have either structure XXVII or XXVIII (eq. 43). Structure XXVIII seems improbable.

3-Amino-4-oxo-3,4-dihydro-1,2,3-benzotriazine (XXIX) may have been first prepared by Finger,[26] who treated the hydrazide of anthranilic acid with nitrous acid to obtain a product which was not analyzed. He did not speculate on possible structures. The first unequivocal synthesis of XXIX was achieved by Heller[30] years later. He treated the acetophenone derivative of anthranilhydrazide with nitrous acid, obtaining thereby the 1-phenylethylidene derivative of XXIX. Hydrolysis of this with 18% hydrochloric acid at room temperature gave XXIX (eq. 44). Heller and Siller[34] then studied the reaction first

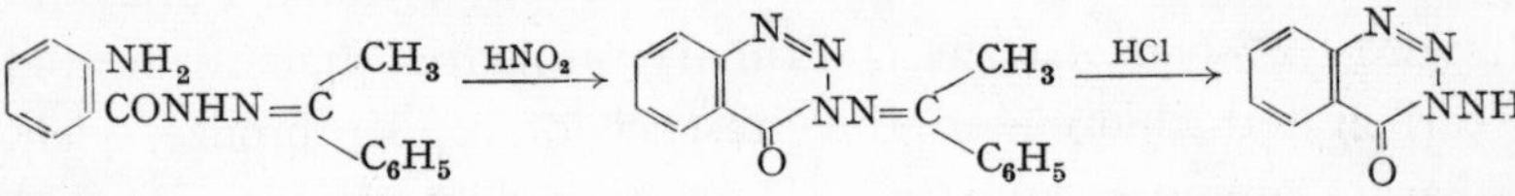

(44)

(XXIX)

employed by Finger. They found that the reaction of nitrous acid with anthranilhydrazide could give any of three products, depending upon reaction conditions. Anthranilhydrazide, treated with sodium nitrite in dilute acetic acid, gives a 45% yield of anthranilazide and a 40% yield of XXIX (eq. 45). When treated with one mole of sodium nitrite

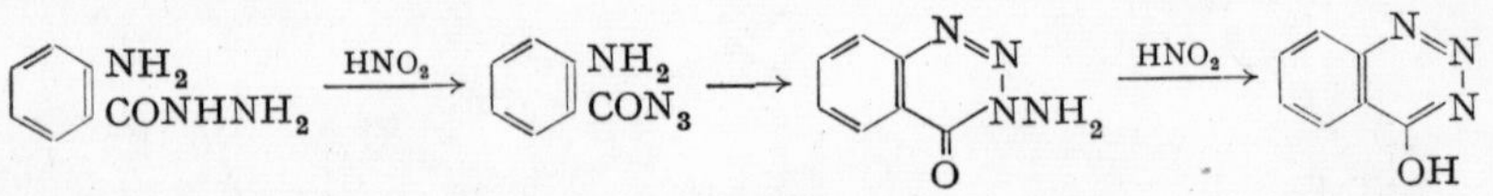

(45)

in 18% hydrochloric acid, it gives only XXIX. When treated with two moles of sodium nitrite in 18% hydrochloric acid, it yields benz-azimide, presumably formed from XXIX. Thode[71] also obtained benz-azimide from anthranilhydrazide and nitrous acid. 3-Amino-4-oxo-3,4-

dihydro-1,2,3-benzotriazine, treated with concentrated hydrochloric acid, is converted to anthranilhydrazide (eq. 46). Dissolved in sulfuric acid, then treated with sodium nitrite and β-naphthol, it forms a coupling product, wherein the triazine ring is presumably intact (eq.

$$\text{(XXIX)} \xrightarrow[\text{HCl}]{\text{conc.}} \begin{array}{c}\text{NH}_2\\\text{CONHNH}_2\end{array} \tag{46}$$

$$\xrightarrow[\beta\text{-naphthol}]{\text{HNO}_2} \quad \text{NN}=\text{NC}_{10}\text{H}_6\text{OH} \tag{47}$$

$$\xrightarrow{\text{C}_6\text{H}_5\text{CHO}} \quad \text{NN}=\text{CHC}_6\text{H}_5 \xrightarrow{\text{NaOH}} \begin{array}{c}\text{NHN}=\text{CHC}_6\text{H}_5\\\text{COONa}\end{array} \tag{48}$$

$$\xrightarrow[\text{CH}_3\text{COOH}]{\text{Zn}} \quad \begin{array}{c}\text{N}\\\text{OH}\end{array} \tag{49}$$

47). 3-Amino-4-oxo-3,4-dihydro-1,2,3-benzotriazine reacts with benzaldehyde, giving a benzylidene derivative; this is said to react with sodium hydroxide, forming the sodium salt of the benzylidene derivative of o-hydrazinobenzoic acid (eq. 48). Zinc dust and acetic acid convert XXIX to benzazimide (eq. 49). The 1-phenylethylidene derivative of XXIX, with hot hydrochloric acid, gives indiazolone (eq. 50).

$$\begin{array}{c}\text{N}=\text{N}\\\text{NN}=\text{C}\begin{array}{c}\text{CH}_3\\\text{C}_6\text{H}_5\end{array}\\\text{O}\end{array} \xrightarrow{\text{hot HCl}} \begin{array}{c}\text{NH}\\\text{NH}\\\text{O}\end{array} \tag{50}$$

Several acyl derivatives of 3-amino-4-oxo-3,4-dihydro-1,2,3-benzotriazine have been prepared by Heller,[30, 31] who employed the usual method of synthesis, treating acyl derivatives of anthranilhydrazide with nitrous acid. In this way he obtained the acetyl and benzoyl

$$\begin{array}{c}\text{NH}_2\\\text{CONHNHCOR}\end{array} \xrightarrow{\text{HNO}_2} \begin{array}{c}\text{N}=\text{N}\\\text{NNHCOR}\\\text{O}\end{array} \xrightarrow[\Delta]{\text{alkali}} \begin{array}{c}\text{N}_3\\\text{COOH}\end{array} \tag{51}$$

(XXX)

derivatives of 3-amino-4-oxo-3,4-dihydro-1,2,3-benzotriazine (**XXX**, R = CH₃ and C₆H₅) and methyl and ethyl *N*-(4-oxo-3,4-dihydro-1,2,3-benzotriazin-3-yl)-carbamates (**XXX**, R = OCH₃ and OC₂H₅) (eq. 51). All of these acylated compounds, when warmed with alkali, yield *o*-azidobenzoic acid.

There is no agreement as to whether 3-anilino-4-oxo-3,4-dihydro-1,2,3-benzotriazine (**XXXI**) has been prepared. Thode[71] stated that the action of nitrous acid upon 2-phenyl-1-anthranilhydrazide gives a nitroso compound (**XXXII**), m.p. 78° (dec.), rather than **XXXI**. He supported this statement with carbon, hydrogen and nitrogen analyses. König and Reissert,[40] on the other hand, claimed to have obtained

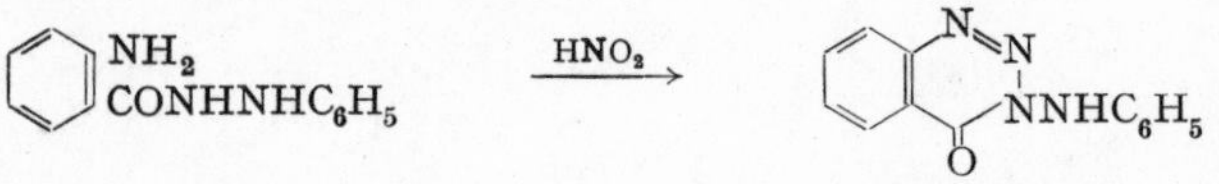

$$(52)$$

(**XXXI**)

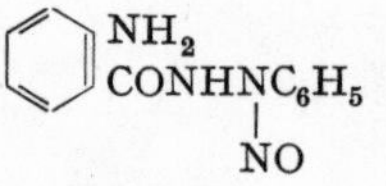

(**XXXII**) 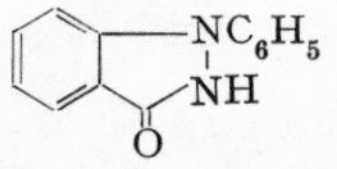   (**XXXIII**)

XXXI by this reaction (eq. 52), although most of the product consisted of 1-phenylindiazolone (**XXXI**). They described their product (**XXXI**) as yellow needles, m.p. 135° (dec.), and obtained carbon, hydrogen, and nitrogen analyses confirming their structure. The König-Reissert product was said to be insoluble in alkali and therefore easily separated from the indiazolone. Perhaps the reaction does give all three products, **XXXI**, **XXXII** and **XXXIII**.

Mercapto and Thioxo Derivatives. Reissert and Grube,[63] by treating *o*-aminothiobenzamide with nitrous acid, obtained 4-mercapto-1,2,3-benzotriazine (eq. 53). They preferred structure **XXXIV**, rather than **XXXV**, and their choice seems to be the better one. In the next chapter

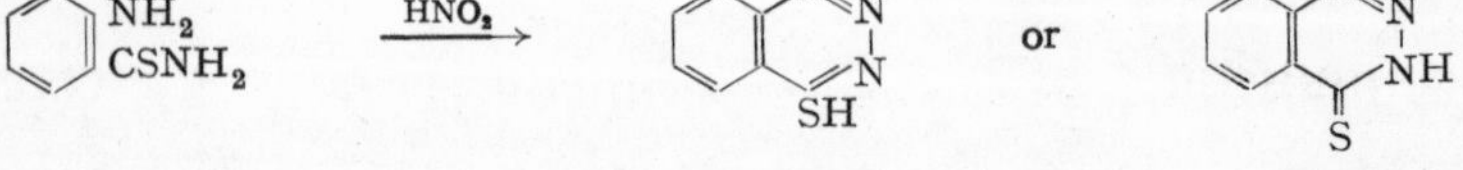

$$(53)$$

(**XXXIV**)   (**XXXV**)

it is shown that 1,2,4-triazines bearing mercapto groups exist in the enolic form although their oxygen analogs may apparently exist, or, at least, react as the keto tautomers. This is true also for acyclic compounds of similar structure, *e.g.*, thiourea. Reissert and Grube prepared *S*-acyl derivatives of 4-mercapto-1,2,3-benzotriazine by treating it with benzoyl chloride and sodium hydroxide or with acetic anhydride and sodium acetate. When treated with sodium and methyl iodide, 4-mercapto-1,2,3-benzotriazine forms the *S*-methyl derivative. Alkaline permanganate converts 4-mercapto-1,2,3-benzotriazine to benzazimide, S being replaced by O. Milder oxidizing agents would presumably convert it to its disulfide.

(2) 1,2,3-Benzotriazines with Valence Bridges

One ring system (*R.I.* 1223) is known of this type. It is named *triazirinoindiazole* by *The Ring Index*. Other names that have been used are *triazirinoindiazene*, *cycloazibenztriazine*, and *endoiminodihydro-benzisodiazole*.

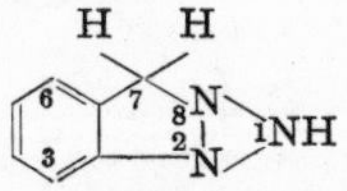

Triazirinoindiazole

Chattaway and Walker[19] observed that bromination or chlorination of *o*-nitrobenzylidene phenylhydrazones yield so-called *ω*-halogen derivatives (XXXVI). These, warmed with alcohol or treated with such bases as sodium acetate, aqueous ammonia, or pyridine, lose hydrogen halide, yielding very explosive compounds. These explosive compounds were at first designated as substituted "isodiazomethanes" (XXXVII) (eq. 54). These reactions are illustrated by the bromination of *o*-nitrobenzylidene phenylhydrazone.

In a second paper, Chattaway and Walker[20] revised their views as to the course of these reactions. They now regarded the cyclization occurring on loss of hydrogen halide as giving a triazine oxide (XXXVIII) which is, of course, isomeric with XXXVII. In support of this view, they reduced compound XXXVIII with stannous chloride to a compound written as XXXIX. Compound XXXIX was converted to two compounds of known structure; alcoholic potassium hydroxide cleaves it to o-(2,4-dibromophenylazoamino)-benzoic acid (XL) (eq. 55) and reduction of XXXIX with tin and hydrochloric acid converts it to o-aminobenzoyl-2,4-dibromophenylhydrazide (XLI) (eq. 56). Compounds XL and XLI are both identical with compounds of known structure, prepared in other ways.

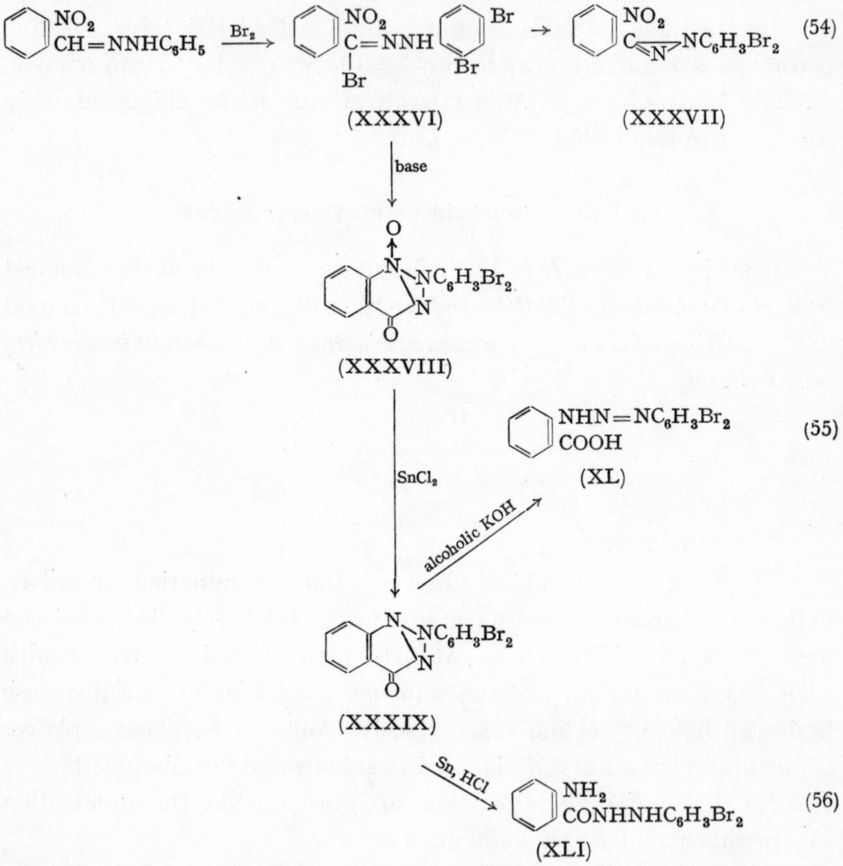

(XXXVI)   (XXXVII)

(XXXVIII)

$$\text{NHN}=\text{NC}_6\text{H}_3\text{Br}_2 \quad (55)$$
$$\text{COOH}$$
(XL)

(XXXIX)

$$\text{NH}_2 \quad (56)$$
$$\text{CONHNHC}_6\text{H}_3\text{Br}_2$$
(XLI)

In later work, Chattaway and colleagues[14-18, 52] prepared many of these bridged 1,2,3-benzotriazines, in each case starting with the action of chlorine or bromine upon o-nitrobenzylidene derivatives of phenylhydrazine, tolylhydrazines, chlorophenylhydrazines and bromophenylhydrazines. In one case,[17] they employed 2,4-dinitrobenzylidene derivatives as well and thereby obtained products where the benzene rings condensed with the triazine ring bore nitro groups. They found that reduction of the triazine oxides (XXXVIII) to the triazines (XXXIX) can be accomplished by boiling with alcohol as well as by the use of stannous chloride. All of these bridged triazines and bridged triazine oxides are listed in Table I–4.

TABLE I-4. 1-Aryl-7-oxo-triazirinoindiazoles

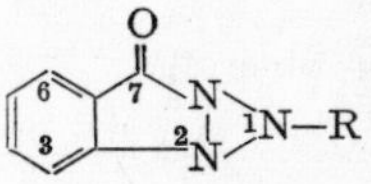

Substituents besides the 7-oxo group	Color, crystal habit	M.p., °C.	Explosion pt., °C.	Ref.
1-(4-Bromophenyl)	Pale yellow needles	197		20
1-(4-Bromophenyl)-2-oxide	Yellow needles		144	19
1-(2-Bromo-4-methylphenyl)	Pale yellow prisms	166		14
1-(4-Bromo-2-methylphenyl)	Pale yellow needles	181		16
1-(2-Bromo-4-methylphenyl)-4-nitro	Colorless prisms	250		17
1-(2-Bromo-4-methylphenyl)-4-nitro-2-oxide	Bright yellow rhombic plates		133	17
1-(2-Bromo-4-methylphenyl)-2-oxide	Bright yellow rhombic plates		139	14
1-(4-Bromo-2-methylphenyl)-2-oxide	Bright yellow prisms		151	16
1-(4-Bromo-2-nitrophenyl)-2-oxide	Bright yellow prisms		142	16
1-(4-Chlorophenyl)-2-oxide	Bright yellow needles		147	19
1-(2-Chloro-4-methylphenyl)	Colorless needles	173		15
1-(2-Chloro-4-methylphenyl)-2-oxide	Bright yellow rhombic plates		134	15
1-(2,4-Dibromophenyl)	Long colorless needles	178		20
1-(2,4-Dibromophenyl)-2-oxide	Long yellow needles		145–146	19
1-(2,6-Dibromo-4-methylphenyl)	Yellow rhombic plates	190 (dec.)		14
1-(2,6-Dibromo-4-methylphenyl)-4-nitro	Colorless prisms	279		17
1-(2,6-Dibromo-4-methylphenyl)-4-nitro-2-oxide	Bright yellow hexagonal plates		142	17
1-(2,4-Dibromo-5-methylphenyl)-2-oxide	Yellow needles		126	52

(Table continued)

TABLE I-4 *(continued)*

Substituents besides the 7-oxo group	Color, crystal habit	M.p.,°C.	Explosion pt., °C.	Ref.
1-(2,4-Dibromo-6-methylphenyl)-2-oxide	Bright yellow tablets		145	16
1-(2,6-Dibromo-4-methylphenyl)-2-oxide	Bright yellow rhombic plates		167	14
1-(2,4-Dichlorophenyl)	Labile form: yellow prisms	167		20
	Stable form: colorless needles	157		20
1-(2,4-Dichlorophenyl)-2-oxide	Slender bright yellow hexagonal prisms		140	19
1-(2,6-Dichloro-4-methylphenyl)	Colorless hexagonal prisms	202		15
1-(2,6-Dichloro-4-methylphenyl)-2-oxide	Bright yellow hexagonal plates		155	15
2-Oxide-1-(pentabromophenyl)	Bright yellow		157	18
2-Oxide-1-(pentachlorophenyl)	Deep yellow		128	18
2-Oxide-1-(2,3,4,5-tetrabromophenyl)	Bright yellow		155	18
2-Oxide-1-*p*-tolyl	Bright yellow prisms		143	14
2-Oxide-1-(2,4,6-trichlorophenyl)	Long bright yellow prisms		163	19
2-Oxide-1-(3,4,5-trichlorophenyl)	Compact yellow plates		151	19
1-(2,4,6-Trichlorophenyl)	Colorless needles	258		20

The triazine oxides of this type are, without exception, very explosive. Their explosion points, however, are distinctive and reproducible. Mixed explosion points are generally depressed like true melting points. Removal of the oxide oxygen by reduction destroys the explosive nature of these compounds. Those triazine oxides with three halogen atoms on the benzene ring are more stable than those with less halogen. All of these compounds are stable towards acids. They are feebly basic and form salts that are very easily hydrolyzed. When oxidized with potassium permanganate, they form *o*-nitrobenzoic acids.

B. Condensed with Naphthalene

(1) Condensed with the 2,3 Positions of Naphthalene

This ring system is preferably named *naphtho[2,3]-v-triazine (R.I.* 1818). Other names that have been used are *lin-1,2,3-naphthotriazine* and *v-naphthotriazine*. The last name, of course, does not uniquely specify the structure.

A solitary compound of this type is known. It was prepared by Fries, Walter, and Schilling[27] by treating 3-aminonaphthalene-2-carboxamide or 3-aminonaphthalene-2-carbohydrazide with nitrous acid (eq. 57). The yield of product is apparently very good. It is ob-

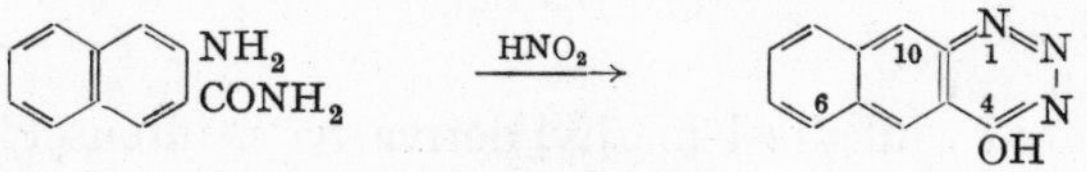

$$\text{(57)}$$

tained as colorless needles, m.p. 250° (dec.), soluble in strong alkali and in acetic acid, less soluble in dioxane and acetone. When heated with resorcinol, it forms a red azo dyestuff.

(2) Condensed with the 1,8 Positions of Naphthalene

This ring system has received several names, being called at various times the *azimide of 1,8-diaminonaphthalene, 1,8-aziminonaphthalene, 1,2,3-triaza-perinaphthindene, α-peri-naphthotriazole* (a very poor name), and, finally, *The Ring Index* name, *1-naphtho[1,8]-triazine (R.I.* 1822).

In 1874 de Aguiar[22] prepared the first 1,2,3-triazine known. He obtained it by the action of nitrous acid upon 1,8-diaminonaphthalene (eq. 58). Not knowing the precise structure of "β-diaminonaphthalene," his starting material, he was not able to assign the correct structure (XLII) to his product. Instead, he wrote XLIII, a structure which is incomplete rather than incorrect. Erdmann[23] was the first to write structure XLII explicitly. Whereas de Aguiar had thought his product unstable, Erdmann reported that it is reasonably stable and can be

volatilized with only partial decomposition. The best description of
1-naphtho[1,8]triazine has been given by Waldmann and Back,[76] who
obtained it in 50% yield by de Aguiar's reaction. It melts at 236–237°
(dec.) upon rapid heating and is very soluble in nitrobenzene, easily
soluble in alcohol, and less soluble in other solvents. According to

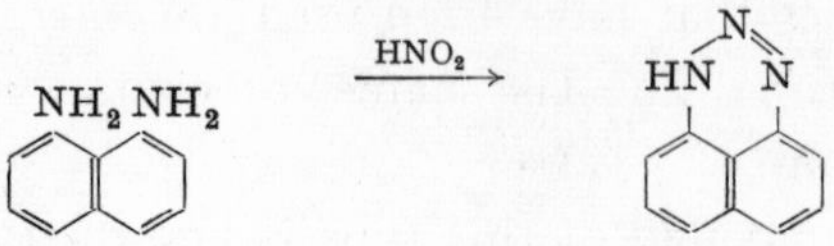

(58)

(XLII)

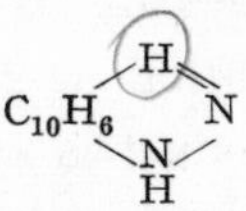

(XLIII)

Sachs,[65] it is red while its 1-methyl derivative is intensely blue, either
in solution or in the solid state. A solution of naphtho[1,8]triazine in
concentrated sulfuric acid is red-brown. Erdmann stated that it forms
salts with acids and with bases; he said nothing about their stability.
De Aguiar reported that salts with either acids or bases are unstable.
Their decomposition is probably by way of ring opening.

A German patent[54] states that naphtho[1,8]triazine is extraordinarily resistant to chemical reagents in general. This does not
appear to be the case. When dissolved in alkali and treated with
methyl iodide or methyl sulfate, naphtho[1,8]triazine yields its
1-methyl derivative (eq. 59).[65] In some of its reactions naphtho[1,8]-

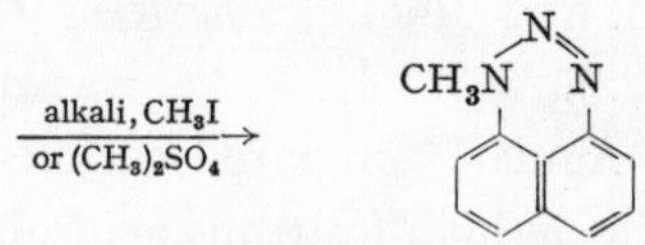

(59)

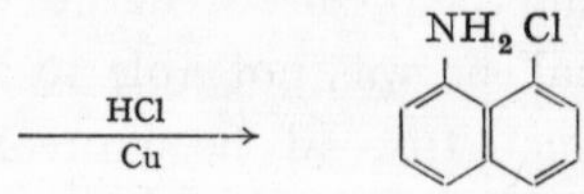

(60)

triazine acts like a diazonium compound. When heated with concentrated hydriodic acid and copper powder on the steam bath, it forms

1,8-diiodonaphthalene.[67] When treated with hydrochloric acid in the presence of copper or cuprous salts even at low temperatures, it is said to form 1-amino-8-chloronaphthalene (eq. 60).[54] This reaction also takes place with the 6-sulfonic and 5,8-disulfonic acid derivatives of naphtho[1,8]triazine.[54] With dichlorobenzoquinone chloroimide, it forms an indophenol, whose structure was not given.[57] It has been observed on several occasions that naphtho[1,8]triazine and its 6-sulfonic acid derivative will both couple readily with diazonium compounds, yielding dyes in which the 1,2,3-triazine ring is intact.[55, 56, 65] These dyes are deeply colored and stable. In only one case has it been reported that the 1,2,3-triazine ring in naphtho[1,8]-triazine behaves like a diazonium grouping towards such compounds as β-naphthol. In this instance, its 1-benzenesulfonyl derivative, dissolved in acetic acid or hydrochloric acid, then poured into an alkaline solution of β-naphthol, gave a coupling product.[47] The coupling was also brought about by heating the triazine with β-naphthol in pyridine on the steam bath. A hydrochloric acid solution of this benzenesulfonyl derivative reacts with platinum chloride, yielding a product said to be a diazonium platinichloride.[47]

Some 1-substituted derivatives of naphtho[1,8]triazine have been prepared by the reactions of nitrous acid with the properly substituted 1,8-diaminonaphthalenes (eq. 61). In this manner, Morgan and

(XLIV)

(61)

Micklethwait[47] prepared the benzenesulfonyl derivative (XLIV, $R = C_6H_5SO_2$). No melting point was given. Waldmann and Back prepared two other derivatives of naphtho[1,8]triazine in a similar manner, obtaining the 1-phenyl derivative in 50% yield and the 1-(2,4-dinitrophenyl) derivative in 70% yield.[76] These compounds are listed in Table I–5. The phenyl derivative gives a red-brown solution in concentrated sulfuric acid, the dinitrophenyl derivative, a yellow solution. The phenyl and the dinitrophenyl derivatives, when heated in

TABLE I-5. Naphtho[1,8]triazines

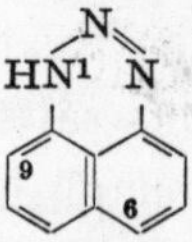

Substituents	Color, crystal habit	M.p., °C.	Ref.
None		236–237 (dec.)	76
	Red		65
	Red microscopic crystals		23
	Light-colored needles		22
1-Benzenesulfonyl	Orange-yellow		47, 49
1-(3-Chloro-2-hydroxy-5- nitro-phenylazo)-6(or 7-)- sulfonic acid[a]	Violet dye		55, 56
1-(2,4-Dinitrophenyl)		163 (dec.)	76
5,8-Disulfonic acid			54
1-Methyl	Intense blue		65
1-Phenyl	Gleaming brownish crystals	134	76*
6-(or 7-)-Sulfonic acid			54

[a] Structure assumed. See text.

boiling naphthalene or nitrobenzene, are converted to benzacridines (eq. 62). This is illustrated with the dinitrophenyl derivative. The same products are obtained by heating in the absence of solvent but the reactions then proceed explosively.

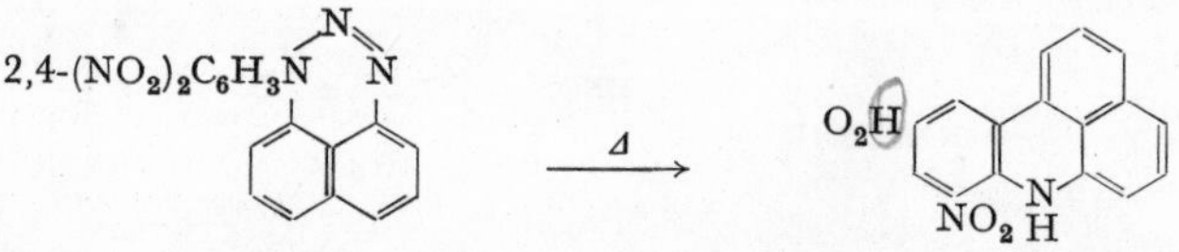

(62)

3. 1,2,3,-TRIAZINE RINGS CONDENSED WITH HETEROCYCLES

A. Condensed through Two Carbon Atoms

(1) Condensed with the Thiazole Ring

This ring system is called *thiazolo[5,4-d]-v-triazine* (*R.I.* 732) in *The Ring Index*. Only one compound containing such a ring system has been reported. Weidel and Niemilowicz[78] treated 5-amino-2-methylthiazole-4-carboxamide with nitrous acid (eq. 63) and obtained

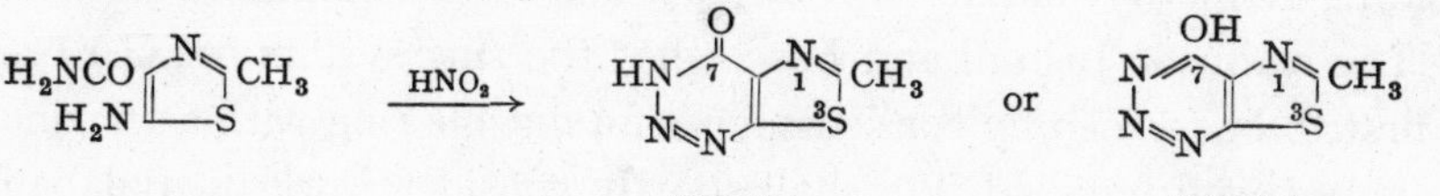

$$\text{(XLVa)} \qquad\qquad \text{(XLVb)} \tag{63}$$

a product (yellowish scales, m.p. 270–280° (dec.)). On the basis of carbon, hydrogen, nitrogen, and sulfur determinations, they assigned it structure XLVa, calling it *μ-methylazimidothiazole-α-carboxylic acid* [sic!]. This name is incorrect. We would like to point out that the corresponding enolic structure, XLVb, should also be considered for the compound.

(2) Condensed with the Pyrazole Ring

The *Chemical Abstracts* name for this ring system is *5′,4′:4,5-pyrazole-(1,2,3)triazine;* in *The Ring Index* it is called *7-pyrazolo-[3,4-d]-v-triazine* (*R.I.* 742). Justoni and Fusco[36] obtained an interesting compound of this type (90% yield, m.p. 160° (dec.)) by the action of nitrous acid upon 1,3-diphenyl-5-aminopyrazole-4-carboxamide (eq. 64). Structure XLVI is a plausible one for this synthesis.

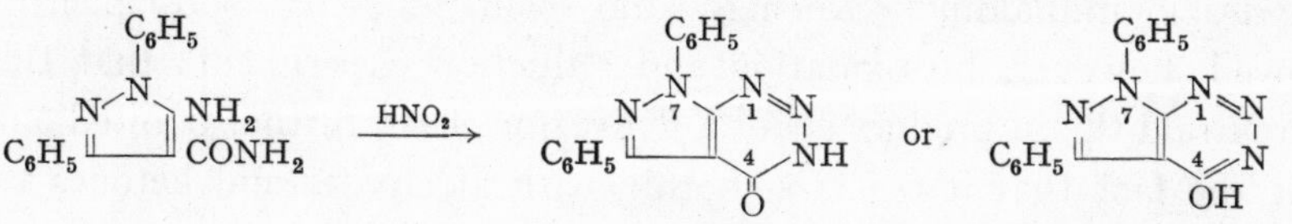

$$\text{(XLVIa)} \qquad\qquad \text{(XLVIb)} \tag{64}$$

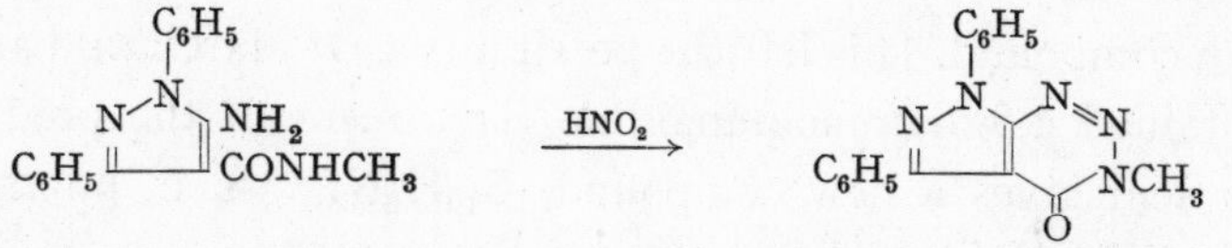

$$\tag{65}$$

However, if the product is XLVI, it is unusual among 1,2,3-triazines in that it is stable to chemical reagents. It is only slightly decomposed by heating for a long time in dilute or concentrated hydrochloric acid. It is soluble in boiling dilute sodium hydroxide solution; upon cooling

such solutions, one obtains the sodium salt, m.p. 230–240° (dec.). An
N-methyl derivative, m.p. 155.5° (dec.) was prepared from the corresponding N-methyl amide (eq. 65). It is insoluble in aqueous alkali.

The claim of Justoni and Fusco that the ring system of XLVI is
the first to be formed by condensation of a diazole ring with a triazine
ring is not well founded. We shall shortly consider work by Balaban
and King which antedates that of Justoni and Fusco.

B. Condensed through a Carbon Atom and a Nitrogen Atom

(1) Condensed with the Pyrazole Ring

This ring system is called *pyrazolo[2,3-c][1,2,3]benzotriazine* in
Chemical Abstracts. It is not named in *The Ring Index*. Two compounds

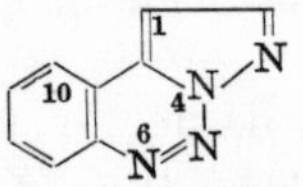

Pyrazolo[2,3-*c*][1,2,3]benzotriazine

of this type are known. The story of the elucidation of their structure
is of some interest. It was reported by Marckwald and Chain[43] that
4-chloroquinaldine, heated with hydrazine hydrate at 150°, yields
4-hydrazinoquinaldine. Koenigs and von Loesch[39] subsequently
showed, however, by oxidation and reduction experiments that the
Marckwald-Chain product is not a hydrazine. They further pointed out
that the fact that it reacts smoothly with aldehydes and ketones to
split out water suggests that an orthodiamine or peridiamine structure
is present. They stated that the material is not 3,4-diaminoquinaldine,
a known compound. This left the possibility that Marckwald and Chain
had obtained 4,5-diaminoquinaldine. Treatment of the product with
nitrous acid gives a new compound, $C_{10}H_8N_4$, which, on this basis,
would be XLVII (eq. 66).

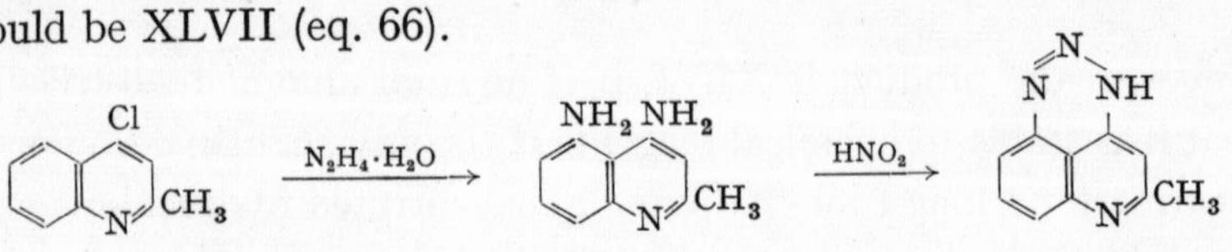

(66)

(XLVII)

Some years later the correct structures were announced by Koenigs and Freund.[38] 4-Chloroquinaldine, when heated with hydrazine hydrate at 150°, undergoes ring opening, followed by a ring closure which yields a pyrazole derivative (XLVIII, R = H). This compound was also synthesized by a different route, starting with o-nitrobenzoylacetone. Compound XLVIII (R = H), treated with nitrous acid, gives a 1,2,3-triazine (XLIX) in nearly quantitative yield. Compound XLIX (R = H) is obtained as colorless needless, m.p. 126°; it is weakly basic and heating with hydrochloric acid converts it to an isomer of unknown structure. Reduction with stannous chloride opens the triazine ring to give 3-methyl-5-o-hydrazinophenylpyrazole (eq. 67); oxidation with

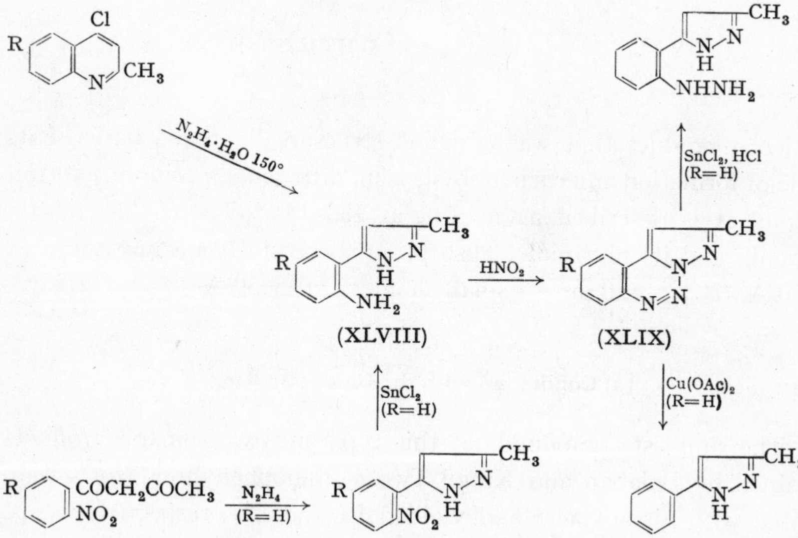

cupric acetate yields 3-methyl-5-phenylpyrazole, a known compound (eq. 68). A similar triazine (XLIX, R = OCH$_3$) is obtained as gleaming flakes, m.p. 212°, by heating 6-methoxy-4-chloroquinaldine with hydrazine hydrate and treating the resulting product with nitrous acid.[38]

(2) Condensed with the Thiazole Ring

One such ring system has been prepared. *Chemical Abstracts* calls it *3H-thiazolo[3,2-c]-v-triazine*. It is not named in *The Ring Index*. In

their study of penicillin, Cook and Heilbron[21] nitrosated the α-amide of
D-benzylpenicillic acid, converted the nitroso derivative to its methyl
ester and then treated the methyl ester with methanolic potassium
hydroxide at room temperature. This sequence of reactions (eq. 69)

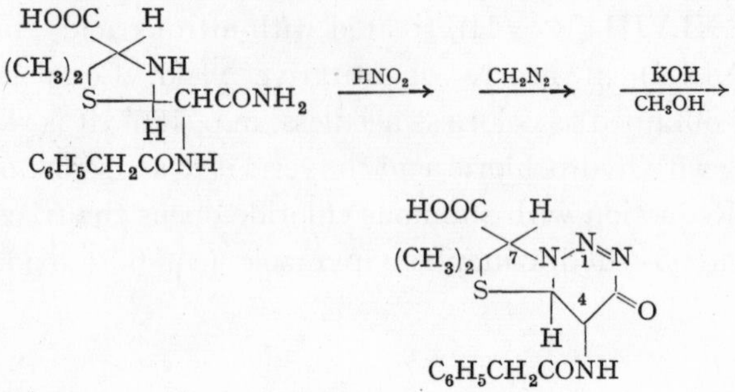

(69)

(L)

yielded a product that was assigned structure L on the basis of its
mode of formation and carbon, hydrogen, nitrogen, and sulfur determinations. It is described as melting at 133–134° (dec.), $\alpha_D^{23} + 16°$ (in
ethanol), and its ultraviolet absorption spectrum has a maximum at
2,650 A. ($E_{1\,cm.}^{1\,\%}$ 420) and a small shoulder at 2,750 A.

(3) Condensed with the Imidazole Ring

The simplest compounds of this type are two isomeric products
obtained by Balaban and King.[1] Two o-aminophenylimidazoles were
treated with nitrous acid and yielded LI and LII, respectively (eqs.
70, 71). Compound LI was described as needles, m.p. 113–114°, and

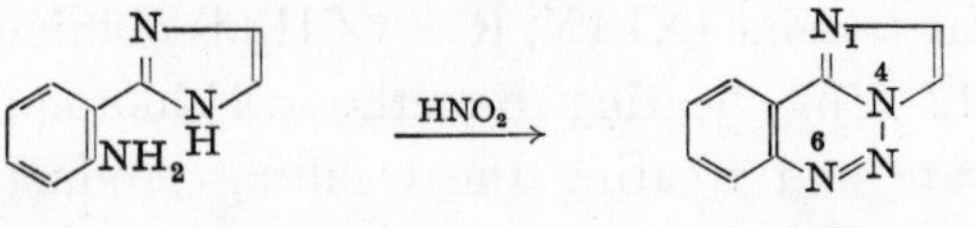

(70)

(LI)

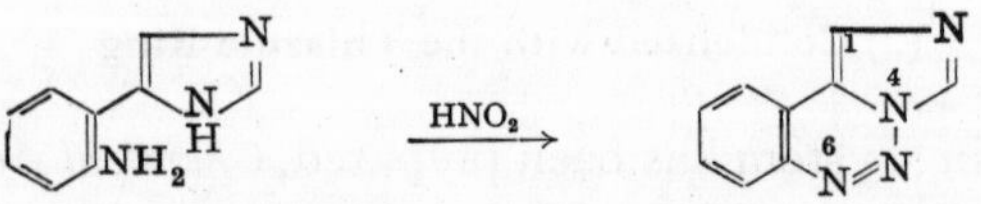

(71)

(LII)

soluble in concentrated hydrochloric acid. Compound LII was described as needles; nothing was said of its melting point or solubility in hydrochloric acid. Both compounds are insoluble in alkali and neither will couple with alkaline β-naphthol. *The Ring Index* calls LI *imidazo[1,2-c][1,2,3]benzotriazine* (R.I. 1555). Compound LII is not named in *The Ring Index* but a suitable name would be *imidazo-[3,4-c][1,2,3]benzotriazine*.

Somewhat more complicated structures of this type (LIII) have been prepared by von Niementowski.[72,73] He called LIII the *azimide* of *o-aminophenylbenzimidazole*. Its *Ring Index* name is *benzimidazo-[1,2-c][1,2,3]benzotriazine* (R.I. 2378). As usual, closure of the triazine ring was brought about by the action of nitrous acid upon compounds containing adjacent amino groups (eq. 72). The yields appear to be

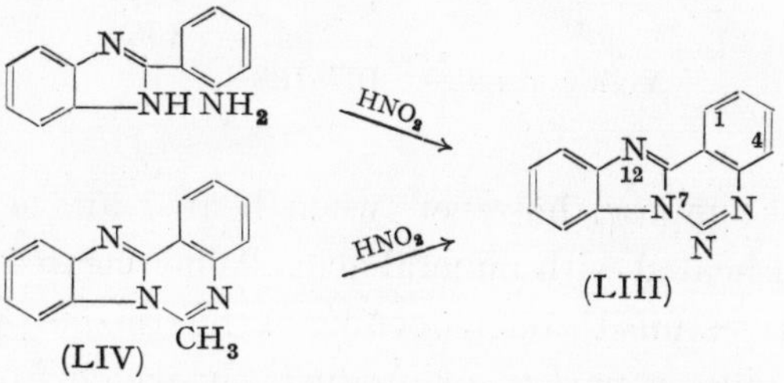

$$(72)$$

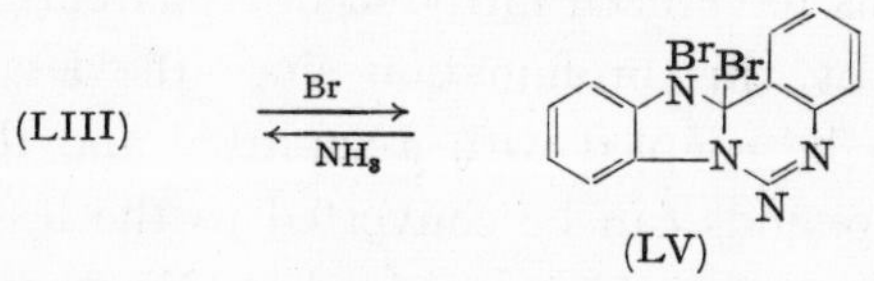

$$(73)$$

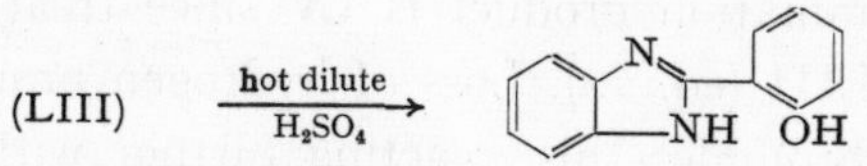

$$(74)$$

very good. A more unexpected synthesis is found in the reaction of nitrous acid with 6-methylbenzimidazo[1,2-c]quinazoline (LIV).[74] Presumably, LIV hydrolyzes, yielding acetic acid and a diamine which then reacts with nitrous acid. 1,2,3-Triazines of this type are listed in Table I–6. They are yellow solids of weakly basic nature, soluble in organic solvents and in strong acids. They are not attacked by boiling

TABLE I-6. Benzimidazo[1,2-c][1,2,3]benzotriazines[72,73]

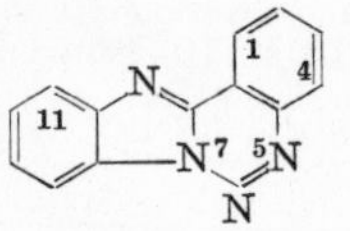

Substituents	Color, crystal habit	M.p., °C.	Derivatives, with m.p.,°C.
None	Bright yellow needles	207–208	Hydrochloride, 200 (dec.). HAuCl₄ deriv., 220 (dec.). Monobromo deriv., two forms, 131–132 and 146. Orange dibromo deriv., 112.
3,9- or 3,10-Dimethyl	Bright yellow needles	197	Monobromo deriv., 254. Pentabromo deriv., 155 (dec.).
3-Methyl	Yellow	185	H_2PtCl_6 deriv., >290. Dibromo deriv., 257. Pentabromo deriv., 120–130 (dec.).
9- or 10-Methyl	Yellow needles	187–188	

alkali. They decompose, however, when heated above their melting points or when heated with mineral acids. When heated with phenols, they form azo dyestuffs through opening of the triazine ring. Treatment with bromine gives a variety of products, in which from one to five bromine atoms have been introduced. Apparently the triazine ring is not affected by this bromination since the less highly brominated materials can be coupled with β-naphthol and the more highly brominated compounds can be converted to the less highly brominated ones by treatment with ammonia. Von Niementowski believed that the first bromination product is LV since treatment with ammonia regenerated LIII (eq. 73). Loss of hydrogen bromide from LV would give a monobromide; this, reacting further with bromine in an unspecified manner, would yield the pentabromide. It is difficult to see how HBr could be split out from LV, however. Compounds such as LIII, treated with hot dilute sulfuric acid, are converted to 2-o-hydroxyphenylbenzimidazoles (eq. 74); here the triazines are obviously behaving as diazonium compounds. Surprisingly, the 3-methyl derivative of LIII is not affected by several days' boiling with potassium permanganate solution.

(4) Condensed with the Pyrimidine Ring

A single compound of this type is known. It was prepared by Sachs and Steiner[66] by the reaction of nitrous acid with 2-*o*-amino-phenylperimidine (eq. 75). Compound LVI has no melting point but

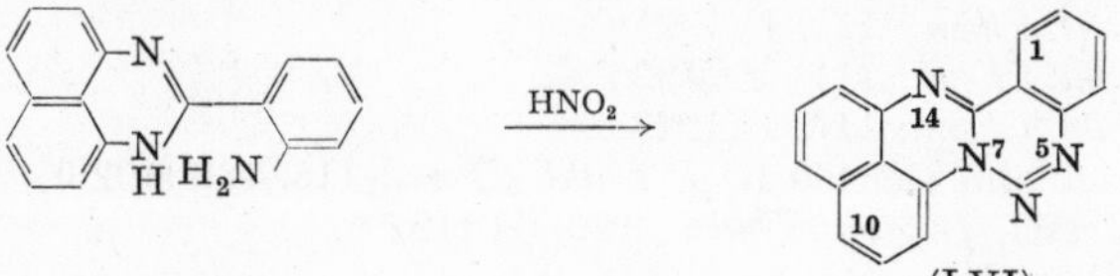

$$\text{(75)}$$

(LVI)

explodes suddenly at 140°. It is soluble in the usual organic solvents and in hot dilute sulfuric acid. In concentrated sulfuric acid it gives a green color, on standing in dilute sulfuric acid, a blue-violet color and, in dilute hydrochloric acid, a blue color. It is not affected by sulfuric acid at 50–60°. It is also stable towards alkali. The original name given this compound is *o-aminophenylperimidine azoimide*. Its *Ring Index* designation is *[1,2,3]benzotriazino[3,4-a]perimidine* (*R.I.* 3187).

Bibliography

1. Balaban and King, *J. Chem. Soc.*, **1927**, 2701 (1925).
2. Bamberger, *Ann.*, **305**, 333 (1899).
3. Bamberger, *Ann.*, **305**, 359 (1899).
4. Bamberger and Demuth, *Ber.*, **34**, 1309 (1901).
5. Bamberger and von Goldberger, *Ber.*, **31**, 2636 (1898).
6. Bamberger and Weiler, *J. prakt. Chem.*, **58**, 349 (1898).
7. Beilstein's *Handbuch der organischen Chemie*, Springer, Berlin, Fourth Edition.
8. Borsche, *Ber.*, **33**, 2995 (1900).
9. Busch, *Ber.*, **25**, 445 (1892).
10. Busch, *J. prakt. Chem.*, **51**, 113 (1895).
11. Busch *J. prakt. Chem.*, **51**, 257 (1895).
12. Busch, *J. prakt. Chem.*, **52**, 373 (1895).
13. Busch, *J. prakt. Chem.*, **55**, 356 (1897).
14. Chattaway and Adamson, *J. Chem. Soc.*, **1930**, 157.
15. Chattaway and Adamson, *J. Chem. Soc.*, **1930**, 843.
16. Chattaway and Adamson, *J. Chem. Soc.*, **1931**, 2787.
17. Chattaway and Adamson, *J. Chem. Soc.*, **1931**, 2792.
18. Chattaway and Parkes, *J. Chem. Soc.*, **1935**, 1005.
19. Chattaway and Walker, *J. Chem., Soc.*, **127**, 2407 (1925).
20. Chattaway and Walker, *J. Chem. Soc.*, **1927**, 323.

21. Cook and Heilbron, in *Chemistry of Penicillin*, edited by Clarke, Princeton University Press, 1949, p. 972.
22. de Aguiar, *Ber.*, **7**, 315 (1874).
23. Erdmann, *Ann.*, **247**, 364 (1888).
24. Fierz and Brütsch, *Helv. Chim. Acta*, **4**, 375 (1921).
25. Finger, *J. prakt. Chem.*, **37**, 431 (1888).
26. Finger, *J. prakt. Chem.*, **48**, 92 (1893).
27. Fries, Walter, and Schilling, *Ann.*, **516**, 280 (1935).
28. Gabriel, *Ber.*, **36**, 805 (1903).
29. Heller, *J. prakt. Chem.*, **111**, 1 (1925).
30. Heller, *J. prakt. Chem.*, **111**, 36 (1925).
31. Heller, *J. prakt. Chem.*, **116**, 1 (1927).
32. Heller, Dietrich and Reichardt, *J. prakt. Chem.*, **118**, 138 (1928).
33. Heller and Hessel, *J. prakt. Chem.*, **120**, 64 (1929).
34. Heller and Siller, *J. prakt. Chem.*, **116**, 9 (1927).
35. Jacini, *Gazz. chim. ital.*, **77**, 308 (1947); through *Chem. Abstracts*, **42**, 2962 (1948).
36. Justoni and Fusco, *Gazz. chim. ital.*, **68**, 59 (1938); through *Chem. Abstracts*, **32**, 6244 (1938).
37. King and Murch, *J. Chem. Soc.*, **125**, 2606 (1924).
38. Koenigs and Freund, *Chem. Ber.*, **80**, 143 (1947).
39. Koenigs and von Loesch, *J. prakt. Chem.*, **143**, 59 (1935).
40. König and Reissert, *Ber.*, **32**, 782 (1899).
41. Kratz, *J. prakt. Chem.*, **53**, 210 (1896).
42. Maccoll, *J. Chem. Soc.*, **1946**, 670.
43. Marckwald and Chain, *Ber.*, **33**, 1898 (1900).
44. Mehner, *J. prakt. Chem.*, **63**, 241 (1901).
45. Meisenheimer, Senn, and Zimmermann, *Ber.*, **60**, 1736 (1927).
46. Meyer, *Ann.*, **351**, 267 (1907).
47. Morgan and Micklethwait, *J. Chem. Soc.*, **89**, 4 (1906).
48. Morgan and Micklethwait, *J. Chem. Soc.*, **89**, 1158 (1906).
49. Morgan and Micklethwait, *J. Chem. Soc.*, **93**, 607 (1908).
50. Niementowski, see refs. 72, 73.
51. Nietzki and Petri, *Ber.*, **33**, 1788 (1900).
52. Parkes and Burney, *J. Chem. Soc.*, **1935**, 1619.
53. German Patent 139,908 (Dec. 3, 1901), to Leopold Cassella & Co.; through *Chem. Zentr.*, **1903**, I, 797.
54. German Patent 147,852 (March 25, 1903), to Badische Anilin und Soda Fabrik; through *Chem. Zentr.*, **1904**, I, 132.
55. German Patent 222,928 (March 5, 1909), to Bayer & Co.; through *Chem. Zentr.*, **1910**, II, 257.
56. German Patent 222,929 (March 20, 1909), to Bayer & Co.; through *Chem. Zentr.*, **1910**, II, 257.
57. German Patent 247,592 (June 17, 1911), to A.G. für Anilin-Fabrikation; through *Chem. Zentr.*, **1912**, II, 165.
58. Patterson and Capell, *The Ring Index*, Reinhold, New York, 1940.
59. Pictet and Gonset, *Arch. sc. phys. Genève*, [4], **3**, 37; through *Chem. Zentr.*, **1897**, I, 413.
60. Pinnow and Sämann, *Ber.*, **29**, 623 (1896).
61. Ramart-Lucas, Hoch, and Grumez, *Bull. soc. chim. France, Mém.*, **1949**, 447.
62. Reich and Ghazarian, *Bull. soc. chim. France, Mém.*, **19**, 261 (1916).
63. Reissert and Grube, *Ber.*, **42**, 3710 (1909).
64. Ruhemann and Morrell, *J. Chem. Soc.*, **61**, 795 (1892).

65. Sachs, *Ann.*, **365**, 59 (1909).
66. Sachs and Steiner, *Ber.*, **42**, 3674 (1909).
67. Scholl, Seer, and Weitzenböck, *Ber.*, **43**, 2206 (1910).
68. Shah, *J. Indian Inst. Sci.*, **7**, 205 (1924).
69. Stolz, *Ber.*, **36**, 3290 (1903).
70. Sumuleau, *Ann. scientif. de l'Univ. de Jassy*, **2**, 131 (1903); through *Chem. Zentr.*, **1903, II**, 31.
71. Thode, *J. prakt. Chem.*, **69**, 92 (1904).
72. (von) Niementowski, *Ber.*, **21**, 1534 (1888).
73. von Niementowski, *Ber.*, **31**, 314 (1898).
74. von Niementowski and Kozakowski, *Ber.*, **32**, 1477 (1899).
75. von Walther and Bamberg, *J. prakt. Chem.*, **71**, 153 (1905).
76. Waldmann and Back, *Ann.*, **545**, 52 (1940).
77. Weddige and Finger, *J. prakt. Chem.*, **35**, 262 (1887).
78. Weidel and Niemilowicz, *Monatsh.*, **16**, 746 (1895).
79. Widman, *J. prakt. Chem.*, **38**, 192 (1888).
80. Zacharias, *J. prakt. Chem.*, **43**, 446 (1891).

CHAPTER II

The 1,2,4-Triazines

Introduction

Compounds with ring system I are most systematically named as *1,2,4-triazines*. The name *isotriazine* is occasionally found, especially in the Italian literature.[133-135] *α-Triazine*, another name for this ring system, seems to have arisen from a proposal by Widman.[196] He suggested that 1,2,4-benzotriazine (II) be called *α-phentriazine* since it

(I)	(II)
1,2,4-Triazine	1,2,4-Benzotriazine
as-Triazine	α-Phentriazine
Isotriazine	
α-Triazine	

contains two nitrogen atoms in positions alpha to the benzene ring. Probably the most commonly used name for I is *as-triazine*, where *as-* denotes asymmetry. It leads to somewhat shorter and simpler names and is preferred by *The Ring Index*[153] and *Chemical Abstracts*.

The 1,2,4-triazine ring is apparently not present in any naturally occurring material of known structure. Numerous compounds of this class have been prepared, however, the first synthesis having been reported in 1889. Much of our knowledge regarding their preparation and properties is a by product of work in other directions. The most important syntheses have received systematic study; these include the reactions of semicarbazide, thiosemicarbazide or aminoguanidine with 1,2-dicarbonyl compounds or their monoximes, with α-keto acids or their esters or amides, or with α-hydroxy ketones. These methods all introduce the N–N–C–N portion of the 1,2,4-triazine ring as a unit. The ring has been built up in other ways as well.

The study of this class of compounds has been made by many workers and in a rather sporadic fashion. Consequently, a survey shows an uneven distribution of the various types possible. While a fairly large number of relatively complex triazines have been prepared, few of the simplest members of this class are known. For example, *as*-triazine itself, as well as its homologs, has never been prepared.

Less attention has been directed to the reactions of the 1,2,4-triazines than to their preparation. In general, reduction, oxidation and alkylation are the reactions that have been most extensively investigated. Such substitution reactions as nitration, chlorination, amination (Tschitschibabin reaction), etc., have received little, if any study. The discussion that follows will show the gaps in our knowledge of these interesting compounds. It will be seen that there is much room for well-planned and exhaustive investigations in this field.

So far as we know, no 1,2,4-triazine has found widespread use. A compound, once believed to be a 1,2,4-triazine, was for a time sold as a sweetening agent under the name "glucin" and apparently attained some popularity in Europe (see p. 101). A U.S. patent, issued to Shoemaker and Loane,[141] has claims covering the use of 1,2,4-triazines as additives for lubricating oils; the permissible substituents listed include alkyl, aryl, aralkyl, alkoxy, mercapto, or amino groups or halogens. However, the patent gives only one example of reduction to practice and this does not mention the use of 1,2,4-triazines. Some 1,2,4-triazines are known to be dyes for wool but it is doubtful whether they are actually used for this purpose. U.S. patents issued to Wolf and Pfister[143-152] state that certain 1,2,4-benzotriazine derivatives show promise in the treatment of malaria.

1. UNCONDENSED 1,2,4-TRIAZINES

A. Unbridged 1,2,4-Triazine Rings

Surprisingly few of the simplest 1,2,4-triazines have been prepared. Relatively few studies have been made with compounds of this type, so few, indeed, that it is difficult to make reliable generalizations for the class as a whole. Further, attempts to prepare the simplest triazines are not always successful. It seems that cyclization reactions leading to the simple triazines may not always proceed as well as those yielding more highly substituted triazines. Table II-1 is a listing of all the reported aromatic, monocyclic 1,2,4-triazines.

TABLE II-1. Substituted *as*-Triazines

Substituents	Color, crystal habit	M.p., °C.	Ref.
3-Acetamido-5,6-diphenyl[a]		151	184
3-Acetamido-5-phenyl	Pale yellow needles	182–184	81
3-Acetamido-6-phenyl	Colorless	219–225 (dec.)	81
3-Acetoxy-5,6-bis(3,4-methylene-dioxyphenyl)[a]		208	22
3-Acetoxy-5,6-bis(*p*-bromo-phenyl)[a]		282	21
3-Acetoxy-5,6-dianisyl[a]		157	22
3-Acetoxy-5,6-dicumyl[a]		136–137	22
3-Acetoxy-5,6-diphenyl[a]	Almost colorless prisms	154	24
3-Amino		171.5–172.5	85
3-Amino-5,6-dimethyl		211–212	85
3-Amino-5,6-diphenyl		175	184
3-Amino-5-phenyl	Light yellow flakes	233–235	81
3-Amino-5-phenyl, hydrochloride	Colorless	213 (dec.)	81
3-Amino-6-phenyl	Pale yellow needles	175	81
3-Amino-6-phenyl, hydrochloride	Colorless	217–220 (dec.)	81
3-Amino-6-phenyl, imino form[a]	Silky straw-colored needles	192–193	81
3-Amino-6-phenyl, imino form,[a] acetyl deriv.		219–221 (dec.)	81
3-Amino-6-phenyl, imino form,[a] hydrochloride		228–235 (dec.)	81
5,6-Bis(3,4-methylenedioxy-phenyl)-3-hydroxy	Lemon-yellow prisms	248	18, 22
5,6-Bis(*p*-bromophenyl)-3-hydroxy	Colorless needles	253	21
3-Chloro-5-phenyl		122–123	198
5,6-Dianisyl-3-hydroxy	Yellow prisms	261–262	18, 22
5,6-Dicumyl-3-hydroxy	Yellow rhombohedra	250–251	18,22

(Table continued)

TABLE II-1 *(continued)*.

Substituents	Color, crystal habit	M.p., °C.	Ref.
5,6-Dimethyl-3-hydroxy		222–223 (dec.)	176
5,6-Diphenyl-3-hydroxy	Pale yellow needles	218	184, 186
		223	79
	Colorless	224–225	18,23
	Yellow prisms	225–226	24
5,6-Diphenyl-3-sulfanilylamino		189	139, 160
3,3′-Dithiobis(6-benzyl-5-hydroxy)	Amorphous yellowish solid	173	63
		172.5	53
3,3′-Dithiobis(5-phenyl)		183	198
3-Hydroxy-5-phenyl		234	197
3-Mercapto-5-phenyl		200	198

[a] May have another structure. See the text.

The parent heterocycle of this class, *as*-triazine (*R.I.* 159), has never been prepared. Nevertheless, Maccoll[120] has carried out some quantum-mechanical computations on this compound. He has found that, of the two non-equivalent Kekulé forms (IIIa, IIIb), IIIa is the

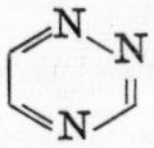

(IIIa) 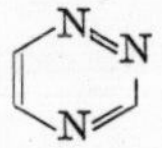   (IIIb)

more stable. The calculated resonance energy of *as*-triazine is 18 kilocalories, relative to structure IIIa. According to Maccoll's calculations, the absorption spectrum should have a band at 3830 A.

There are at least two possible methods of preparing *as*-triazine from known compounds containing this ring system. The first involves diazotization of 3-amino-*as*-triazine, followed by reduction of the

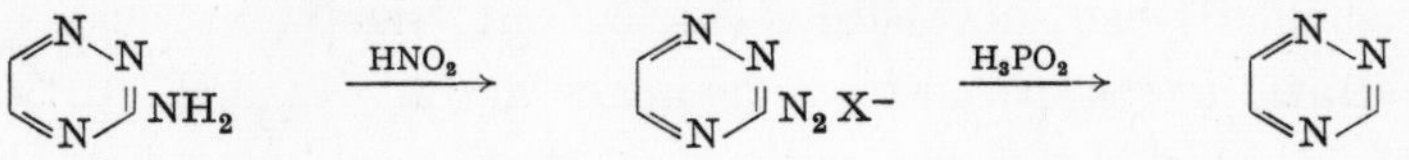

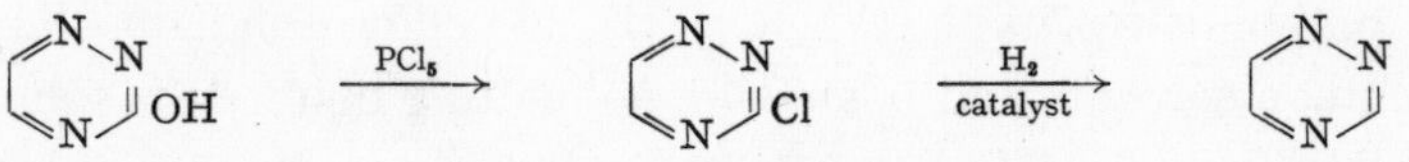

diazonium compound with hypophosphorus acid (eq. 1). A second method would entail treatment of 3-hydroxy-*as*-triazine with phosphorus pentachloride, followed by removal of chlorine by catalytic hydrogenation (eq. 2).

Presumably, *as*-triazine could also be prepared by reaction of formhydrazidine (or its tautomer, formamide hydrazone) with glyoxal. The reaction of glyoxal with the hydrazidines of other aliphatic and aromatic acids would be expected to yield 3-alkyl- or 3-aryl-*as*-triazines. 5-Alkyl-, 5-aryl-, 6-alkyl-, 6-aryl-, and 5,6-dialkyl- and 5,6-diaryl- substituted *as*-triazines would presumably be obtained by the use of other 1,2-dicarbonyl compounds than glyoxal (eq. 3). This type of reaction has apparently not been explored with aliphatic hydrazidines. Pinner,[156] however, attempted to prepare 3-phenyl-*as*-triazine from glyoxal and benzhydrazidine. Instead of the desired product, he obtained an osazone-like compound (eq. 4). It appears to us

$$
\begin{array}{c}
\text{RCO} \\
| \\
\text{R'CO}
\end{array}
+
\begin{array}{c}
\text{H}_2\text{N} \\
\diagdown \text{NH} \\
| \\
\text{CR''} \\
\text{HN}\diagup
\end{array}
\longrightarrow
\begin{array}{c}
\text{R} \diagup\!\!\!{}^{\text{N}}\diagdown_{\text{N}} \\
\text{R'}\diagdown_{\text{N}}\diagup\!\!{}_{\text{R''}}
\end{array}
+ \quad 2\,\text{H}_2\text{O} \qquad (3)
$$

$$
\begin{array}{c}
\text{NH}_2 \\
| \\
\text{C}_6\text{H}_5\text{C}=\text{NNH}_2
\end{array}
\xrightarrow{\text{CHOCHO}}
\begin{array}{c}
\text{NH}_2 \\
| \\
\text{C}_6\text{H}_5\text{C}=\text{NN}=\text{CH} \\
| \\
\text{C}_6\text{H}_5\text{C}=\text{NN}=\text{CH} \\
| \\
\text{NH}_2
\end{array}
\qquad (4)
$$

that by proper choice of experimental conditions the reaction might be made to follow the desired course. Perhaps, in very dilute solutions, one molecule of benzhydrazidine could react with one of glyoxal and then cyclize to 3-phenyl-*as*-triazine before the reaction to form the osazone took place.

Dedichen[73] has successfully carried out triazine syntheses with oxalhydrazidine (prepared from cyanogen and hydrazine) (eq. 5). The reaction of this compound with glyoxal in weakly acidic solution yields 3,3'-bi-*as*-triazinyl (IV, R = H), a yellow solid, insoluble in the common solvents and possessing no melting point. It is soluble in strong formic acid and in concentrated sulfuric acid. It is very resistant towards oxidizing agents. The tetramethyl analog (IV, R = CH₃) was obtained by reaction of oxalhydrazidine with biacetyl. It forms yellowish needles, m.p. 166°, soluble in alcohol, acetone, chloroform, and pyridine and very soluble in hot water. The tetraphenyl compound (IV, R = C_6H_5) was not formed as readily as the other bi-*as*-triazinyls.

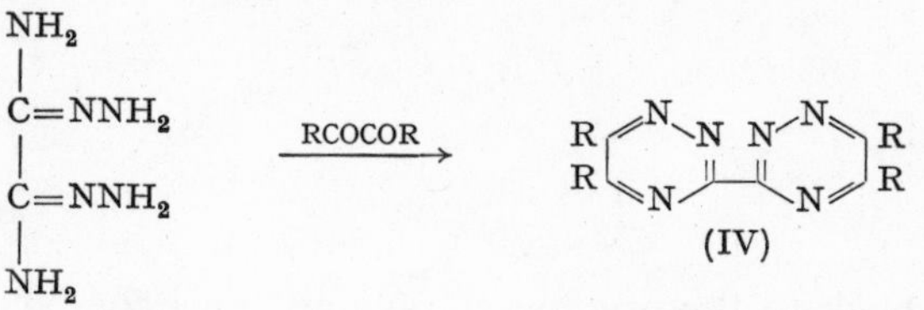

$$
\begin{array}{c}
NH_2 \\
| \\
C=NNH_2 \\
| \\
C=NNH_2 \\
| \\
NH_2
\end{array}
\xrightarrow{\text{RCOCOR}}
\quad (IV)
\qquad (5)
$$

It was obtained by refluxing an alcoholic solution of benzil and oxalhydrazidine, containing a few drops of hydrochloric acid, for three to four hours. Recrystallization from toluene gave yellow needles, m.p. 297°, soluble with difficulty in the common organic solvents and insoluble in water, acids, or alkali. This compound is soluble in a mixture of concentrated sulfuric acid and nitric acid and is somewhat soluble in hot pyridine and in hot acetic anhydride.

Wolff and Lindenhayn[198] found that α-cyanoazoacetophenone, when treated with cold concentrated hydrochloric acid, forms an addition product with hydrogen chloride. This, upon standing in cold alcoholic solution, loses hydrogen chloride and cyclization occurs, yielding 3-chloro-5-phenyl-*as*-triazine (eq. 6). This compound is

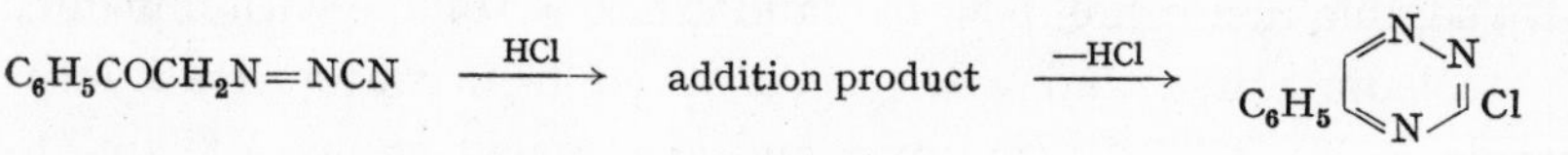

$$
C_6H_5COCH_2N=NCN \xrightarrow{\text{HCl}} \text{addition product} \xrightarrow{\text{—HCl}} \qquad (6)
$$

soluble in organic solvents and in concentrated hydrochloric acid; it is only slightly soluble in water. It is stable towards boiling water or alcohol but is attacked slowly by cold sodium hydroxide solution. Boiling dilute potassium carbonate solution replaces the chlorine by a hydroxyl group.

Biquard[26] has described the preparation of a dihydro-*as*-triazine by an unusual ring closure. The semicarbazone of acetophenone, when treated with a Grignard reagent, such as ethylmagnesium bromide or butylmagnesium chloride, is converted in 60–70% yield to a product, m.p. 126°, which had the composition $C_9H_9N_3$ (eq. 7). Biquard believed that this compound is 6-phenyl-1,4-dihydro-*as*-triazine (V) because of

its reactions. With bromine in chloroform, it forms a dibromo derivative. It is basic and forms a hydrochloride. The monoacetyl derivative is soluble in hydrochloric acid. The diacetyl derivative can be

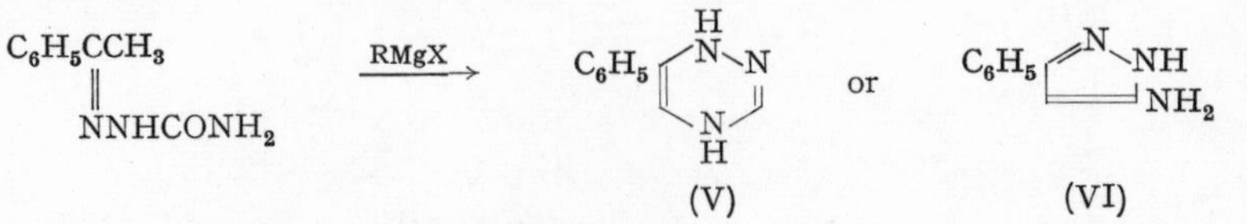

$$
\underset{\substack{\parallel \\ NNHCONH_2}}{C_6H_5CCH_3} \quad \xrightarrow{RMgX} \quad C_6H_5 \text{(V)} \quad \text{or} \quad C_6H_5 \text{(VI)} \tag{7}
$$

hydrolyzed back to the original compound. This compound does not
react with Grignard reagents except to give the active hydrogen
reaction. It appears from unpublished work by Searles and Kash[175]
that this $C_9H_9N_3$ is probably 3-amino-5-phenylpyrazole (VI), whose
structure is also consistent with the reactions observed.

Busch and Küspert[44] obtained 2,6-diphenyl-2,3-dihydro-*as*-
triazine (VII) by treating 4-amino-2,6-diphenyl-2,3,4,5-tetrahydro-*as*-
triazine with hydrochloric acid, whereupon there is loss of ammonia
(eq. 8). Compound VII was described as yellow needles, m.p. 94°. It is

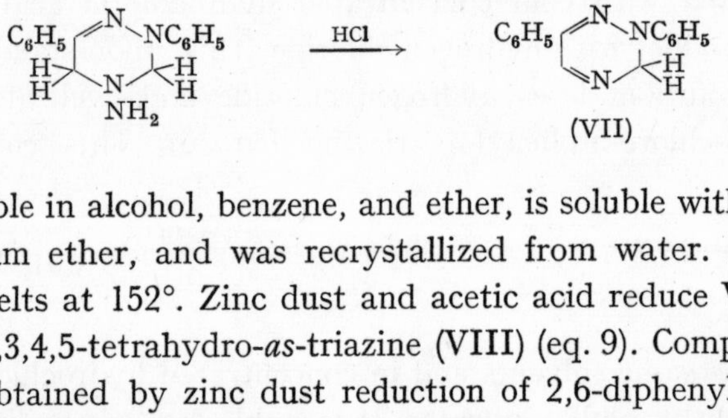

$$
\text{(structure)} \quad \xrightarrow{HCl} \quad \text{(VII)} \tag{8}
$$

easily soluble in alcohol, benzene, and ether, is soluble with difficulty
in petroleum ether, and was recrystallized from water. Its hydrochloride melts at 152°. Zinc dust and acetic acid reduce VII to 2,6-
diphenyl-2,3,4,5-tetrahydro-*as*-triazine (VIII) (eq. 9). Compound VIII
was also obtained by zinc dust reduction of 2,6-diphenyl-4-nitroso-
2,3,4,5-tetrahydro-*as*-triazine (eq. 9). In a similar manner, Busch and

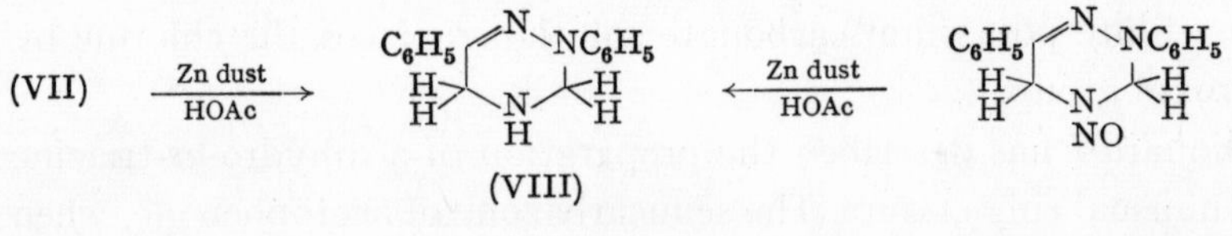

$$
\text{(VII)} \quad \xrightarrow[\text{HOAc}]{\text{Zn dust}} \quad \text{(VIII)} \quad \xleftarrow[\text{HOAc}]{\text{Zn dust}} \quad \text{(structure)} \tag{9}
$$

Küspert[44] treated 4-benzylideneamino-2,3,6-triphenyl-2,3,4,5-tetra-
hydro-*as*-triazine with concentrated hydrochloric acid. The product,
2,3,6-triphenyl-2,3-dihydro-*as*-triazine, was isolated as leaflets, m.p.
164°, easily soluble in benzene and less soluble in other solvents.

Busch and Hefele[43] and Busch, Friedenberger, and Tischbein[4] prepared several tetrahydro-*as*-triazine derivatives by the action of aldehydes upon hydrazones of phenacylamines (eq. 10). The products

$$C_6H_5CCH_2NHR \ + \ R''CHO \ \underset{\text{dilute } H_2SO_4}{\overset{\Delta}{\rightleftarrows}} \ \begin{array}{c} C_6H_5 \\ H \\ H \end{array} \begin{array}{c} N \\ N \\ R \end{array} NR' \ + \ H_2O \quad (10)$$

$$\underset{\text{NNHR'}}{\parallel}$$

$$(IX)$$

are listed in Table II-2. Only the *syn* forms of the hydrazones form triazines. These compounds (IX) are produced in very good yields by heating the reagents for a few minutes at 120°. Compounds with structure IX are not very stable towards water and warming them with dilute sulfuric acid causes hydrolysis to the parent aldehydes and phenacylamine hydrazones. They are readily soluble in benzene and in chloroform, less soluble in most other organic solvents.

Amino Derivatives. Thiele and Dralle[185] attempted unsuccessfully to prepare 3-amino-5-chloro-*as*-triazine by reaction of chloral with aminoguanidine (eq. 11). There was first formed a very unstable

$$Cl_3CHO \ \xrightarrow{NH_2NHCNH_2} \ \underset{Cl_3CCH=NNHCNH_2}{\overset{NH}{\parallel}} \ \xrightarrow{\ \ //\ \ } \ Cl \underset{N}{\overset{N}{\diagdown}} \underset{N}{\overset{N}{\diagup}} NH_2 \quad (11)$$

$$\downarrow H_2O$$

$$\underset{HOOCCH=NNHCNH_2}{\overset{NH}{\parallel}}$$

hydrazone; this, rather than cyclizing, was hydrolyzed to the guanyl-hydrazone of glyoxylic acid. From the reactions of aminoguanidine hydrochloride or dinitrate with such carbonyl compounds as chloro-acetaldehyde, dichloroacetaldehyde, glyoxal, biacetyl, and dihydroxy-tartaric acid, Thiele and Dralle obtained only osazone-like compounds (X). Apparently, under the reaction conditions employed, cyclization of the monoguanylhydrazones could not compete successfully with formation of the bisguanylhydrazones. However, Erickson[85] has found that glyoxal and biacetyl react readily with aminoguanidine bicar-bonate in aqueous suspension at room temperature to yield the expected

TABLE II-2. 2,3,4,5-Tetrahydro-*as*-triazines

Substituents	Color, crystal habit	M.p., °C.	Ref.
4-Amino-2,6-diphenyl	Leaflets	130	44
4-Amino-3-oxo-6-phenyl	Colorless needles	200	44
4-*p*-Anisyl-3-*p*-chlorophenyl-6-phenyl-2-*o*-tolyl	Colorless prisms	139–140	42
4-*p*-Anisyl-3-*p*-dimethylamino-phenyl-2,6-diphenyl	Yellowish needles	158	42
4-*p*-Anisyl-3,6-diphenyl-2-*o*-tolyl	Colorless needles	170	42
4-*p*-Anisyl-3-methyl-6-phenyl-2-*o*-tolyl		127–128	42
4-*p*-Anisyl-6-phenyl-2-*o*-tolyl	Colorless needles	143–144	42
4-Benzylideneamino-2-carbamyl-3,6-diphenyl	Prisms	205–206	44
4-Benzylideneamino-3,3-dimethyl-2,6-diphenyl	Needles	176	44
4-Benzylideneamino-2,6-diphenyl	Colorless needles	159–160	44
4-Benzylideneamino-2,6-diphenyl-3-methyl	Needless	126	44
4-Benzylideneamino-2,6-diphenyl-3-oxo		199	44
4-Benzylideneamino-3-methyl-2,3,6-triphenyl	Colorless needles	153–154	44
4-Benzylideneamino-3-oxo-6-phenyl		203	44
4-Benzylideneamino-2,3,6-triphenyl	Needles	159	44
5,6-Bis(3,4-methylenedioxy-phenyl)-2,4-diacetyl-3-oxo[a]		163	25
5,6-Bis(3,4-methylenedioxy-phenyl)-2,4-dibenzoyl-3-oxo[a]		212–213	25
5,6-Bis(3,4-methylenedioxy-phenyl)-3-oxo		285	18, 25
6-Bromomethyl-5-ethyl-3-oxo *or* 6-(1-bromopropyl)-3-oxo		115–117 (dec.)	74,75
6-*p*-Bromophenyl-4-*p*-chloro-benzylideneamino-2,3-diphenyl	Yellow	163–164	41

(Table continued)

TABLE II-2 *(continued)*

Substituents	Color, crystal habit	M.p., °C.	Ref.
6-*p*-Bromophenyl-4-*p*-chloro-benzylideneamino-3-methyl-2-phenyl	Colorless needles	166	41
6-*p*-Bromophenyl-4-*p*-chloro-benzylideneamino-2-phenyl	Colorless needles	180 (dec.)	41
2,4-Diacetyl-5,6-di-*p*-anisyl-3-oxo[a]	Fine needles	132	25
2,4-Diacetyl-5,6-dicumyl-3-oxo[a]	Fine needles	123	25
2,4-Diacetyl-5,6-diphenyl-3-oxo[a]	Colorless, silky needles	138	25
5,6-Di-*p*-anisyl-2,4-dibenzoyl-3-oxo[a]	Colorless	194–195	25
5,6-Di-*p*-anisyl-3-oxo[a]	Needles	212–213	18, 25
3,4-Di-*p*-anisyl-6-phenyl-2-*o*-tolyl	Needles	166	42
2,4-Dibenzoyl-5,6-dicumyl-3-oxo[a]		188	25
2,4-Dibenzoyl-5,6-diphenyl-3-oxo[a]	Colorless prisms	188–189	25
5,6-Dicumyl-3-oxo[a]	Compact, colorless needles	255–256	18, 25
2,6-Diphenyl	Colorless	160	44
2,6-Diphenyl-hydrochloride	Colorless	190	44
2,6-Diphenyl-3-*o*-hydroxyphenyl-4-*p*-tolyl		156–163[b]	43
5,6-Diphenyl-2-methyl-3-oxo[a]	Compact granules	199	25
2,6-Diphenyl-4-nitroso	Yellow needles	109–110	44
4,6-Diphenyl-3-oxo		181 (dec.)	43
5,6-Diphenyl-3-oxo[a]	Colorless needles	275–276	18, 25
6-Methyl-3-oxo	Long, prismatic needles	200–202	124
3-Oxo-6-phenyl	Long needles	224–228	44
3-Oxo-6-phenyl-4-*p*-tolyl		208	43
3-Oxo-6-(3-semicarbazonopropyl)		222	159
4-*p*-Tolyl-2,3,6-triphenyl		126[c]	43

[a] Other structures are possible. See the text.
[b] M.p. 156–163°, from alcohol-ether. M.p. 149–153°, from benzene-petroleum ether.
[c] M.p. 126°, from acetone. M.p. 76–77°, from ether-alcohol. M.p. 78–83°, from benzene-petroleum ether. The melting point is said to vary because different amounts of solvents are held by the recrystallized product.

triazines (eq. 12). 3-Amino-*as*-triazine (XI, R = H) and 3-amino-5,6-dimethyl-*as*-triazine (XI, R = CH$_3$) were obtained in this manner in 50–60% and 80% yields, respectively. These successful results are

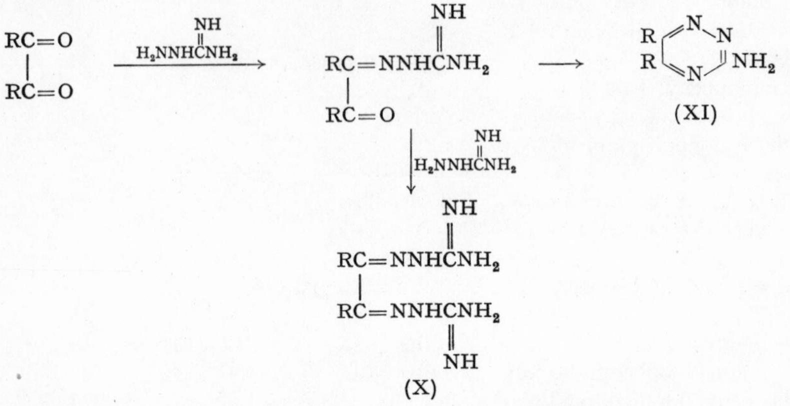

presumably due to a difference between the properties of the amino-guanidine salts. The bicarbonate is relatively insoluble in water; its solutions therefore contain much lower concentrations of amino-guanidine salt than was the case with the hydrochloride or nitrate. As a result, the monoguanylhydrazone is given a greater opporunity to cyclize before further reaction with aminoguanidine occurs, yielding the osazone.

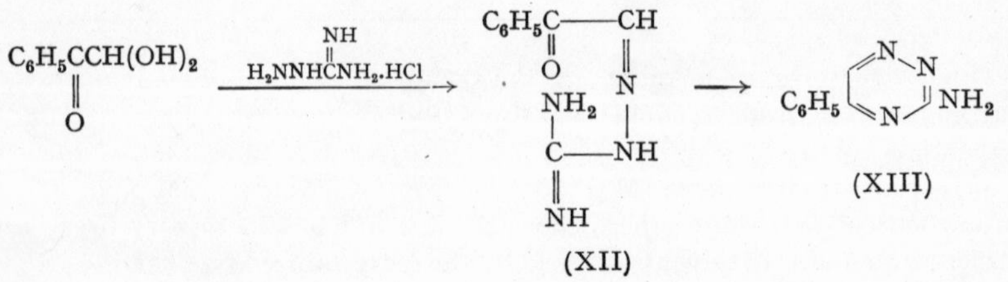

According to Ekeley, Carlson, and Ronzio,[81] the course taken by the reaction between phenylglyoxal hydrate and aminoguanidine depends upon the experimental conditions. If the reaction is carried out in acidic solution, an intermediate condensation product, believed to be XII, may be isolated. This, when heated, loses water and ring closure takes place (eq. 13), giving 3-amino-5-phenyl-*as*-triazine (XIII) in 87% yield. This same product was obtained in 52% yield when the reaction was carried out by heating an aqueous solution of phenyl-glyoxal hydrate and aminoguanidine bicarbonate to boiling and adding an excess of 30% sodium hydroxide solution. The structure of XIII is rather strongly supported by the fact that, when this compound is treated with nitrous acid or with boiling potassium hydroxide solution, it is converted to 3-hydroxy-5-phenyl-*as*-triazine. The structure of this latter compound seems well established by an independent synthesis.

By mixing phenylglyoxal hydrate and aminoguanidine hydrochloride in aqueous solution, then slowly adding excess potassium hydroxide solution (eq. 14), Ekeley, Carlson, and Ronzio obtained a 30% yield of another product. This they designated as 3-amino-6-phenyl-*as*-triazine (XIV). Another variation in the order of mixing reagents gave still another product. The addition of aminoguanidine hydrochloride to a strongly alkaline solution of phenylglyoxal hydrate (eq. 15) resulted in a 30% yield of another compound, said to be the imino

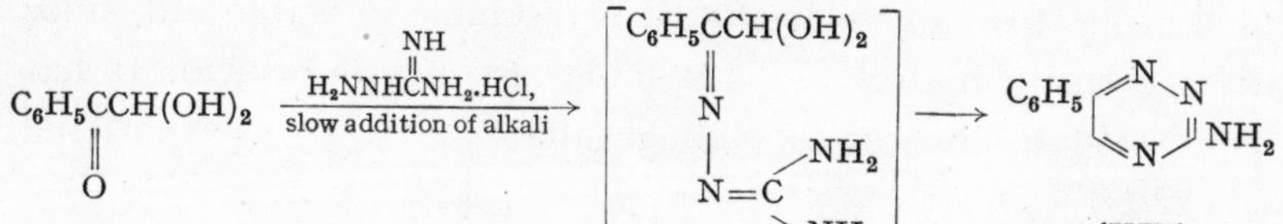

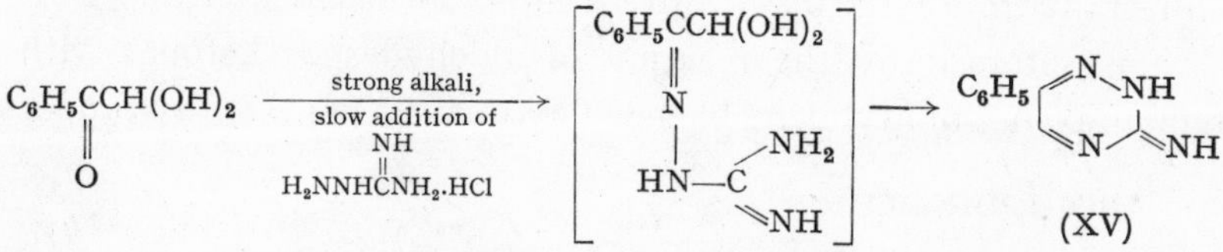

form (XV) of compound XIV. Compounds XIV and XV form hydrochlorides and acetyl derivatives of distinctly different melting points (see Table II-1). If compounds XIV and XV are truly enamine-ketimine tautomers, the process of forming these derivatives should convert the less stable form to the more stable. Accordingly, one would expect to obtain the same hydrochloride or acetyl derivative, no matter which of the tautomers was the starting material. There is, therefore, some doubt as to the structures of these compounds. Despite this doubt, we have listed the compounds in Table II-1. They are all yellow solids, not very soluble in the usual solvents with the exception of hot alcohol, which dissolves them readily. Ekeley and colleagues gave the absorption spectra of all of these products.

According to Thiele and Bihan,[184] benzil reacts slowly with aminoguanidine dinitrate in alcoholic solution (eq. 16) to yield 3-amino-

$$C_6H_5C=O \quad \xrightarrow[\text{then alkali}]{\overset{\text{NH}}{\underset{\parallel}{H_2NNHCNH_2 \cdot 2HNO_3,}}} \quad \begin{array}{c} C_6H_5 \\ C_6H_5 \end{array} \!\!\! \begin{array}{c} N\!\!-\!\!N \\ \diagdown \\ N \end{array} \!\! NH_2 \qquad (16)$$
$$C_6H_5C=O$$

(XVI)

5,6-diphenyl-*as*-triazine (XVI). This product, which was obtained in unstated yield, was precipitated by the addition of alkali. With boiling acetic anhydride it forms the acetyl derivative. Boiling potassium hydroxide solution replaces the amino group in XVI by a hydroxyl group; nitrous acid is said to have no effect upon XVI. These latter reactions may indicate that the compound exists mainly as the imino tautomer or tautomerizes readily to the imino form. Compound XVI is soluble in most organic solvents; it is insoluble in water and, since its salts are easily hydrolyzed, insoluble also in dilute acid. It has been converted to the corresponding sulfanilamide by conventional methods.[139, 160]

Busch and associates [41, 44] have prepared several 4-arylideneamino-2,3,4,5-tetrahydro-*as*-triazines (XVII). These are listed in Table II-2. They were obtained by the reaction of aldehydes or ketones with phenylhydrazones of arylidene phenacylhydrazines (eq. 17). By proper

$$\begin{array}{c} RCCH_2NHN=CHR' \\ \parallel \\ NNHC_6H_5 \end{array} \xrightarrow{R''CHO} \quad \begin{array}{c} C_6H_5 \\ H\!-\! \\ H \end{array} \!\!\! \begin{array}{c} N\!\!-\!\!NC_6H_5 \\ \diagup \quad H \\ N \quad R'' \\ | \\ N=CHR' \end{array} \qquad (17)$$

(XVII)

choice of reagents, a wide variety of products can be obtained. The yields were not given in most cases. A 90% yield was obtained in one case, however.

4-Benzylideneamino-2,6-diphenyl-2,3,4,5-tetrahydro-*as*-triazine, treated with phenylhydrazine, is converted to 4-amino-2,6-diphenyl-2,3,4,5-tetrahydro-*as*-triazine (eq. 18).[44] On the other hand, ring opening takes place when 4-benzylideneamino-2,3,6-triphenyl-2,3,4,5-tetrahydro-*as*-triazine (XVIII) reacts with phenylhydrazine (eq. 19). Compound XVIII, under the action of concentrated hydrochloric acid, splits out the elements of benzylideneimine and XIX is formed (eq. 20). A similar reaction takes place when 4-amino-2,6-diphenyl-2,3,4,5-tetrahydro-*as*-triazine reacts with hydrochloric acid, ammonia being lost; when this compound is treated with nitrous acid, its amino group is converted to a nitroso group (eq. 21).

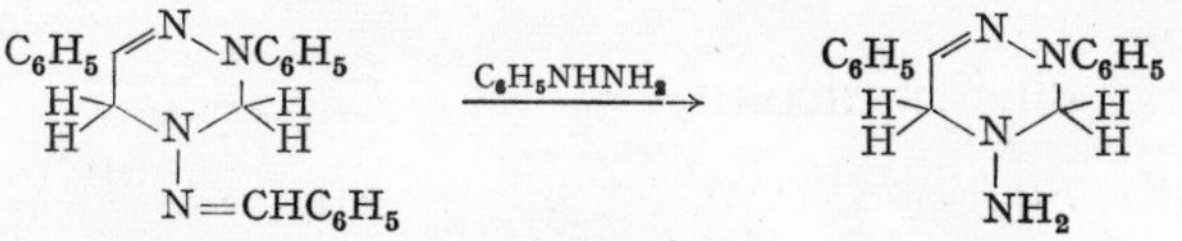

$$\text{(18)}$$

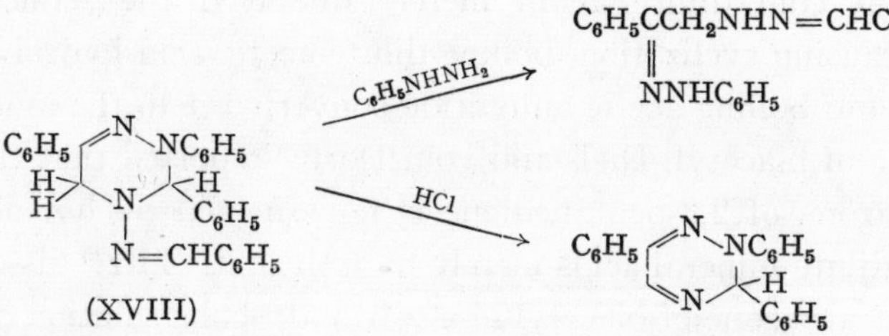

$$\text{(19)}$$

$$\text{(XVIII)}$$

$$\text{(20)}$$

$$\text{(XIX)}$$

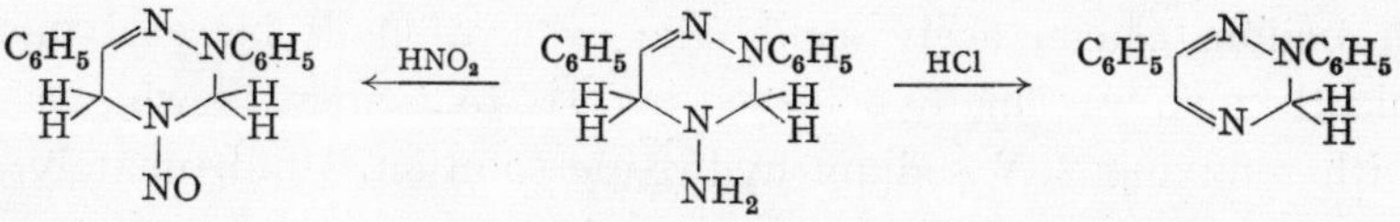

$$\text{(21)}$$

Hydroxy and Oxo Derivatives. Wolff[197] performed an elegant synthesis of an *as*-triazine. α-Carbamylazoacetophenone, heated briefly with sodium hydroxide solution and then acidified, is converted to 3-hydroxy-5-phenyl-*as*-triazine (eq. 22). This compound is readily soluble in concentrated hydrochloric acid; it is apparently soluble in alkali also, although this was not stated.

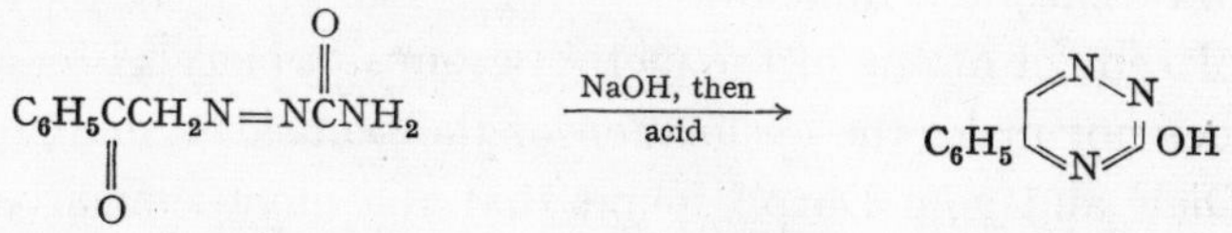

$$\text{(22)}$$

Just as 1,2-diketones and aminoguanidine cyclize to 3-amino-*as*-triazines, so 3-hydroxy-*as*-triazines can be obtained from 1,2-dicarbonyl compounds and semicarbazide. These ring closures do not proceed nearly as readily with semicarbazide as with aminoguanidine. The ease of reaction appears to be greatly affected by the nature of sub-stituent groups, for aromatic diketones give much more satisfactory results than do diketones containing aliphatic groups. Several un-successful attempts were made to prepare 3-hydroxy-5,6-dimethyl-*as*-triazine from the monosemicarbazone of biacetyl (eq. 23). Diels[77]

$$
\begin{array}{c}
CH_3C{=}NNHCONH_2 \\
| \\
CH_3C{=}O
\end{array}
\quad \longrightarrow \quad
\begin{array}{c}
CH_3 \\
CH_3
\end{array}
\!\!\!
\begin{array}{c}
N\,{\diagdown}\,N \\
\diagdown N \diagup\!\!OH
\end{array}
\qquad\qquad (23)
$$

found that cold dilute alkali merely dissolved the semicarbazone without causing cyclization, boiling dilute acetic acid hydrolyzed it to biacetyl, and boiling acetic anhydride converted it to the monoacetyl-hydrazone of biacetyl. Diels and vom Dorp[79] reported that the mono-semicarbazone of 2,3-pentanedione is not affected by hot alkali and that hot dilute mineral acids merely hydrolyze it. Biltz[20] dissolved the monosemicarbazone of biacetyl in a warm alcoholic solution of sodium ethoxide and recovered it unchanged. Biltz also found that the semi-carbazone of biacetyl monoxime is not cyclized after long heating with boiling glacial acetic acid. The cyclization of biacetyl mono-semicarbazone was finally achieved in 1947 by Seibert,[176] who heated it with refluxing 2 *N* sodium hydroxide solution. Unfortunately, he did not state the reaction time required. 3-Hydroxy-5,6-dimethyl-*as*-triazine decolorizes a cold solution of potassium permanganate in sulfuric acid. Its crystallization from water or acetic acid is very slow and requires weeks for completion. Perhaps earlier workers actually obtained small amounts of this triazine and failed to isolate it because of this slow crystallization. However, whether or not they missed small amounts of this compound, it is clear that the cyclization of biacetyl monosemicarbazone is difficult.

Replacement of one of the methyl groups in biacetyl by a phenyl group does not make the cyclization of the semicarbazone noticeably easier. Diels and vom Dorp[79] found that the monosemicarbazone of methylphenylglyoxal is not affected by hot alkali and is hydrolyzed by hot dilute mineral acids. No one seems to have tried to close the triazine ring with the semicarbazone of phenylglyoxal. When two aryl groups are present in the diketone, cyclization proceeds with ease. Thus, Thiele and Stange[186] showed that benzil, heated with semicarbazide hydrochloride and magnesium carbonate in alcoholic solution, yielded only 3-hydroxy-5,6-diphenyl-as-triazine (XX) (eq. 24). The

$$
\begin{array}{l}
\text{C}_6\text{H}_5\text{C}=\text{O} \\
\quad | \qquad\qquad \xrightarrow{\text{NH}_2\text{NHCONH}_2} \\
\text{C}_6\text{H}_5\text{C}=\text{O}
\end{array}
\qquad
\begin{array}{l}
\text{C}_6\text{H}_5 \\
\text{C}_6\text{H}_5
\end{array}\!\!
\begin{array}{c}
\nearrow^{\text{N}}\!\!\searrow_{\text{N}} \\
\diagdown_{\text{N}}\!\!\diagup \text{OH}
\end{array}
\qquad (24)
$$

(XX)

preparation of XX from benzil and semicarbazide has been repeated by others,[18, 22–25, 113] especially by Biltz and co-workers, who have devoted the most study to this reaction. They have found that benzil and semicarbazide, reacting in an aqueous-alcoholic solution at room temperature, will yield the monosemicarbazone of benzil. If a solution of these reagents is heated, one obtains a mixture of XX and the disemicarbazone of benzil. Compound XX is also formed in quantitative yield by simply heating the monosemicarbazone of benzil in alcoholic solution or in 84% yield by refluxing an acetic acid solution of benzil and semicarbazide hydrochloride for several hours. Biltz and colleagues[18, 21, 22] used this technique to prepare several other 3-hydroxy-5,6-diaryl-as-triazines, apparently in very good yields. They are listed in Table II-1. Hopper[113] has found that the reaction between benzil and semicarbazide hydrochloride stops at the monosemicarbazone stage when it is carried out in pyridine solution.

Compound XX has also been prepared by the action of hot potassium hydroxide solution on the corresponding 3-amino compound. Biltz and colleagues found that XX can also be obtained by heating

$$
\begin{array}{l}
\text{C}_6\text{H}_5\text{C}=\text{O} \\
\quad | \qquad\qquad \xrightarrow[\Delta]{\text{NH}_2\text{NHCONH}_2} \\
\text{C}_6\text{H}_5\text{CHOH}
\end{array}
\quad
\begin{array}{l}
\qquad\quad \text{H} \\
\text{C}_6\text{H}_5\text{C}-\text{N} \\
\qquad\quad \| \qquad\quad \diagdown \\
\text{C}_6\text{H}_5\text{C}-\text{N} \qquad \diagup^{\text{C}=\text{O}} \\
\qquad\quad \text{H}
\end{array}
\!\cdot\!
\begin{array}{l}
\text{C}_6\text{H}_5 \\
\text{C}_6\text{H}_5
\end{array}\!\!
\begin{array}{c}
\nearrow^{\text{N}}\!\!\searrow_{\text{N}} \\
\diagdown_{\text{N}}\!\!\diagup \text{OH}
\end{array}
\quad (25)
$$

benzoin with semicarbazide[19, 24, 25]; this procedure yields a material that has been shown to be an addition product of one molecule of XX

and one molecule of 4,5-diphenyl-3-oxoimidazoline (eq. 25). The
components of this addition compound can be separated by dissolving
it in hot acetic acid and then cooling, whereupon the imidazolone is
precipitated. An oxidation must have occurred in the formation of XX
from benzoin; there is no evidence to show whether this oxidation
took place before or after ring formation.

The 3-hydroxy-5,6-diaryl-*as*-triazines are relatively insoluble in
water, but, in general, are soluble in most of the common organic
solvents. They are also soluble in dilute alkali, a fact that suggests they
are indeed aromatic hydroxy compounds. The hydrochlorides are
apparently very easily hydrolyzed. The acetyl derivatives, formed by
the action of hot acetic anhydride, are very readily saponified. We
cannot decide from this whether they are *O*-acetyl or *N*-acetyl derivatives. Biltz favored the *O*-acetyl structure. Treatment of the sodium
derivative of XX with methyl sulfate gives a monomethyl derivative,
m.p. 152–153°[24]; with ethyl iodide a monoethyl derivative, m.p. 105°,
is formed.[186] These alkylated compounds are not *O*-alkyl ethers; the
methyl derivative, heated with concentrated hydriodic acid, yields no
methyl iodide. The alkyl groups are presumably attached to nitrogen
at either position 2 or position 4. Biltz favored attachment of the alkyl
groups to nitrogen at position 2. In the formation of these alkylated
derivatives, compound XX reacted as the keto tautomer. A final
choice between the keto and enol forms under other reaction conditions
is not possible in the absence of further information.

The 3-hydroxy-5,6-diaryl-*as*-triazines can be smoothly reduced
with zinc in alcohol-acetic acid or with zinc and hydrochloric acid.[25]
Dihydro derivatives (3-oxo-tetrahydro-*as*-triazines (XXI)) are formed
in 80–90% yields (eq. 26). The two atoms of hydrogen are added in the
4,5 positions, according to Biltz. They may also be added in the 5,6
positions, however. Hydrogenation in the 4,5 positions seems reasonable since, according to Biltz,[25] the same products can be obtained in a
different manner. A mixture of semicarbazide and benzoin, heated in
refluxing acetic acid containing a small amount of hydrochloric acid,
gave a 35% yield of the tetrahydro-*as*-triazine (eq. 26); benzil and compound XX were also formed. These 3-oxo-5,6-diaryl-2,3,4,5-tetra-
hydro-*as*-triazines are soluble in chloroform, acetic acid, and benzene

and less soluble in most of the other organic solvents. They form salts
with neither acids nor bases but will dissolve in concentrated sulfuric
acid, from which they are precipitated unchanged by the addition of

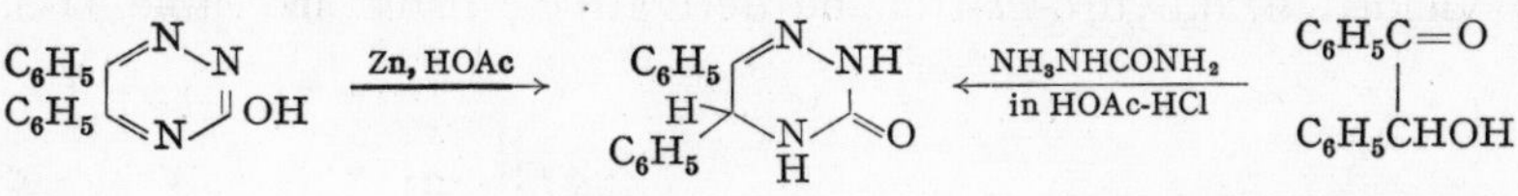

$$
\underset{(XXI)}{}
$$

(26)

water. With acetic anhydride or with benzoyl chloride and pyridine
they form diacyl derivatives; the acyl groups are presumably attached
to the nitrogen atoms at positions 2 and 4. Compound XXI can not be
reduced further by long heating with zinc and acetic acid. It is not
affected by short heating with phosphorus and hydriodic acid. The
ring in compound XXI is ruptured between the 1 and 2 positions when
this compound is heated with red phosphorus and hydriodic acid for
four to five hours at 180°; a subsequent ring closure occurs with the
formation of 4,5-diphenylimidazolone in 75% yield (eq. 27). The only

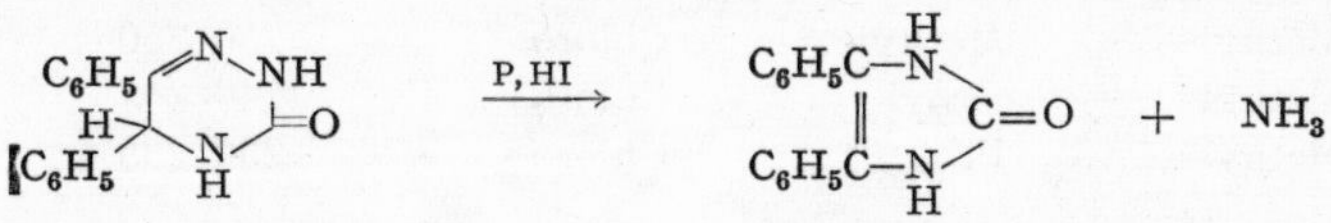

(27)

other product obtained from this reduction was ammonia. Although compound XXI cannot be methylated, its methyl derivative was obtained
in 80% yield by reducing the methyl derivative of compound XX with
zinc and alcoholic acetic acid.[25] The position of the methyl group, of
course, is not known.

Rolla[165] prepared 2,5,6-triphenyl-3-oxo-2,3-dihydro-as-triazine by
the reaction of benzil with 2-phenylsemicarbazide (eq. 28). This product

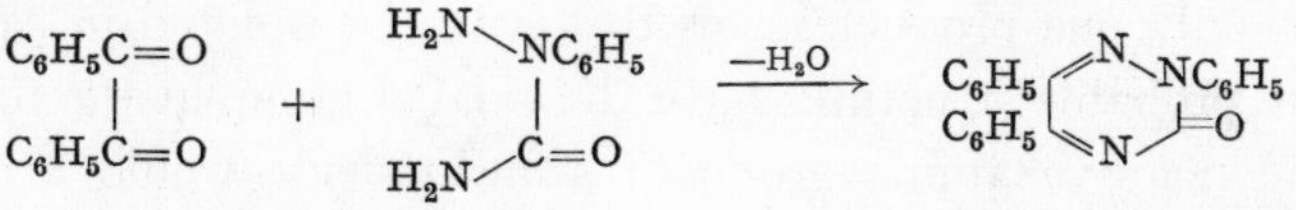

(28)

is described as melting at 170°, insoluble in alkali, and giving a red
color in concentrated sulfuric acid.

Ekeley and O'Kelly[82] found an interesting method of preparing *as*-triazines from aliphatic 1,2-diketones and semicarbazide. They converted the diketones to the sodium bisulfite addition products, which were then treated with semicarbazide hydrochloride (eq. 29). This yielded hexahydro-*as*-triazine derivatives, listed in Table II-3.

TABLE II-3. 3-Oxo-hexahydro-*as*-triazines [a]

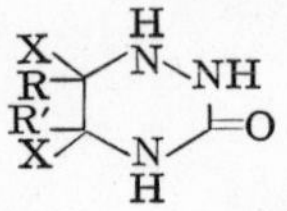

R	R′	X	Decomposition temp., °C.
H	H	Hydroxy	265–270
H	Methyl	Hydroxy	250–255
Methyl	Methyl	Hydroxy	240–245
Methyl	Ethyl	Hydroxy	230–235
Methyl	Propyl	Hydroxy	240–245
Methyl	Butyl	Hydroxy	230–235
Methyl	Amyl	Hydroxy	100–105
H	H	Chloro	265–270
H	Methyl	Chloro	260–270
Methyl	Methyl	Chloro	250–260
Methyl	Ethyl	Chloro	240–245
Methyl	Propyl	Chloro	230–235

[a] Prepared by Ekely and O'Kelly[82].

4-Methyl-2,3-pentanedione (isobutyrylacetyl) did not give the expected triazine but instead formed a soluble compound of unknown structure. The structures of these triazines are indicated by elementary analyses. A compound of this type, in which R and R′ are of different chain lengths, may presumably have either of two structures; R may be at the 5 or the 6 position (with R′ at the 6 or the 5 position). Actually, however, only one product seems to have been isolated in each case. The more probable structures have the smaller group at the 6 position since the reactive amino group in semicarbazide would attack the carbonyl-bisulfite group attached to the less hindered alkyl group. These dihydroxy triazines are unexpectedly stable. They can be recrystallized from hot glacial acetic acid as colorless solids that do not melt but instead decompose, mostly at temperatures over 200°. They are decomposed by hot strong acids but form salts in the cold. These compounds are stable towards hot alkali. With the lower members of the series, the two hydroxyl groups are replaced by chlorine upon treatment with phosphorus trichloride; the higher members of the series are decomposed by this reagent. The dichloro compounds so obtained are listed in Table II-3. They too decompose rather than melt when heated.

Biltz[20] attempted unsuccessfully to bring about ring closure by heating the semicarbazone of acetoin at 270° and also by heating it with boiling acetic acid (eq. 30). Others appear to have been successful

$$
\begin{array}{c}
\text{OH} \\
| \\
\text{RCSO}_3\text{Na} \\
| \\
\text{R'CSO}_3\text{Na} \\
| \\
\text{OH}
\end{array}
\xrightarrow{\text{NH}_2\text{NHCONH}_2.\text{HCl}}
\quad
\xrightarrow{\text{PCl}_3}
\quad (29)
$$

in preparing *as*-triazines from aliphatic acyloins and semicarbazide. Their work was not described in satisfactory detail, however. Speck and Bost[179] treated a series of aliphatic acyloins with semicarbazide (prolonged heating with a solution of semicarbazide hydrochloride and sodium acetate in dilute alcohol) to obtain high-melting, crystalline products that were not characterized. These products were thought to be triazines; this does indeed seem likely.

The literature contains several examples of *as*-triazines being formed from ketones containing alpha functional groups other than hydroxy. Michael,[124] on repeated recrystallization of the semicarbazone of chloroacetone from hot water, obtained 6-methyl-3-oxo-2,3,4,5-tetrahydro-*as*-triazine as long, prismatic needles, m.p. 200–202° (eq. 31). Delaby[74, 75] has carried out similar reactions. Thus, 1,3-dibromo-2-

$$
\begin{array}{c}
\text{CH}_3\text{C}=\text{NNHCONH}_2 \\
| \\
\text{CH}_3\text{CHOH}
\end{array}
\quad \xrightarrow{\quad //\quad} \quad (30)
$$

pentanone reacts with semicarbazide (eq. 32) to yield a product, m.p. 115–117° (dec.), which may be 6-(1-bromopropyl)-3-oxo-2,3,4,5-tetrahydro-*as*-triazine (XXII) or 6-bromomethyl-5-ethyl-3-oxo-2,3,4,5-tetrahydro-*as*-triazine (XXIII). 1,2-Dibromo-3-pentanone, on the other hand, with semicarbazide (eq. 33) gives a bromine-free product, m.p. 229–230° (dec.), which Delaby thought might be either 3-oxo-6-(1-semicarbazonopropyl)-hexahydro-*as*-triazine (XXIV) or 3-oxo-5-(1-semicarbazonopropyl)-hexahydro-*as*-triazine (XXV). It may also be 6-ethyl-3-oxo-5-(1-semicarbazidomethyl)-2,3,4,5-tetrahydro-*as*-triazine

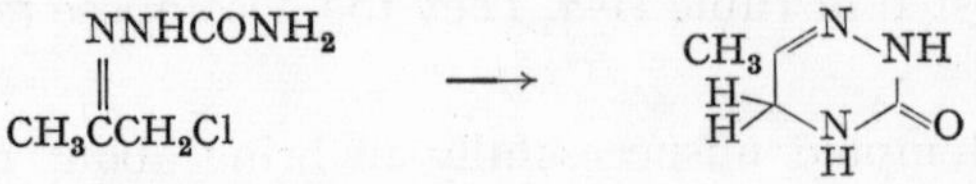

$$
\begin{array}{c}
\text{NNHCONH}_2 \\
\| \\
\text{CH}_3\text{CCH}_2\text{Cl}
\end{array}
\quad \longrightarrow \quad
\text{(structure)}
\qquad (31)
$$

(XXVI). Pummerer and Gump[159] reported that the reaction of semicarbazide with 1,5,5-trimethoxy-2-pentanone gives 3-oxo-6-(3-semicarbazonopropyl)-2,3,4,5-tetrahydro-*as*-triazine (eq. 34).

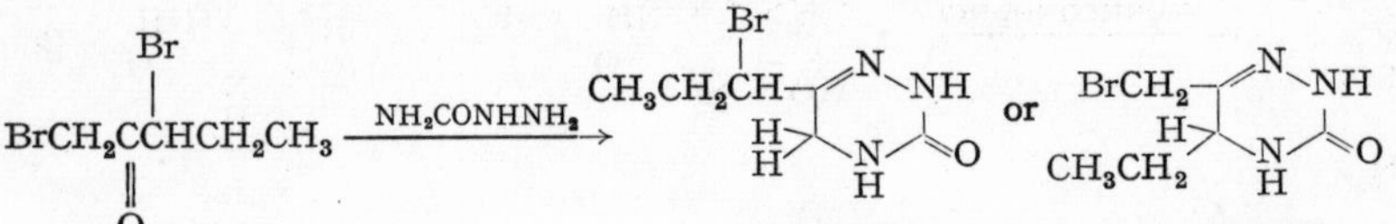

$$
\begin{array}{c}
\text{Br} \\
| \\
\text{BrCH}_2\text{CCHCH}_2\text{CH}_3 \\
\| \\
\text{O}
\end{array}
\xrightarrow{\text{NH}_2\text{CONHNH}_2}
\quad \text{(XXII)} \quad \text{or} \quad \text{(XXIII)}
\qquad (32)
$$

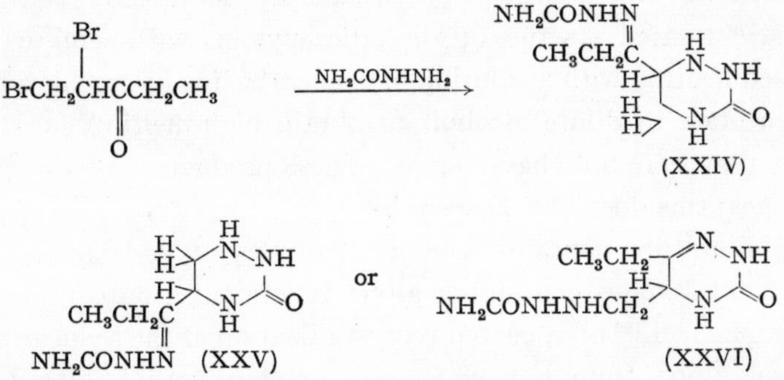

$$
\begin{array}{c}
\text{Br} \\
| \\
\text{BrCH}_2\text{CHCCH}_2\text{CH}_3 \\
\| \\
\text{O}
\end{array}
\xrightarrow{\text{NH}_2\text{CONHNH}_2}
\quad \text{(XXIV)} \quad \text{or}
$$

$$
\text{(XXV)} \quad \text{or} \quad \text{(XXVI)}
\qquad (33)
$$

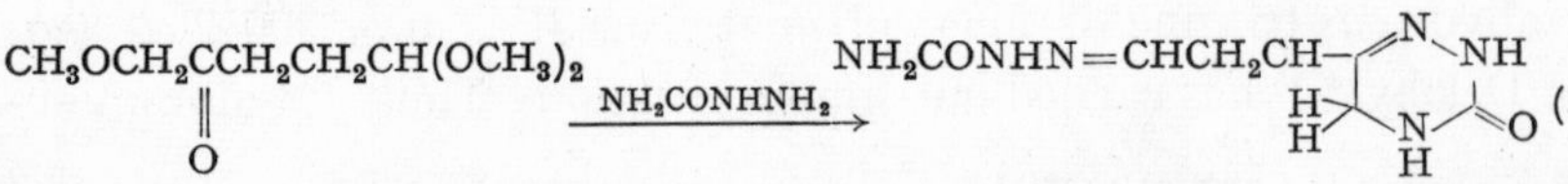

$$
\begin{array}{c}
\text{CH}_3\text{OCH}_2\text{CCH}_2\text{CH}_2\text{CH(OCH}_3)_2 \\
\| \\
\text{O}
\end{array}
\xrightarrow{\text{NH}_2\text{CONHNH}_2}
\quad \text{NH}_2\text{CONHN}{=}\text{CHCH}_2\text{CH-}\text{(triazine)}
\qquad (34)
$$

Scholtz[174] found that, when the semicarbazone of mesityl oxide is heated above its melting point or when it is distilled, a new substance is formed, isomeric with the semicarbazone. This new product melts at 129° and boils, with slight decomposition, at 212–213°. Scholtz thought that this new compound and the parent semicarbazone are geometric isomers. Harries and Kaiser[110] suggested that the new compound might be a pyrazoline (**XXVII** or **XXVIII**). This compound was later prepared by Rupe and Schlochoff,[169] who also prepared reaction products of semicarbazide with other unsaturated ketones. Rupe and Kessler[168] stated that the compound melts at 131° and that it very slowly evolves ammonia when heated with 10–15% sodium hydroxide solution. Such

$$(CH_3)_2 \diagup CH_3$$
$$HN\!\!-\!\!NCONH_2$$
(XXVII)

$$\overset{H}{}\ \overset{H}{}$$
$$(CH_3)_2 \diagup CH_3$$
$$H_2NCON\!\!-\!\!N$$
(XXVIII)

$$(CH_3)_2CH \quad \overset{H}{\underset{}{N}}\diagdown NH$$
$$CH_3 \diagdown \underset{\overset{|}{H}}{N} \diagup O$$
(XXIX)

$$\overset{CH_3}{}$$
$$CMe_2 \quad \overset{H}{\underset{}{N}}\diagdown NH$$
$$CH_3 \diagdown \underset{\overset{|}{H}}{N} \diagup O$$
(XXX)

resistance to alkali is not characteristic of semicarbazones. The suggestion that this material might be a triazine came from Rupe, Werder, and Takagi.[170] They proposed structure **XXIX**, without giving any mechanism whereby it might be formed. An analogous structure (**XXX**) was suggested for the reaction product (m.p. 223–224°) of semicarbazide and camphorylideneacetone; it too is very resistent to boiling alkali. These structures are, of course, merely tentative. Further work in this direction seems worthwhile.

A few miscellaneous syntheses of monooxo-*as*-triazines remain to be discussed. Von Walther and Hübner[193] reported that the reactions

$$\begin{array}{c} C_6H_5NNH_2 \\ | \\ (CH_3)_2CCONH_2 \end{array} \xrightarrow[\text{HCl}]{\text{RCHO}} \begin{array}{c} C_6H_5NN\!\!=\!\!CHR \\ | \\ (CH_3)_2CCONH_2 \end{array} \text{ or } \begin{array}{c} C_6H_5 \\ | \\ (CH_3)_2 \diagup \overset{N}{}\diagdown NH \\ O \diagup \underset{\overset{|}{H}}{N} \diagdown \overset{H}{\underset{R}{}} \end{array} \quad (35)$$

(XXXI)   (XXXII)

of aromatic aldehydes with α-(1-phenylhydrazino)isobutyramide lead to compounds that may be triazines (eq. 35). They suggested structures **XXXI** and **XXXII** for the products. Since they did no structure proof, they left the question of structure open. The product from benzaldehyde was isolated as gleaming white needles, m.p. 128°, soluble in the usual organic solvents. The product from salicylaldehyde is insoluble in ligroin. Widmann[195] heated the phenylhydrazide of

$$
\begin{array}{l}
\text{C}_6\text{H}_5\text{NNH}_2 \\
\quad | \\
\text{O}=\text{CCH}_2\text{NHC}_6\text{H}_5
\end{array}
\quad \xrightarrow[\Delta]{\text{HCOOH}} \quad
\text{(structure)}
\qquad (36)
$$

phenylglycine with anhydrous formic acid to obtain a compound thought to be a triazine (eq. 36). It was isolated as silky needles, m.p. 173–174°, not very soluble in organic solvents but soluble in concentrated hydrochloric acid.

Sen,[177] by heating phenylhydrazine with several N-acetyl-N-arylglycines, obtained products said to be as-triazines (eq. 37). The experimental conditions employed involved heating molar amounts of

$$
\begin{array}{l}
\text{R} \\
| \\
\text{CH}_3\text{CONCH}_2\text{COOH}
\end{array}
\quad \xrightarrow{\text{C}_6\text{H}_5\text{NHNH}_2} \quad
\text{(structure)}
\qquad (37)
$$

$$(\text{XXXIII})$$

reagents in alcohol solution for 6–8 hours on the steam bath. In this way, Sen prepared XXXIII (R = C_6H_5, rectangular plates, m.p. 163–164°) in 53% yield, XXXIII (R = o-$\text{CH}_3\text{C}_6\text{H}_4$, rectangular plates, m.p. 183–184°) in 49% yield, and XXXIII (R = α-C_{10}H_7, fine scales, m.p. 221°) in 60% yield. These compounds were described as insoluble in dilute and concentrated alkali, soluble in concentrated hydrochloric acid but insoluble in this reagent after dilution, and giving bright rose-red solutions in concentrated sulfuric acid. They are insoluble in ether and in ligroin and soluble in most other organic solvents.

Sen stated that compounds with structure XXXIII could not be prepared by reactions of 1-acetyl-2-phenylhydrazine with N-arylglycines. He further declared that by heating acetylglycine or hippuric acid with phenylhydrazine he obtained mixtures (XXXIV) of as-triazines and imidazolones. Ohta[137] has challenged Sen's statements regarding this reaction; he asserted that Sen obtained hippuric phenyl-hydrazide (XXXV) rather than an *as*-triazine.

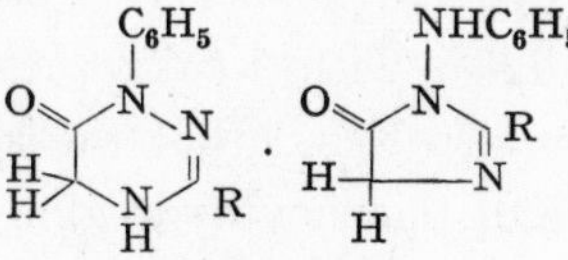

(XXXIV)   (XXXV)

$C_6H_5CONHCH_2CONHNHC_6H_5$

According to Harries[109] ethyl phenylhydrazinoacetate, heated at 130–160° with formamides, yields *as*-triazines (eq. 38). The product from formamide (XXXVI, R = H) was obtained in 20% yield. It is described as melting at 203–204° (dec.), soluble in alkali and insoluble in acid. It is decomposed by boiling alkali. The product from methyl-formamide (XXXVI, R = CH₃, m.p. 179–180°) was also produced by methylation of the product from formamide. Methyl iodide and

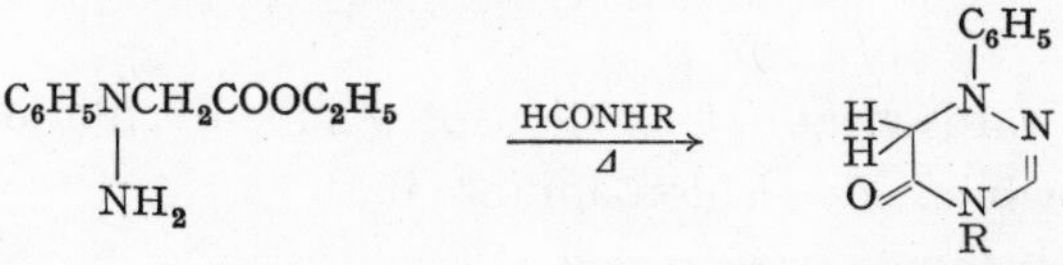

$$C_6H_5NCH_2COOC_2H_5 \xrightarrow[\Delta]{HCONHR}$$

(38)

(XXXVI)

alcoholic potassium hydroxide were employed in the methylation reaction, which also gave a considerable amount of methylamine. The 4-phenyl analog (XXXVI, R = C₆H₅), m.p. 204–205°, was prepared from formanilide. It is said to be soluble with difficulty in organic solvents.

Busch and Küspert[44] found that the semicarbazone of phenacyl-hydrazine, upon standing with alkali or being heated on the steam bath,

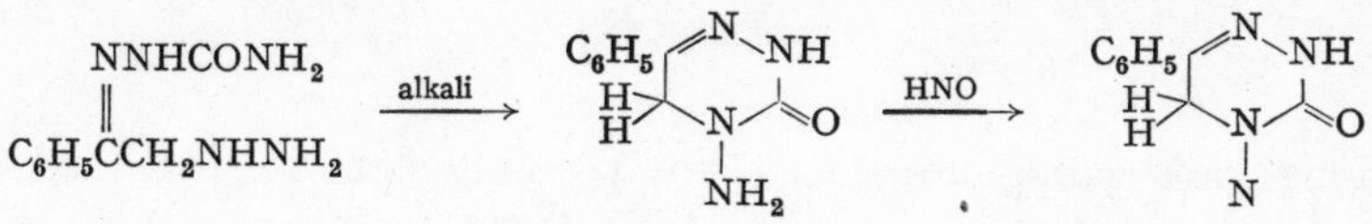

(39)

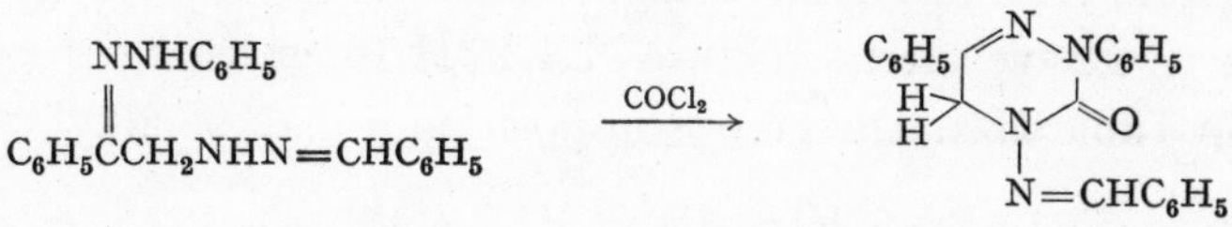

(40)

is cyclized to 4-amino-3-oxo-6-phenyl-2,3,4,5-tetrahydro-*as*-triazine (eq. 39). Nitrous acid removes the amino group from this compound, yielding 3-oxo-6-phenyl-2,3,4,5-tetrahydro-*as*-triazine. This product is described as long needles, m.p. 224–228°, with weakly acidic and weakly basic properties. These workers also found that the action of phosgene on the benzylidene derivative of phenacylhydrazine phenyl-hydrazone produces a 50% yield of 4-benzylideneamino-3-oxo-6-phenyl-2,3,4,5-tetrahydro-*as*-triazine, m.p. 199° (eq. 40).

Fusco and Romani[97] reported the preparation of an *as*-triazine by the reaction of equation 41. The product is described as a lemon-yellow material, m.p. 216–217°, insoluble in aqueous acids and alkali

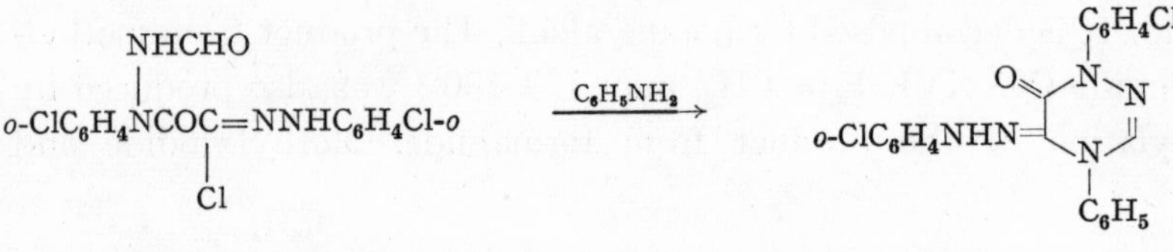

$$o\text{-ClC}_6\text{H}_4\text{NCOC}{=}\text{NNHC}_6\text{H}_4\text{Cl-}o \quad \xrightarrow{\;C_6H_5NH_2\;} \qquad (41)$$

and stable towards heat. The action of stannous chloride upon this compound slowly yields *o*-chloroaniline.

The most common preparation of dihydroxy- or dioxo-*as*-triazines is the cyclization of semicarbazones of α-keto acids (eq. 42). These

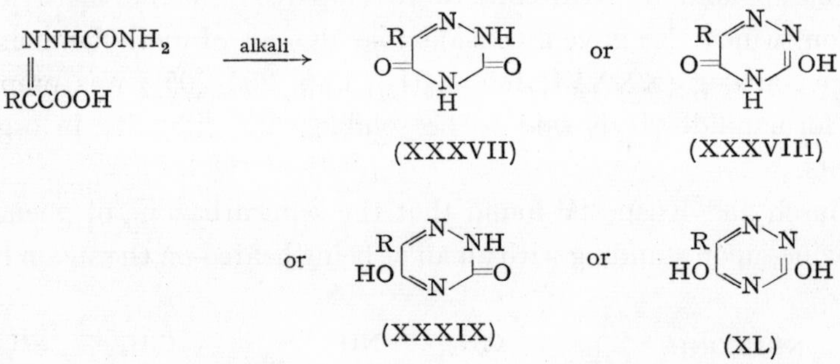

(XXXVII)   (XXXVIII)

(XXXIX)   (XL)   (42)

reactions yield compounds that are possibly best regarded as 3,5-dioxo-2,3,4,5-tetrahydro-*as*-triazines (XXXVII), although monoenolic forms (XXXVIII and XXXIX) and the dienolic form (XL) cannot be excluded. We have used structure XXXVII when listing these compounds in Table II-4. The groups in position 6 may be alkyl, aryl, or aralkyl.

TABLE II-4. 3,5-Dioxo-2,3,4,5-tetrahydro-*as*-triazines

Substituents	Color, crystal habit	M.p., °C.	Ref.
None	Leaflets	272	176
4-Acetyl-6-benzyl		110	54
6-*p*-Anisyl		273	29
6-(1-*p*-Anisylethyl)	Brilliant plates	220.5	47
6-(1-*p*-Anisylethyl)-4-benzyl		206	47, 56
6-(1-*p*-Anisylethyl)-2,4-dibenzyl		160.5–161.5	47, 56
6-(1-*p*-Anisylethyl)-2,4-diethyl	Liquid		47, 56
6-(1-*p*-Anisylethyl)-2,4-dimethyl		142.5	47, 56
6-(1-*p*-Anisylethyl)-4-ethyl		132	47, 56
6-(1-*p*-Anisylethyl)-4-methyl		159–160	47, 56
6-Benzyl		208	29
6-Benzyl-2,4-dichloro		119 (expl. 150)	34, 67
6-Benzyl-2,4-diethyl	Liquid		29
6-Benzyl-2,4-dimethyl		96	29
6-Benzyl-2-ethyl		103	54, 57
6-Benzyl-4-ethyl		117	29
2-Benzyl-6-*p*-methoxybenzyl		120	98
4-Benzyl-6-*p*-methoxybenzyl		136	98
6-Benzyl-2-methyl		137	54, 57
6-Benzyl-4-methyl		150	29
4-Benzyl-6-*β*-naphthyl		217	157
6-Butyl		135	100
6-Isobutyl		185	100
6-*sec*-Butyl		206–207	117
6-*tert*-Butyl		285	29
6-Carbethoxycarbamyl-2-*p*-nitrophenyl	Garnet-red prisms	205	194
6-Carbethoxycarbamyl-2-phenyl	Buff-colored, feathery crystals	203 (dec.)	194
6-Carbethoxycarbamyl-2-*p*-tolyl	Buff, silky needles	218	194
6-(8-Carboxyoctyl)		128–132	200
2-Chloro-4,6-dibenzyl		153	34, 67
2,6-Dibenzyl		113	54, 57
4,6-Dibenzyl		161	29
2,4-Dibenzyl-6-*p*-methoxybenzyl		71	98
2,4-Dibenzyl-6-*β*-naphthyl		179	157
6-(1,4-Dicarbethoxybutyl)	Colorless prisms	158–159	1
2,4-Dichloro-6-phenylethyl		130 (expl. 160)	34,67

(*Table continued*)

TABLE II-4 *(continued)*

Substituents	Color, crystal habit	M.p., °C.	Ref.
2,4-Diethyl-6-*p*-methoxybenzyl		72	98
2,4-Dimethyl-6-*p*-methoxybenzyl		89	98
2,4-Dimethyl-6-phenyl		118	29
6-(1,2-Diphenyl-2-hydroxyethyl)		226	29
6-(1,2-Diphenyl-2-hydroxyethyl- 4-methyl)		184	29
6-Ethyl		152	100
4-Ethyl-6-*p*-methoxybenzyl		140	98
6-*p*-Methoxybenzyl		177	99
		215	98
6-*p*-Methoxybenzyl-4-methyl		144	98
6-Methyl		209	182
4-Methyl-6-phenyl		205	29
6-(3,4-Methylenedioxystyryl)		282	29
6-*β*-Naphthyl		289	157, 158
2-*m*-Nitrophenyl-6-*o*-nitro- phenylazo	Red rhomboids	224	194
6-Phenyl		262	29
2-Phenyl-6-phenylazo	Orange needles	256	194
6-(2-Phenyl-2-thiosemicarba- zonoethyl)		187.5	64
6-(2-Phenylethyl)		194	29
6-Styryl		266	29
2-*p*-Tolyl-6-*p*-tolylazo	Orange-red needles	246	194
2,4,6-Tribenzyl		108	29
6-Veratryl		212	92

The cyclizations of semicarbazones of α-keto acids are usually carried out in the presence of some alkaline substance. Thus, Siebert[176] obtained the simplest triazine of this type, 3,5-dioxo-2,3,4,5-tetrahydro-*as*-triazine itself (XXXVII, R = H), by refluxing a solution of glyoxylic acid semicarbazone in 2 N sodium hydroxide, then acidifying. Similar cyclizations failed completely with the semicarbazone of pyruvic acid (using excess dilute aqueous alkali)[29,30] and the semicarbazone of ethyl pyruvate (with sodium ethoxide).[6] Unchanged starting material was recovered in the latter case. Higher homologs have been obtained without difficulty, however; 6-*sec*-butyl-3,5-dioxo-2,3,4,5-tetrahydro-*as*-triazine was prepared from the ester of the corresponding keto acid[117] and the 6-*tert*-butyl derivative from the keto acid[29]. The 6-aryl and -6aralkyl derivatives are easily prepared by this method. Bougalt thought that the success of this cyclization increased with the electronegativity of the group in the 6-position. The yields are frequently very good but an appreciable evolution of ammonia also occurs and this, of course, prevents the yields from being theoretical. In general, it is desirable, from the viewpoint of good yields, to permit the semicarbazone of the keto acid to stand with a slight excess of dilute alkali (sodium hydroxide or sodium carbonate) at room temperature; several weeks may be necessary for reaction to take place. By raising the temperature to the boiling point of the mixture, one may shorten the reaction time to a few hours but the yields are usually decreased.

Adickes[1] found that ethyl α-ethoxalyladipate reacts with semicarbazide hydrochloride, ring closure taking place without benefit of added alkali. Surprisingly, ethyl α-ethoxalylpimelate could not be induced to react with semicarbazide, thiosemicarbazide, phenylhydrazine, or benzhydrazide. Zakutskaya[200] has stated that α-oxoundecanoic acid yields a semicarbazide which loses water to form a triazine; no details were given.

A few less important preparations of 3,5-dioxo-2,3,4,5-tetrahydro-*as*-triazines remain to be mentioned. When the semicarbazone of 4,5-dioxo-2,3-diphenyl-tetrahydrofuran is treated with dilute alkali,

$$
\begin{array}{ccc}
\text{(structure)} & \xrightarrow[\text{alkali}]{\text{dilute}} & \text{(structure)} \quad (43)
\end{array}
$$

$$
\begin{array}{ccc}
\text{(structure)} & \longrightarrow & \text{(structure)} \xleftarrow[\text{H}_2\text{O}]{\text{Br}_2} \text{(structure)} \quad (44)
\end{array}
$$

a rearrangement occurs and an *as*-triazine is formed in 80% yield (eq. 43).[29] The semicarbazone of an α-oxo acid may be an intermediate in this reaction. 6-Methyl-3,5-dioxo-2,3,4,5-tetrahydro-*as*-triazine, which could not be prepared from the semicarbazones of pyruvic acid or its ethyl ester, has been obtained by the cyclization of ethyl α-1-(1-*m*-nitrophenylazosemicarbazido)propionate (eq. 44).[7] It was also prepared by the oxidation of the hexahydro-*as*-triazine with bromine water (eq. 44).[182] Sodium hypobromite solution has been found to replace the thioxo groups in 3-oxo-5-thioxo-2,3,4,5-tetrahydro-*as*-triazines with oxo groups. This reaction is discussed at greater length in the section dealing with thioxo compounds.

Whiteley and Yapp[194] have prepared *as*-triazines from malonylurethan. In the first step, they carried out the reaction between

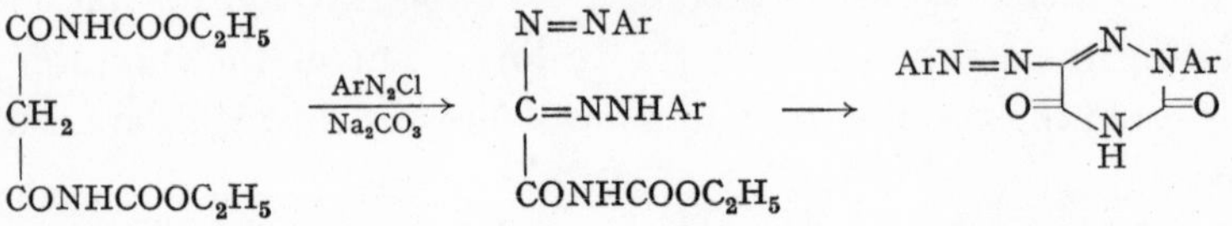

$$\underset{\substack{|\\ \text{CH}_2 \\ |\\ \text{CONHCOOC}_2\text{H}_5}}{\overset{\text{CONHCOOC}_2\text{H}_5}{\,}} \xrightarrow[\text{Na}_2\text{CO}_3]{\text{ArN}_2\text{Cl}} \underset{\substack{|\\ \text{C}=\text{NNHAr} \\ |\\ \text{CONHCOOC}_2\text{H}_5}}{\overset{\text{N}=\text{NAr}}{\,}} \longrightarrow \quad \text{(ring structure)} \qquad (45)$$

$$\text{(ring structure)} \xrightarrow{\text{dilute KOH}} \underset{\substack{|\\ \text{C}=\text{NNHAr} \\ |\\ \text{COOH}}}{\overset{\text{N}=\text{NAr}}{\,}} \qquad (46)$$

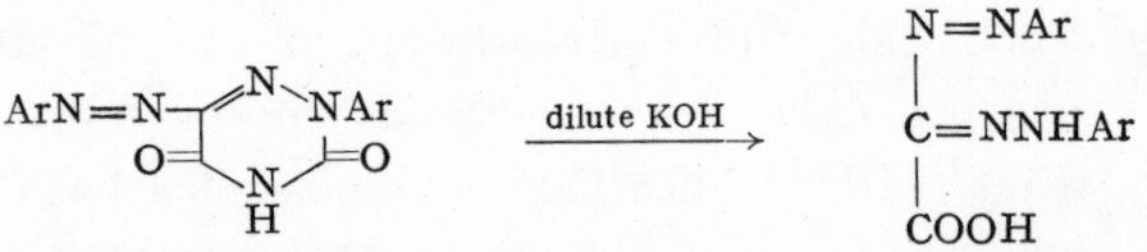

malonylurethan and aryldiazonium chloride in the presence of sodium carbonate. The formazyl compounds so formed were cyclized to *as*-triazines (eq. 45) by heating in boiling xylene or by dissolving in warm alcoholic potassium hydroxide, diluting with water and acidifying with dilute acid. These products are also listed in Table II-4. When heated with dilute potassium hydroxide solution, they undergo ring opening and formazylacetic acids are formed (eq. 46).

The 3,5-dioxo-2,3,4,5-tetrahydro-*as*-triazines are monobasic acids;

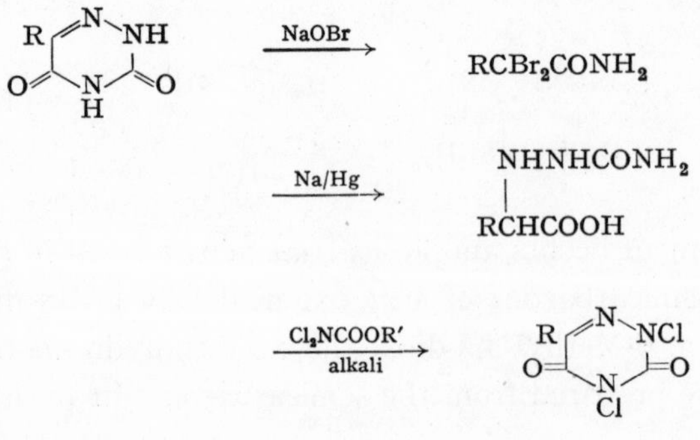

$$\text{(ring structure)} \xrightarrow{\text{NaOBr}} \text{RCBr}_2\text{CONH}_2 \qquad (47)$$

$$\xrightarrow{\text{Na/Hg}} \underset{\substack{|\\ \text{RCHCOOH}}}{\overset{\text{NHNHCONH}_2}{\,}} \qquad (48)$$

$$\xrightarrow[\text{alkali}]{\text{Cl}_3\text{NCOOR}'} \text{(ring structure)} \qquad (49)$$

they can be titrated with phenolphthalein as indicator and some of their alkali metal salts have been isolated. Sodium hypobromite solution opens the triazine ring in these compounds and dibromo amides are formed (eq. 47).[29, 31, 55] The triazine ring can also be opened by reducing agents; the action of sodium amalgam yields α-1-semicarbazido acids (eq. 48).[98, 157] 3,5-Dioxo-2,3,4,5-tetrahydro-as-triazines can be chlorinated with N,N-dichlorocarbamic esters in alkaline solution (eq. 49).[34, 67] The few compounds which have been prepared in this manner are listed in Table II-4. The 2,4-dichloro compounds may explode after melting; the 2-chloro-4-alkyl compounds do not appear to be as unstable.

Alkali metal derivatives of 3,5-dioxo-2,3,4,5-tetrahydro-as-triazines react with alkyl halides to form two types of product, monoalkyl and dialkyl derivatives (eq. 50).[29, 30] These may easily be separated since

$$
\begin{array}{c}
\underset{\substack{R \\ O=\overset{N}{\underset{H}{\big|}}}}{\overset{N}{\big\Vert}} \overset{NH}{\underset{}{\big|}}=O \xrightarrow[R'X]{\text{alkali}}
\end{array}
\quad
\begin{array}{c}
\underset{R'}{\overset{R}{O=}} \overset{N}{\underset{N}{\big\Vert}} \overset{NH}{\big|} =O \xrightarrow{H_2O} R'NHCONHNH_2 \longrightarrow R'NH_2 \\[2em]
+ \\[1em]
\underset{R'}{\overset{R}{O=}} \overset{N}{\underset{N}{\big\Vert}} \overset{NR'}{\big|} =O
\end{array}
\qquad (50)
$$

the monoalkyl derivatives are soluble in alkali, while the dialkyl derivatives are not. A monomethyl derivative, so obtained, when heated with sodium hydroxide solution, gives only methylamine as the gaseous product. Furthermore, the monobenzyl, monomethyl, and monoethyl derivatives can be converted by cautious hydrolysis to 4-alkylsemicarbazides (eq. 50).[29, 32] These facts show clearly that the monoalkyl derivatives are 4-alkyl-as-triazines. The dialkylated compounds are 2,4-dialkyl-as-triazines. Many such alkyl derivatives have been prepared and are listed in Table II-4.

2-Alkyl derivatives of 3,5-dioxo-2,3,4,5-tetrahydro-as-triazines have been prepared in other ways. One of these includes the acid hydrolysis of the dialkyl derivatives of 3-thioxo-5-oxo-2,3,4,5-tetrahydro-as-triazines and will be discussed in a subsequent section. Another method of preparation involves the reaction of an α-oxo acid with 2-alkylsemicarbazides (eq. 51).[49, 54, 57] The 2-alkyl and 4-alkyl derivatives of 3,5-dioxo-2,3,4,5-tetrahydro-*as*-triazines, converted to their alkali metal salts and treated with alkyl halides, yield the same dialkyl derivatives. This fact further establishes the structures of these compounds. Sodium amalgam converts the monoalkyl derivatives to semicarbazido acids.[55]

$$
\begin{array}{ccc}
\text{RCCOOH} & \xrightarrow{\underset{}{NH_2CONHN_2}} & \\
\underset{\parallel}{} & & \\
O & &
\end{array}
\qquad (51)
$$

6-Benzyl-3,5-dioxo-2,3,4,5-tetrahydro-*as*-triazine, treated with acetic anhydride, is converted to a monoacetyl derivative that is very easily hydrolyzed.[54] The exact position of the acetyl group was not determined but it was presumed to be in the 4 position.

Attempts to prepare 6,6-dimethyl-3,5-dioxo-3,4,5,6-tetrahydro-*as*-triazine by cyclization of a substituted isobutyric ester or by oxidation of the corresponding hexahydro-*as*-triazine failed (eq. 52).[7] Decomposition occurred, giving molecular nitrogen.

$$
\begin{array}{ccccc}
\overset{CH_3}{\underset{|}{}} & & & & \\
NH_2CON{=}NCCOOC_2H_5 & \xrightarrow{\;\;\Delta\;\;}\!\!\!/\!\!/ & (CH_3)_2 & \xleftarrow{Br_2,\,H_2O}\!\!\!/\!\!/ & (CH_3)_2 \\
\underset{|}{} & & & & \\
CH_3 & & & &
\end{array}
\qquad (52)
$$

A few 3,5-dioxo-hexahydro-*as*-triazines have been synthesized and are summarized in Table II-5. The preparative methods all involve cyclization of α-hydrazino acid derivatives. Thus, the simplest member of this group, 3,5-dioxohexahydro-*as*-triazine, was prepared by Bailey and Read,[8] who treated ethyl 4-semicarbazidoacetate with sodium ethoxide (eq. 53). In a similar manner, other 3,5-dioxohexahydro-*as*-triazines

$$
\begin{array}{ccc}
NHNHCONH_2 & \xrightarrow{\;NaOC_2H_5\;} & \\
\underset{|}{} & & \\
CH_2COOC_2H_5 & &
\end{array}
\qquad (53)
$$

were obtained from the esters of α-4-semicarbazidopropionic acid and α-4-semicarbazidoisobutyric acid.[6] Ethyl α-4-semicarbazidopropionate was cyclized quantitatively by sodium ethoxide, in 83% yield by cold alcoholic potassium hydroxide and in much lower yield by heating at 120°.[6]

TABLE II-5. 3,5-Dioxo-hexahydro-*as*-triazines

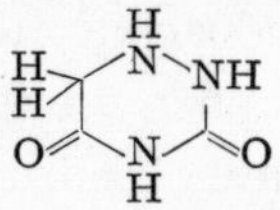

Substituents	M.p., °C.	Ref.
None	221	8
1-Benzoyl-6-methyl		6
1-Carbethoxymethyl	138.5	8
1-Carbomethoxymethyl	183.5	8
4-(*N*-Carboxymethyl-*N*-phenylamino)-1-phenyl	176	39
6,6-Dimethyl	230	6
6,6-Dimethyl-1-*m*-nitrophenylazo	133 (expl.)	7
1,4-Diphenyl	257–258	167
4-Ethyl-1-phenyl	135–136	39
6-Methyl	214	182
6-Methyl-1-*m*-nitrophenylazo		7
1-Phenyl	225	39
	229	96

Several examples have been provided wherein substituted semi-carbazido groups are involved in the ring closure. Bailey[6] converted ethyl α-(4-benzoyl-4-semicarbazido)propionate to 1-benzoyl-3,5-dioxo-6-methylhexahydro-*as*-triazine (XLI, R $= C_6H_5CO$, R' $=$ H, R'' $= CH_3$) by the use of sodium ethoxide (eq. 54). Bailey and Knox[7] used potas-

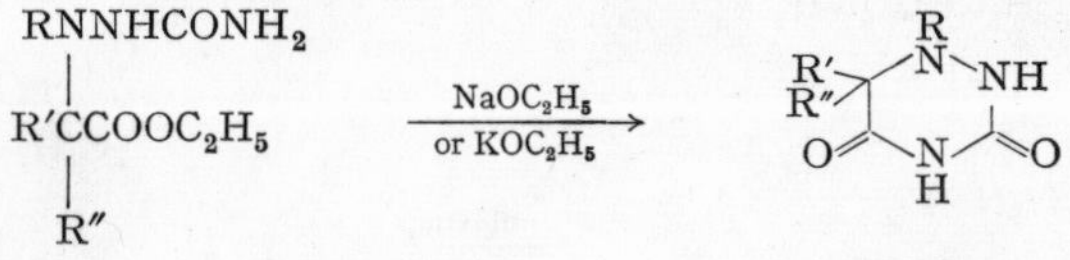

$$\begin{array}{c} \text{RNNHCONH}_2 \\ | \\ \text{R'CCOOC}_2\text{H}_5 \\ | \\ \text{R''} \end{array} \xrightarrow[\text{or KOC}_2\text{H}_5]{\text{NaOC}_2\text{H}_5} \quad \text{(XLI)} \tag{54}$$

sium ethoxide in cyclizing ethyl α-(4-*m*-nitrophenylazo-4-semicarba-zido)isobutyrate; the same product (XLI, R $= m\text{-NO}_2\text{C}_6\text{H}_4\text{N} = \text{N-}$, R' $=$ R'' $= CH_3$) was obtained by treating 6,6-dimethyl-3,5-dioxo-hexahydro-*as*-triazine (XLI, R' $=$ R'' $= CH_3$) with *m*-nitrobenzene-diazonium chloride. Bailey and Read[8] treated 4,4-semicarbazidedi-acetic esters with sodium alkoxides to obtain hexahydro-*as*-triazines (XLI, R $= \text{CH}_2\text{COOCH}_3$ or $\text{CH}_2\text{COOC}_2\text{H}_5$, R' $=$ R'' $=$ H). The carbomethoxymethyl derivative was formed in 70% yield.

Using alcoholic potassium hydroxide, Busch[39] cyclized esters of

α-4-semicarbazidoacetic acids to *as*-triazines (eq. 55). The reaction fails when R is phenyl but proceeds, apparently quite well, when R is hydrogen or ethyl. A substituted carbazide was used in the preparation of another *as*-triazine (eq. 56); this compound was obtained in very poor yield.

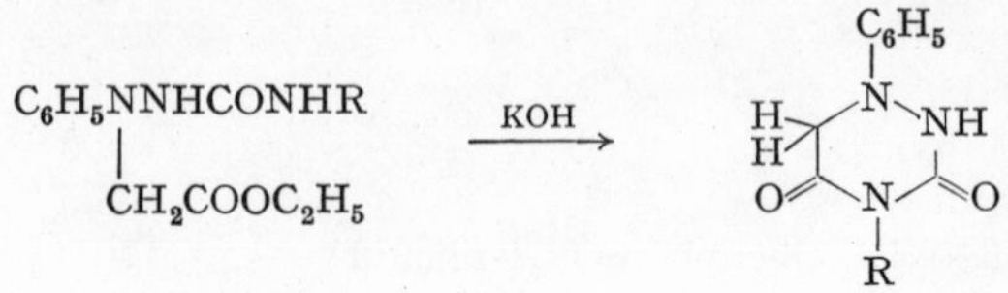

$$
\begin{array}{c}
C_6H_5NNHCONHR \\
| \\
CH_2COOC_2H_5
\end{array}
\xrightarrow{\text{KOH}}
\quad
\text{(55)}
$$

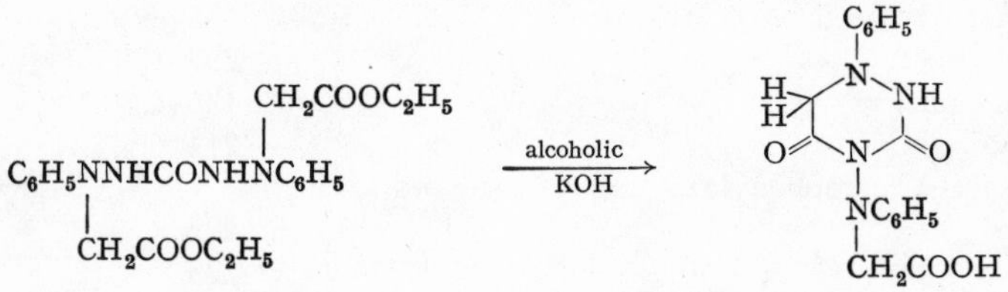

$$
\begin{array}{c}
CH_2COOC_2H_5 \\
| \\
C_6H_5NNHCONHNC_6H_5 \\
| \\
CH_2COOC_2H_5
\end{array}
\xrightarrow[\text{KOH}]{\text{alcoholic}}
\quad
\text{(56)}
$$

α-4-Semicarbazidopropionamide, heated with hydrochloric acid gives a 15% yield of 3,5-dioxo-6-methylhexahydro-*as*-triazine (eq. 57).[182] Apparently, no hydrolysis to carboxylic acid takes place. α-1-Phenylhydrazinoacetylurea, heated in refluxing alcohol, loses

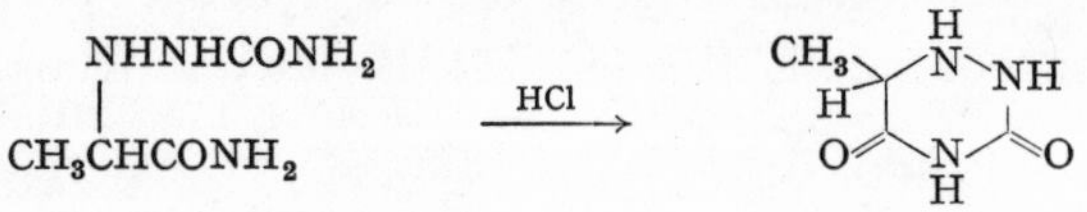

$$
\begin{array}{c}
NHNHCONH_2 \\
| \\
CH_3CHCONH_2
\end{array}
\xrightarrow{\text{HCl}}
\quad
\text{(57)}
$$

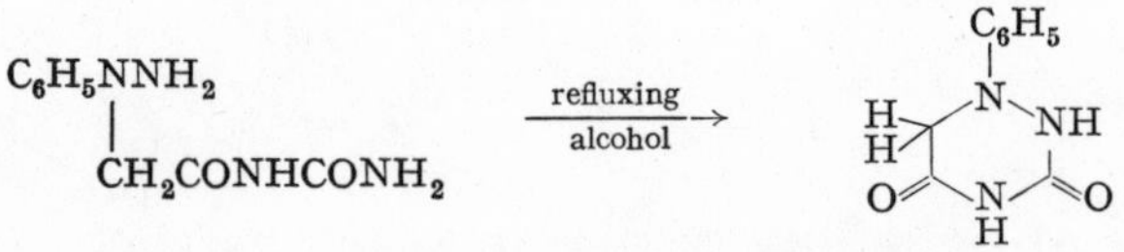

$$
\begin{array}{c}
C_6H_5NNH_2 \\
| \\
CH_2CONHCONH_2
\end{array}
\xrightarrow[\text{alcohol}]{\text{refluxing}}
\quad
\text{(58)}
$$

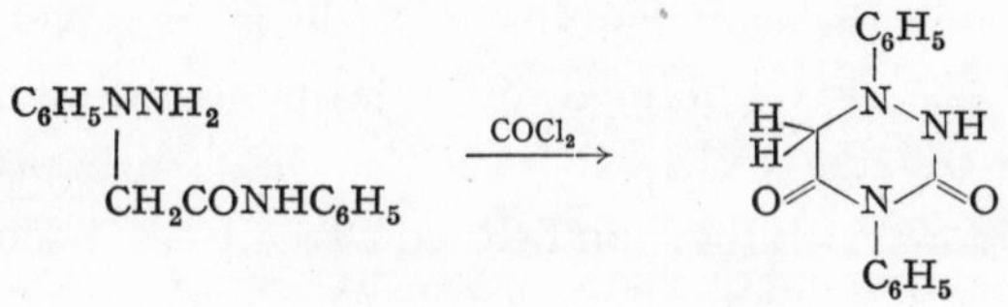

$$
\begin{array}{c}
C_6H_5NNH_2 \\
| \\
CH_2CONHC_6H_5
\end{array}
\xrightarrow{\text{COCl}_2}
\quad
\text{(59)}
$$

ammonia to form 3,5-dioxo-1-phenylhexahydro-*as*-triazine (eq. 58).[96] A similar compound was obtained by Rupe and Heberlein[167] by treating α-1-phenylhydrazinoacetanilide with phosgene (eq. 59).

3,5-Dioxohexahydro-*as*-triazine is readily soluble in water, soluble with difficulty in alcohol, and insoluble in the other common organic solvents. With increasing substitution, the 3,5-dioxohexahydro-*as*-triazines become less soluble in water and more easily soluble in organic solvents. 3,5-Dioxo-1,4-diphenylhexahydro-*as*-triazine, however, is insoluble in all organic solvents. insoluble in acids, and soluble with difficulty in alkali. The 3,5-dioxohexahydro-*as*-triazines are, as a rule, easily hydrolyzed in alkaline solution to form semicarbazido acids (eq. 60). Somewhat different behavior is shown by 1-benzoyl-3,5-dioxo-6-methylhexahydro-*as*-triazine. When subjected to the action of 10% potassium hydroxide solution, it is converted to a triazole (eq. 61).[6]

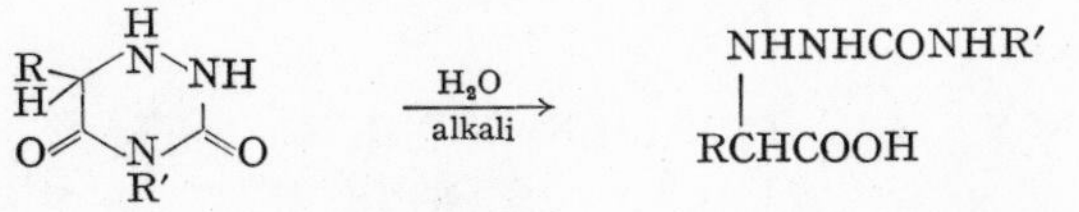

$$\xrightarrow[\text{alkali}]{\text{H}_2\text{O}}$$

$$
\begin{array}{c}
\text{NHNHCONHR}' \\
| \\
\text{RCHCOOH}
\end{array}
$$

(60)

$$\xrightarrow{10\%\,\text{KOH}}$$

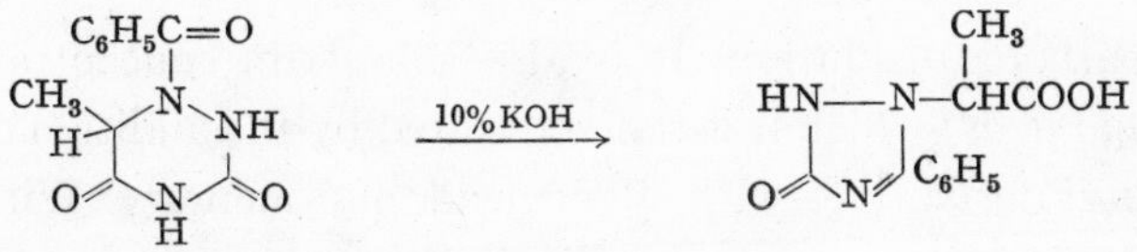

(61)

Many of the 3,5-dioxohexahydro-*as*-triazines are easily oxidized, especially when positions 1 and 2 are unsubstituted. Thus, 3,5-dioxo-6-methylhexahydro-*as*-triazine is oxidized by bromine water to a compound presumed to be 3,5-dioxo-6-methyl-3,4,5,6-tetrahydro-*as*-triazine (eq. 62).[182] However, bromine water destroys 6,6-dimethyl-3,5-

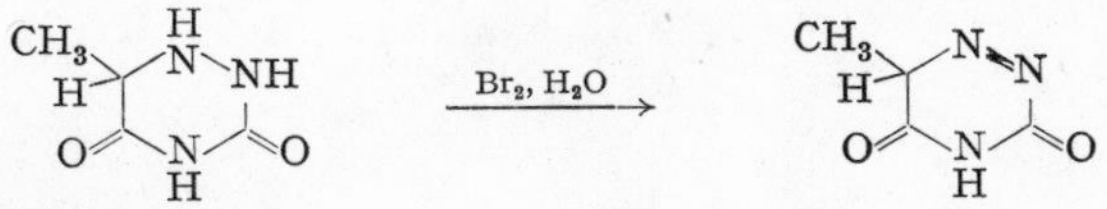

$$\xrightarrow{\text{Br}_2,\,\text{H}_2\text{O}}$$

(62)

dioxohexahydro-*as*-triazine; nitrogen is formed.[7] Even substituted compounds of this class are easily oxidized. Thus 3,5-dioxo-1,4-diphenylhexahydro-*as*-triazine, in which both 1 and 4 positions bear phenyl groups, is said to be oxidized by Fehling's solution.

3,5-Dioxo-6-methylhexahydro-*as*-triazine reacts with *m*-nitrobenzenediazonium chloride, forming 1-*m*-nitrophenylazo-6-methyl-

3,5-dioxohexahydro-*as*-triazine (eq. 63).[7] The 6,6-dimethyl analog behaves similarly.[7]

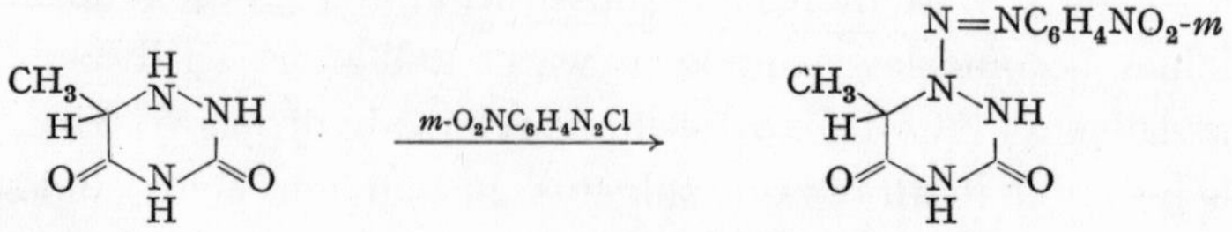

$$\text{(63)}$$

Mercapto and Thioxo Derivatives. A single mercapto *as*-triazine has been described. Wolff and Lindenhayn[198] converted α-cyanoazoaceto-phenone to its thioamide by treatment with hydrogen sulfide. When heated with potassium carbonate, this thioamide was cyclized to 3-mercapto-5-phenyl-*as*-triazine (eq. 64). This compound is soluble in

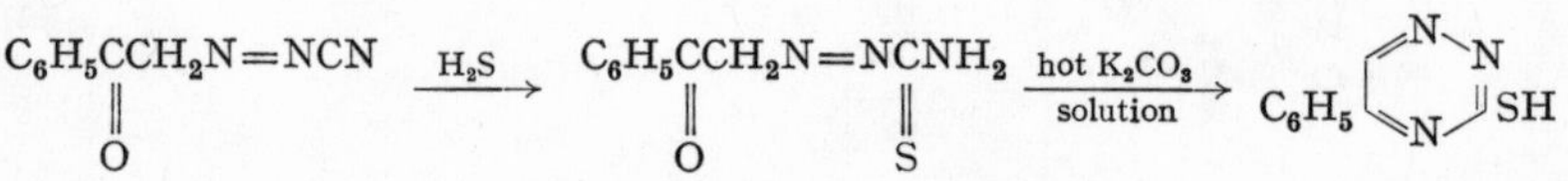

$$\text{(64)}$$

sodium carbonate solution. It is also soluble in concentrated hydro-chloric acid, from which it is reprecipitated by the addition of water. It forms metal derivatives with silver, lead, and mercury. With hot 20% nitric acid, it is converted to a disulfide. These compounds are listed in Table I1-1. The ring closure of thiosemicarbazones of α-oxo acids gives products that may have any of the structures, XLII, XLIII, or XLIV (eq. 65). On the basis of the acidity of the products and the struc-

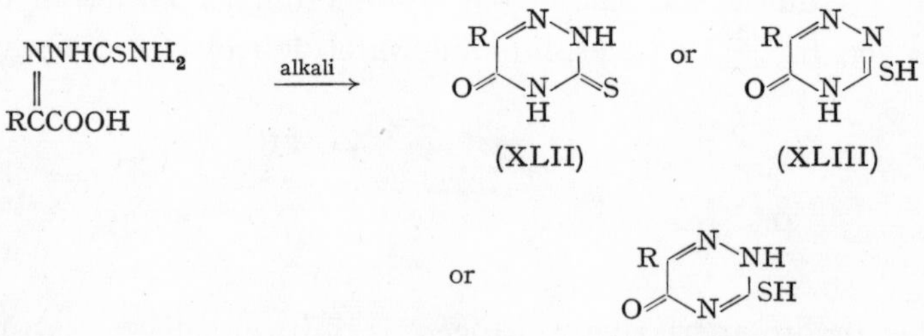

$$\text{(65)}$$

tures of their alkylated derivatives, it has been generally agreed that structure XLIV is probably the best one. It has therefore been used throughout this discussion and the products are listed under this structure in Table II-6. The cyclization takes place under the influence

TABLE II-6. 3-Mercapto-5-oxo-2,5-dihydro-*as*-
triazines, Tautomers[a] and Derivatives

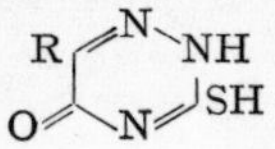

Substituents	M.p., °C.	Ref.
6-(1-*p*-Anisylethyl)	171	61
6-(1-*p*-Anisylethyl)-*S*-benzyl	165.5	61
6-(1-*p*-Anisylethyl)-*S*-benzyl, dihydro deriv.	135	61
6-(1-*p*-Anisylethyl)-*S*-ethyl	126	61
6-(1-*p*-Anisylethyl)-*S*-methyl	216.5	61
6-(1-*p*-Anisylethyl)-*S*-methyl, dihydro deriv.	174	61
6-Benzyl	194	35
6-Benzyl-*S*-carboxymethyl	160	65
6-Benzyl-2,*S*-diethyl	Liquid	52, 58
6-Benzyl-4,*S*-diethyl	Liquid	52, 60
6-Benzyl-2,4-dimethyl	83	52
6-Benzyl-2,*S*-dimethyl	116.5	52, 58
6-Benzyl-4,*S*-dimethyl	112	60
6-Benzyl-*S*-ethyl	200–201	50
6-Benzyl-*S*-ethyl, dihydro deriv.	108.5	50
6-Benzyl-4-ethyl	175	51
	176	60
6-Benzyl-4-ethyl, dihydro deriv.	127–128[b]	51
S-Benzyl-6-*p*-methoxybenzyl	184	98
S-Benzyl-6-*p*-methoxybenzyl, dihydro deriv.	72[c]	98
6-Benzyl-2-methyl	152.5	49
	153.5	59
6-Benzyl-4-methyl	175.5	51, 60
6-Benzyl-4-methyl, dihydro deriv.	140–143	51
6-Benzyl-*S*-methyl	202	50
6-Benzyl-*S*-methyl, dihydro deriv.	129	50
6-Butyl	143	100
6-Isobutyl	182	100
S-Carboxymethyl-6-phenyl	160–162	65
2,6-Dibenzyl	123	49, 59
6,*S*-Dibenzyl	166–167	50
	167	58
6,*S*-Dibenzyl, dihydro deriv.	123–124	50
	125	53, 58
2,*S*-Dibenzyl-6-*p*-methoxybenzyl	Liquid	98
4,6-Dimethyl-2-phenyl	150[d]	83
6-Ethyl	165	100
S-Ethyl-6-*p*-methoxybenzyl	187	98

(Table continued)

TABLE II-6 *(continued)*

Substituents	M.p., °C.	Ref.
6-*p*-Methoxybenzyl	177	98
	215	99
6-*p*-Methoxybenzyl-*S*-methyl	211	98
6-Methyl	220	36
6-*β*-Naphthyl	274	157, 158
6-Phenyl	256	35
6-(2-Phenyl-2-thiosemicarbazonoethyl)	250	64, 66
6-(2-Phenylethyl)	210	35
6-Propyl	149	100
2,6,*S*-Tribenzyl	106	52, 58
2,6,*S*-Tribenzyl, dihydro deriv.	Liquid	53, 58

[a]See text for a discussion of tautomeric forms.
[b]Prisms
[c]Needles.
[d]Needles. Light absorption in ethanol, maxima at 2270 A. ($\varepsilon = 17,260$ and 2740 A. ($\varepsilon = 14,300$).

of alkali and proceeds more readily than the ring closure of the semi-carbazones.[35] The yields frequently approach theoretical. Many compounds have been prepared in this manner. Godfrin[100] has used the reaction of thiosemicarbazide with the oximes of several α-oxo esters to prepare these compounds. A closely related synthesis is illustrated by the reaction of β-*p*-anisyl-α-mercaptoacrylic acid with thiosemicarbazide (eq. 66); a thiosemicarbazone is doubtless an intermediate in this reaction.[98]

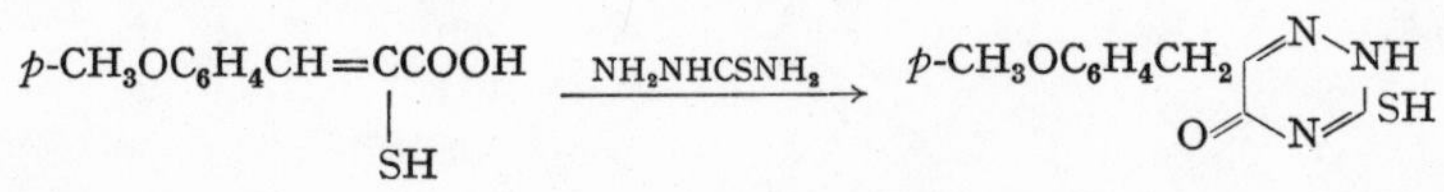

$$p\text{-CH}_3OC_6H_4CH{=}CCOOH \xrightarrow{\text{NH}_2\text{NHCSNH}_2} p\text{-CH}_3OC_6H_4CH_2 \qquad (66)$$

The 3-mercapto-5-oxo-2,5-dihydro-*as*-triazines (XLIV) are acidic, more so than the 3,5-dioxo-2,3,4,5-tetrahydro-*as*-triazines, and, like them, can be titrated with phenolphthalein as indicator. The action of sodium amalgam and water brings about combined reduction and ring opening, just as with the dioxo compounds, and α-4-thiosemicarbazido acids are formed.[37, 157] When compounds with structure XLIV are treated with Raney nickel, the sulfur is replaced by oxygen, not by hydrogen as is usual with many thio compounds.[33] The effect of bromine or iodine in alkaline solution is to replace the sulfur in XLIV with oxygen (eq. 67).[63] The salt of an intermediate sulfonic acid may be for-

$$
\begin{array}{ccc}
\underset{O}{\overset{R}{\diagdown}}\underset{N}{\overset{N}{\diagup}}\overset{NH}{\underset{SH}{}} & \xrightarrow{\text{NaOBr}} & \left[\underset{O}{\overset{R}{\diagdown}}\underset{N}{\overset{N}{\diagup}}\overset{NH}{\underset{SO_3Na}{}} \right] & \xrightarrow[-SO_2]{H^+} & \underset{O}{\overset{R}{\diagdown}}\underset{\underset{H}{N}}{\overset{N}{\diagup}}\overset{NH}{\underset{O}{}} & (67)
\end{array}
$$

med since there is no evolution of sulfur dioxide until the reaction mixture is acidified.[36, 46, 53, 99] However, the cleavage of sulfur dioxide may take place on the alkaline side; the sulfur dioxide could not be evolved until acidification. Use of a great excess of bromine in alkaline solution causes ring opening to give dibromo amides, just as with the 3,5-dioxo-2,3,4,5-tetrahydro-as-triazines. This ring opening does not occur with iodine. Phenolphthalein may be used as indicator in the bromometric determination of 3-mercapto-5-oxo-2,5-dihydro-as-triazines.[46] These compounds, when treated either with iodine in neutral solution or with cupric sulfate, are converted to the disulfides (eq. 68). The disulfide

$$
\underset{O}{\overset{R}{\diagdown}}\underset{N}{\overset{N}{\diagup}}\overset{NH}{\underset{SH}{}} \underset{HI}{\overset{I_2}{\rightleftarrows}} \underset{O}{\overset{R}{\diagdown}}\underset{N}{\overset{N}{\diagup}}\overset{NH}{\underset{S-S}{}} \underset{N}{\overset{N}{\diagup}}\underset{O}{\overset{HN}{\diagdown}}R \xrightarrow{\text{Na/Hg}} \underset{RCHCOOH}{\overset{NHNHCSNH_2}{|}} \quad (68)
$$

from 6-benzyl-3-mercapto-5-oxo-2,5-dihydro-as-triazine, for instance, is an amorphous yellowish solid, m.p. 173°. These disulfides are reduced back to the parent triazines by hydriodic acid, ammonium sulfide, or sodium bisulfite; they are reduced by sodium amalgam to α-thiosemicarbazido acids.[53, 63] The disulfides are acidic and may be titrated with phenolphthalein as indicator. They also form colored cuprous and cupric derivatives.[53, 63] 3-Mercapto-5-oxo-2,5-dihydro-as-triazines are oxidized by cupric sulfate to the cuprous derivatives of the corresponding disulfides.[63]

Alkyl derivatives of the 3-mercapto-5-oxo-2,5-dihydro-as-triazines are prepared in various ways. They also are listed in Table II-6. Direct alkylation, via the alkali metal derivatives and alkyl halides, yield the S-alkyl ethers.[35, 48, 50, 57, 58, 61, 65, 98] The structures of these S-ethers are clearly shown by the fact that acid hydrolysis yields alkyl mercaptans and 3,5-dioxo-2,3,4,5-tetrahydro-*as*-triazines (eq. 69). These *S*-ethers are also obtained by alkylation of the thiosemicarbazones, cyclization occurring concurrently, or, in a similar way, by treating the α-oxo acid with the *S*-methyl derivative of thiosemicarbazide

$$\underset{O}{\overset{R}{\diagdown}}\!\!\!\!\!\!\!\!\!\!\!\!\!\!\!\!\!\overset{N\diagup NH}{\underset{N\diagdown SNa}{}} \quad \xrightarrow{R'X} \quad \overset{R}{\diagdown}\overset{N\diagup NH}{\underset{N\diagdown SR'}{}} \quad \xrightarrow[H^+]{H_2O} \quad \overset{R}{\diagdown}\overset{N\diagup NH}{\underset{\underset{H}{N}\diagdown}{}}\!\!\!O \quad + \ R'SH \quad (69)$$

$$\underset{C_6H_5CH_2CCOOH}{\overset{NNHCSNH_2}{\|}} \xrightarrow{\text{alkylation}} \overset{C_6H_5CH_2}{\diagdown}\overset{N\diagup NH}{\underset{N\diagdown SR'}{}} \xleftarrow{RCOCOOH} \underset{SCH_3}{\overset{H_2NNHC=NH}{|}} \quad (70)$$

$$\overset{C_6H_5CH_2}{\underset{O}{\diagdown}}\overset{N\diagup NH}{\underset{N\diagdown SCH_2C_6H_5}{}} \xrightarrow{\text{Raney Ni}} \overset{C_6H_5CH_2}{\underset{O}{\diagdown}}\overset{N\diagup NH}{\underset{\underset{H}{N}\diagdown}{}}\!\!\!O \quad + \ CH_3C_6H_5 \quad (71)$$

(eq. 70.).[50] The *S*-alkyl ethers are more soluble than the unalkylated compounds. They are acidic and can be titrated with phenolphthalein as indicator. Some of their salts can be salted out of solution.[50] Raney nickel causes replacement of the sulfur by oxygen and 3,5-dioxo-2,3,4,5-tetrahydro-*as*-triazines result (eq. 71).[33]

2-Alkyl-3-mercapto-5-oxo-2,5-dihydro-*as*-triazines are prepared by reactions of α-oxo acids with 2-alkylthiosemicarbazides (eq. 72).[49, 52, 57, 59] These too are acidic and can be titrated. The 2-alkyl and the *S*-alkyl derivatives, upon further alkylation with alkali and alkyl halides, yield

$$RCOCOOH \quad \xrightarrow[]{\overset{R'}{\overset{|}{H_2NNCSNH_2}}} \quad \overset{R}{\underset{O}{\diagdown}}\overset{N\diagup NR'}{\underset{N\diagdown SH}{}} \quad (72)$$

$$\underset{\underset{R'}{|}}{\overset{NH}{\overset{\|}{R'SCNNH_2\cdot HI}}} \quad \xrightarrow{RCOCOOH} \quad \overset{R}{\underset{O}{\diagdown}}\overset{N\diagup NR'}{\underset{N\diagdown SR'}{}} \quad (73)$$

the same type of product, bearing alkyl groups on both the 2 position and the S atom (eq. 73).[49, 50, 52, 58] Another method of preparing these dialkyl derivatives involves the reaction of α-oxo acids with dialkyl derivatives of thiosemicarbazide.[52]

4-Alkyl-3-mercapto-5-oxo-2,5-dihydro-*as*-triazines are prepared by reactions of α-oxo acids with 4-alkylthiosemicarbazides (eq. 74).[51, 60] The cyclization fails when the alkyl group involved is benzyl.[60] These 4-alkyl derivatives, treated with alkali and alkyl halides, yield the S-alkyl ethers (eq. 74).[51, 52, 60] 6-Benzyl-2,4-dimethyl-5-oxo-3-thioxo-2,3,4,5-tetrahydro-as-triazine has been obtained by reaction of 2,4-dimethylthiosemicarbazide with phenylpyruvic acid (eq. 75).[52] 4,6-Dime-

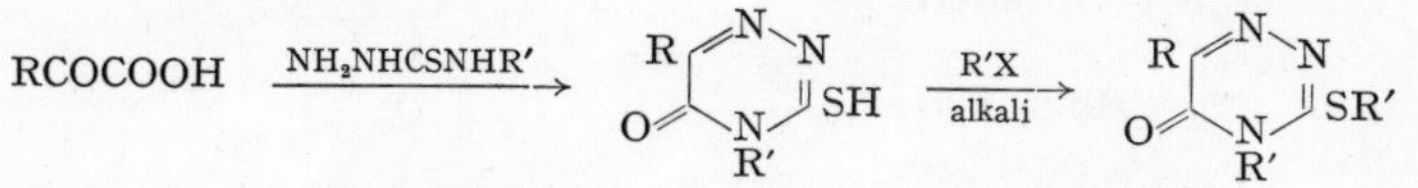

$$RCOCOOH \xrightarrow{\text{NH}_2\text{NHCSNHR}'} \quad \xrightarrow{\text{R}'X \atop \text{alkali}} \qquad (74)$$

$$C_6H_5CH_2COCOOH \xrightarrow{\text{CH}_3\text{NHCSNNH}_2} \qquad (75)$$

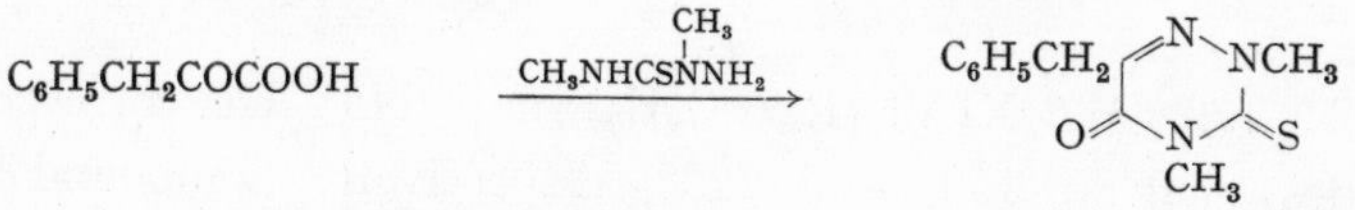

thyl-2-phenyl-5-oxo-3-thioxo-2,3,4,5-tetrahydro-as-triazine was prepared in a similar manner from 4-methyl-2-phenylthiosemicarbazide and pyruvic acid.[83] All of the S-alkyl ethers, when treated with acid, yield alkyl mercaptans and the S-alkyl grouping is replaced by oxygen. None of these alkyl derivatives is affected by sodium hypobromite solution when the sulfur atom is alkylated; otherwise the sulfur atom is replaced by oxygen.[50–52, 98] The presence of an alkyl group on the 2 position appears to make these derivatives resistant to the action of sodium amalgam, but, with this exception, the alkyl derivatives, whether S-alkylated or not, are reduced to dihydro derivatives by this reagent.[48, 50, 51, 55, 60–62, 98] These dihydro products are listed in Table II-6. Their precise structures are not known. They can no longer be titrated and the two added hydrogens can be removed by oxidation with iodine in alkaline solution.

Tingle and Bates[187] prepared a camphorylidene-substituted

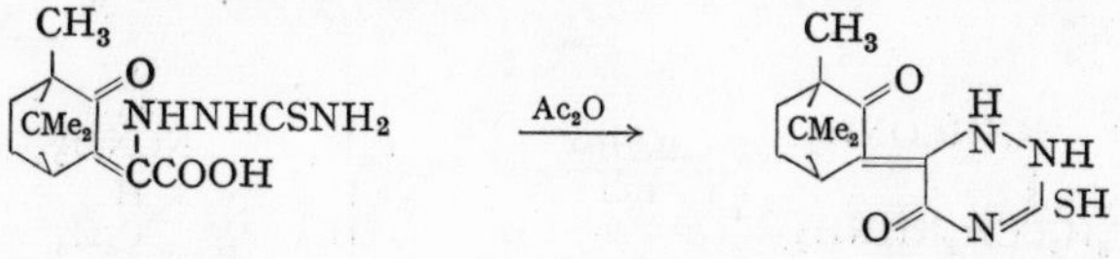

$$\xrightarrow{\text{Ac}_2\text{O}} \qquad (76)$$

(XLV)

mercapto-as-triazine (eq. 76). It melts at 148–149° and is soluble in most organic solvents and in sodium carbonate solution. Structures isomeric with XLV are also possible. According to Busch and Meuss-dörfer,[45] α-(1-phenyl-1-thiosemicarbazido)acetic acid esters, in the presence of alkali, are cyclized to as-triazines (XLVI), which appear to exist in an enolized form since they are readily oxidized to disulfides (eq. 77). Two compounds were prepared in this manner; XLVI (R=H),

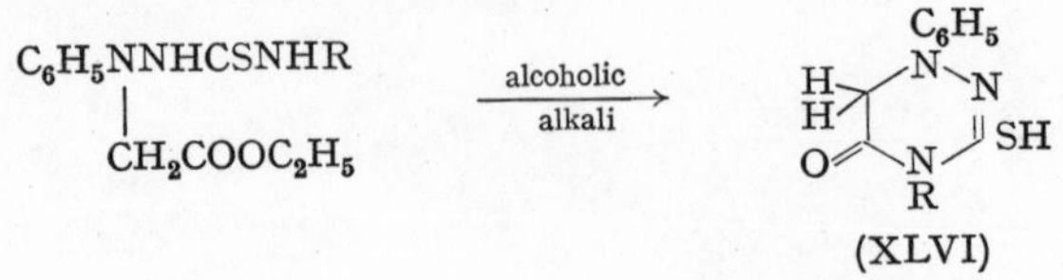

$$C_6H_5NNHCSNHR \atop | \atop CH_2COOC_2H_5 \quad \xrightarrow[\text{alkali}]{\text{alcoholic}} \quad \text{(XLVI)} \tag{77}$$

m.p. 172–173°, and XLVI (R = C_2H_5) m.p. 145°. The corresponding disulfides melt at 159° and 123°, respectively. Compound XLVI (R = H) was converted to its S-methyl derivative, m.p. 196–197°, by treating its potassium salt with methyl iodide. This methyl derivative, upon treatment with aqueous alkali, yields methyl mercaptan.

Carboxylic Acid Derivatives. Whiteley and Yapp[194] have found that arylhydrazones of mesoxalylurethans, treated with warm 10% potassium hydroxide solution, are cyclized to as-triazines bearing carboxylic

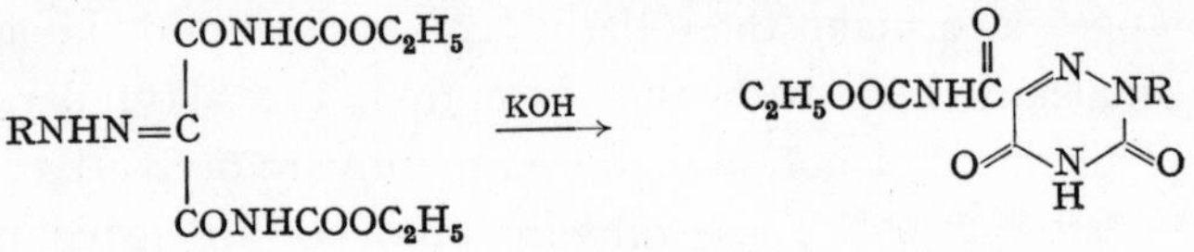

$$\begin{array}{c} CONHCOOC_2H_5 \\ | \\ RNHN=C \\ | \\ CONHCOOC_2H_5 \end{array} \quad \xrightarrow{\text{KOH}} \tag{78}$$

acid functions (eq. 78). These are listed in Table II-4. It was not possible to obtain the 2-*m*-nitrophenyl compound. The 2-*o*-nitrophenyl compound was prepared but not described.

According to Busch and Küspert,[44] the hydrochloride of phenacyl-

$$\begin{array}{c} NNHCONH_2 \\ \| \\ C_6H_5CCH_2NHNH_2 \end{array} \quad \xrightarrow[\text{HCl}]{C_6H_5CHO} \tag{79}$$

hydrazine semicarbazone, treated with benzaldehyde, yields an as-triazine (eq. 79), m.p. 205–206°.

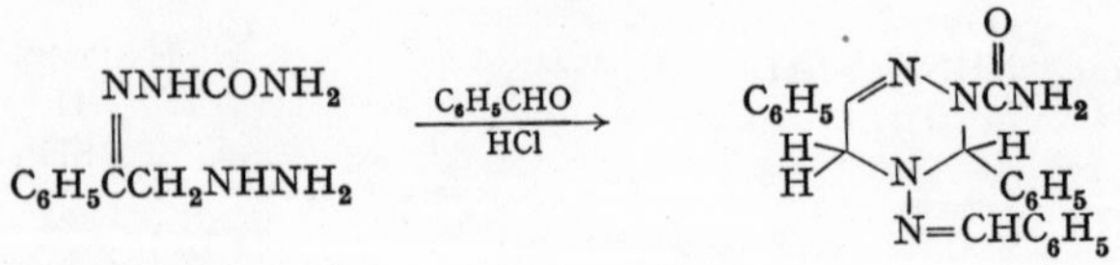

B. 1,2,4-Triazine Rings with Valence Bridges

It is very probable that compounds of this type have never been prepared. A ring system of this type, however, has been recognized by *The Ring Index*, which gives it the name *2,3,6-triazabicyclo[3.1.0]-hexane* (*R.I.* 449). The evidence for this structure will now be discussed.

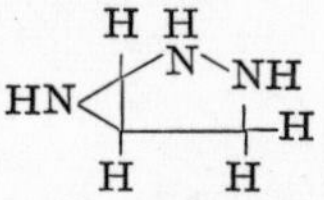

2,3,6-Triazabicyclo[3.1.0]hexane

None of the compounds mentioned in the following discussion was identified by any other means than analyses, frequently only nitrogen analyses.

Michaelis and Brust[126] observed that 3-amino-4-halo-5-methyl-2-phenylpyrazoles, when treated with excess halogen or, better, nitrous acid, are converted to substances having two hydrogens less than the starting materials. Some years later, Michaelis and Schäfer[128] reported that 3-amino-5-methyl-2-phenylpyrazole, a colorless compound, reacts vigorously with hydrogen peroxide in acetic acid solution, yielding a yellow-brown product, m.p. 109°. Elementary analyses and molecular weight determinations indicated a product differing by two hydrogens from the starting material. When heated with sodium hydrosulfite solution, this product was converted to 5-methyl-3-oxo-2-phenyl-

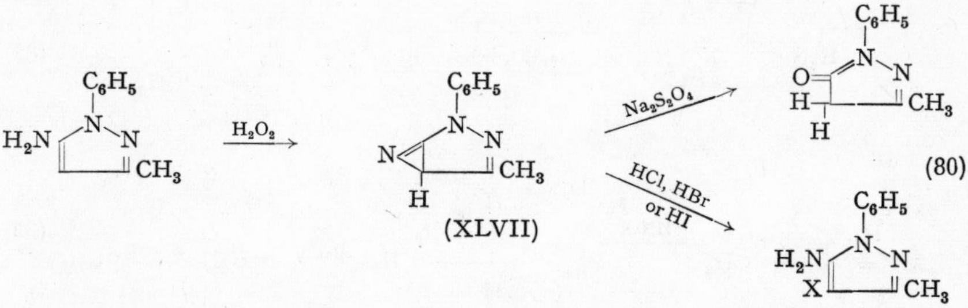

(80)

dihydropyrazole; warmed with concentrated hydrogen halide acids, it yielded 3-amino-4-halo-5-methyl-2-phenylpyrazoles (eq. 80). From these results, Michaelis and Schäfer concluded that a bridged *as-*

triazine ring (XLVII) had been formed. They bestowed the name *azipyrazole* upon this type of compound.

It was said that halogenated azipyrazoles could be prepared by the action of chloride, bromine or bleaching powder upon 3-amino-5-methyl-2-phenylpyrazole (eq. 81).[128] They were also formed by treatment of 3-amino-4-halo-5-methyl-2-phenylpyrazole with nitrous acid or hydrogen peroxide (eq. 81).[128] Michaelis and Klappert[127] carried out

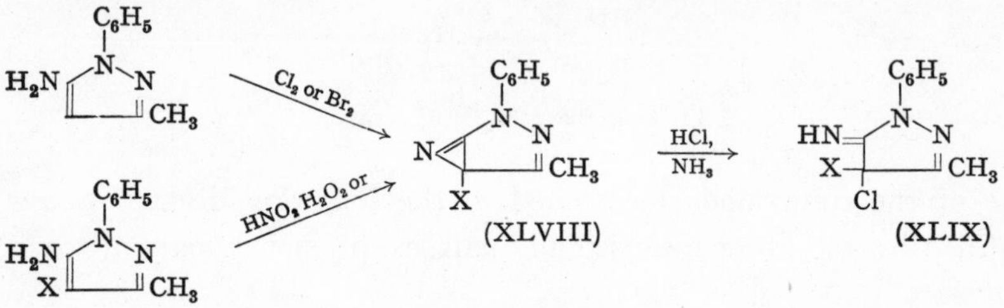

similar reactions, using chlorine, bromine or iodine with 3-amino-5-methyl-2-*o*-tolylpyrazole. Michaelis and Schäfer stated that their products (XLVIII), dissolved in hydrochloric or hydrobromic acids and treated with excess ammonia, are converted to 4,4-dihalo-3-imino-5-methyl-2-phenyl-3,4-dihydropyrazoles (XLIX). A methyl homolog of these azipyrazoles was prepared by treating a hydrochloric acid solution of 3-amino-4,5-dimethyl-2-phenylpyrazole with hydrogen peroxide.[128] When it was treated with sodium hydrosulfite or with tin and hydrochloric acid, it regenerated the starting pyrazole (eq. 82).

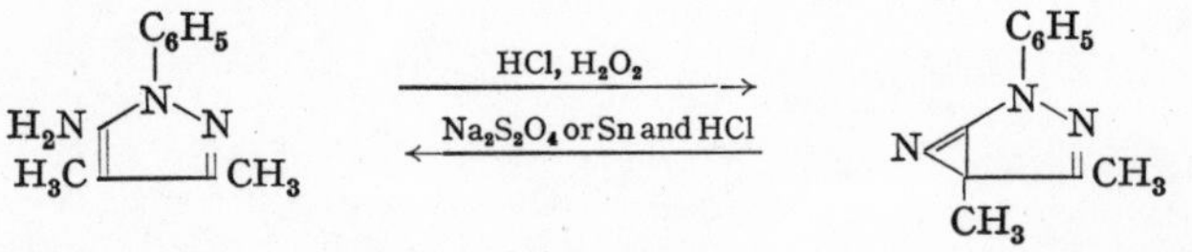

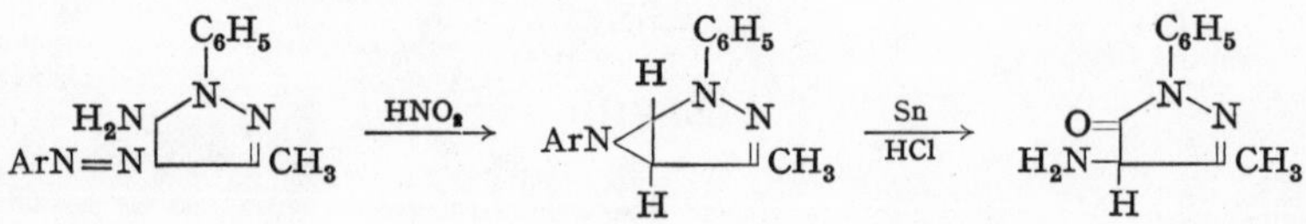

Aryl analogs were formed by the action of nitrous acid on arylazo derivatives (eq. 83),[128] certainly an unexpected reaction. Also surprising is the alleged conversion of these compounds to 4-amino-5-methyl-3-

oxo-2-phenyl-3,4-dihydropyrazoles (eq. 83). The action of hydrogen peroxide on 4-amino-5-methyl-2-phenylpyrazole, rather than producing dehydrogenation, yields a compound $C_{10}H_{11}N_3O_2$, said to be 3-hydroxy-4-oximino-5-methyl-2-phenyl-3,4-dihydropyrazole.[129]

The proof of structure of these azipyrazoles is clearly quite inadequate. As remarked above, analyses constitute the only evidence for these formulations of Michaelis and co-workers. Certainly, there is little reason to accept these structures. What reasons have we for rejecting them? In the first place, these structures contain a double bond at the bridgehead in a bicyclic system, wherein a 3-membered ring is fused with a 5-membered ring. Such a system would be very highly strained (Bredt's rule).[86] Another objection to the azipyrazole structure arises from the behavior of these compounds during syntheses involving free chlorine or bromine. The C_6H_5N grouping in XLVII would be expected to behave very much like aniline in the presence of halogen-that is, halogenation of the phenyl ring should occur readily. However, no such reactions seem to have occurred.

On the basis of the meager experimental results given us by Michaelis, we cannot confidently give any one explanation of these reactions. However, recent work with those heterocyclic compounds known as sydnones may make it possible to suggest a very tentative solution. Baker,[9] who calls such compounds as sydnones "mesoionic," has shown that the physical and chemical properties of sydnones are best explained by considering their structures as resonance hybrids, to which a great many forms contribute. Perhaps a similar situation exists with the azipyrazoles. It can be postulated that the effect of oxidizing agents upon 3-amino-5-methyl-2-phenylpyrazoles is removal of one hydrogen from the amino group and one hydrogen from the methyl group. The oxidized product, rather than closing a new ring, could be stabilized by resonance among many contributing forms, some of which are:

(La)   (Lb)   (Lc)

As Baker has pointed out in connection with the sydnones, the C_6H_5N grouping in such resonance hybrids does not resemble aniline so much as it does the anilinium ion. In accepting this explanation, of course, one assumes that halogens oxidize the amino and methyl groups much faster than they can halogenate the phenyl ring.

It is obvious that a good deal of further work should be done in this field. Quite possibly, the correct structures of the azipyrazoles, when elucidated, will prove to be neither those proposed by Michaelis nor those suggested here.

2. 1,2,4-TRIAZINE RINGS CONDENSED WITH CARBOCYCLES

A. As Parts of Spiro Ring Systems

Two compounds are known in which a 1,2,4-triazine ring has one carbon atom in common with an alicyclic ring and shares no other atom. The fundamental ring systems of these compounds are not listed in *The Ring Index*. In *Chemical Abstracts*, similar compounds are named as aza derivatives of spiroalkanes.

Venus-Danilova[188] found that the monomer or dimer of 1-hydroxy-cyclopentanecarboxaldehyde reacts with semicarbazide, yielding 7-oxo-6,8,9-triazaspiro[4.5]-9-decene, m.p. 216–218° (eq. 84). She also

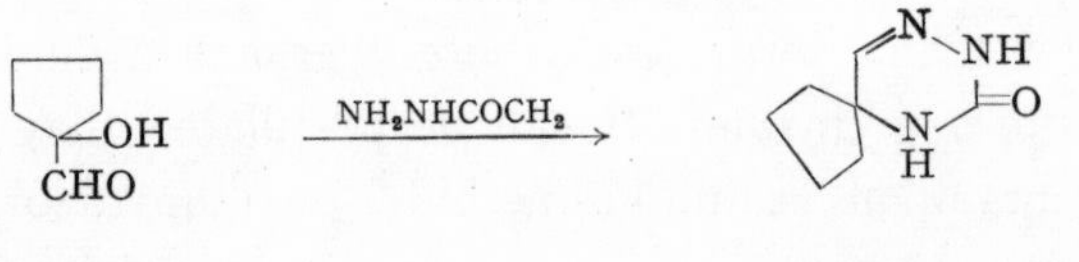

$$\text{(84)}$$

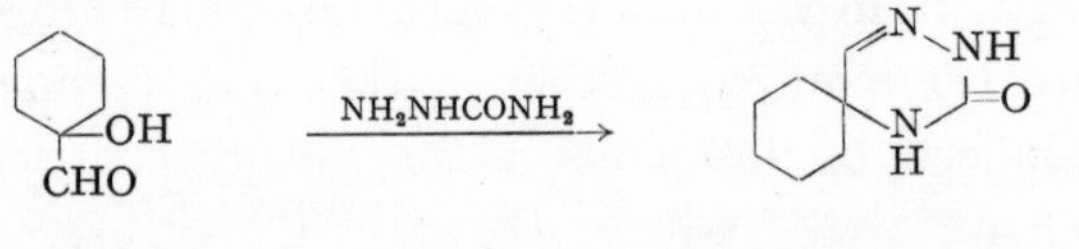

$$\text{(85)}$$

found[189] that the monomer or polymer of 1-hydroxy-cyclohexane-carboxaldehyde, heated two hours with semicarbazide at 110°, forms 2-oxo-1,3,4-triazaspiro[5.5]-4-hendecene, a fluffy light yellow material, m.p. 221–223° (dec.) (eq. 85). This structure is confirmed by the fact that a mixture of this compound with the alternative possibility, the isomeric semicarbazone of tetrahydrobenzaldehyde, shows a depression in melting point. Both of these triazaspiro compounds are soluble in warm acidic or basic solution and are reprecipitated unchanged upon neutralization.

B. Condensed with Alicyclic Ring Systems in 1,2-Positions

(1) Condensed with Cyclopentane

One compound of this type has been reported. The ring system is not listed in *The Ring Index*. Venus-Danilova[190] observed that the reaction of 2-hydroxycyclopentanone with semicarbazide does not produce the semicarbazone. Instead, 3-oxo-2,3,4,4a,6,7-hexahydrocyclopenta-1,2,4-triazine is formed (eq. 86). It is a light yellow powder, m.p. 194° (dec.) soluble in warm acids or bases.

$$\text{(86)}$$

(2) Condensed with the Norcamphane System

Ring systems of this type are hydrogenated forms of a parent system which is called 5,8-methano-1,2,4-benzotriazine (*R.I.* 1448) by *The Ring Index*. In our present compounds the carbocyclic ring is

5,8-Methano-1,2,4-benzotriazine

hydrogenated, the carbon atom at position 9 bears two methyl groups and there is a methyl group at position 5 or position 8. These compounds are listed in Table II-7.

It appears that camphorquinone reacts with carbonyl reagents, such as hydrazine,[178] in such a way that the carbonyl group further removed from the 1-methyl group is first replaced. In this way, Forster

TABLE II-7. 9,9-Dimethyl-5,6,7,8-tetrahydro-
5,8-methano-1,2,4-benzotriazines

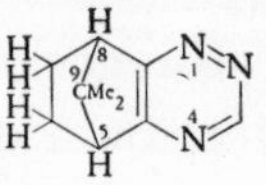

Substituents	Color, crystal habit	M.p., °C.	Ref.
3-Hydroxy-5-methyl	Colorless pyramids	166–167[a]	94
3-Hydroxy-5-methyl, acetyl deriv.		168–169	94
3-Hydroxy-5-methyl, benzoyl deriv.		193–194	94
3-Mercapto-5-methyl	Yellow prisms	207[b]	95
3-Mercapto-8-methyl-?,?-dihydro	Hexagonal plates	239[c]	119
3-Mercapto-8-methyl-2-phenyl-2,4a-dihydro	Small needles	235	93
8-Methyl-3-methylmercapto-?,?dihydro	Prisms	107[d]	119
3-Oxo-8-methyl-2,3,4,4a-tetrahydro	Needles	314–315	166
3-Oxo-8-methyl-2,3,4,4a-tetrahydro, acetyl deriv.		183	166

$^a[\alpha]_D$ +22.6. $^b[\alpha]_D$ —73.3. $^c[\alpha]_D$ +281.5. $^d[\alpha]_D$ —57.4.

and Zimmerli[94] obtained the *syn* and *anti* forms of camphorquinone monosemicarbazone. The *anti* form is stable towards alkali but the *syn* form, treated with 10% sodium hydroxide solution at room temperature, is readily cyclized (eq. 87). Diels and vom Dorp[79] stated in an

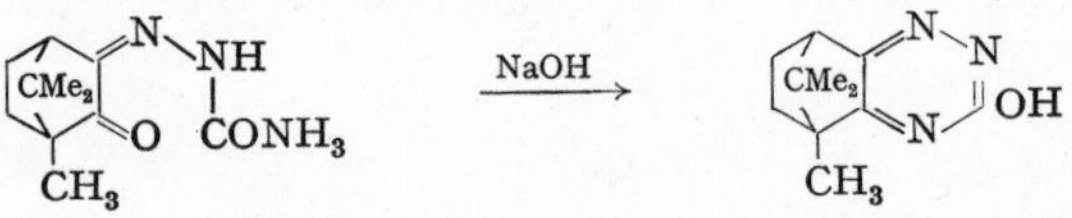

(87)

(LI)

earlier article that the monosemicarbazone of camphorquinone cannot be cyclized, that hot alkali produces no change, and that hot dilute mineral acids merely hydrolyze it. Presumably, they worked with the *anti* form of this compound. Compound LI is soluble in alkali and forms colored salts with copper, nickel, and iron. Acetyl and benzoyl derivatives have been prepared; the structures of these compounds are not known. Rupe and Buxtorf[166] treated 3-camphorylurethan with hydrazine to obtain a product similar to LI (eq. 88). This is soluble in concentrated hydrochloric acid and insoluble in alkali. With acetic anhydride it forms a monoacetyl derivative.

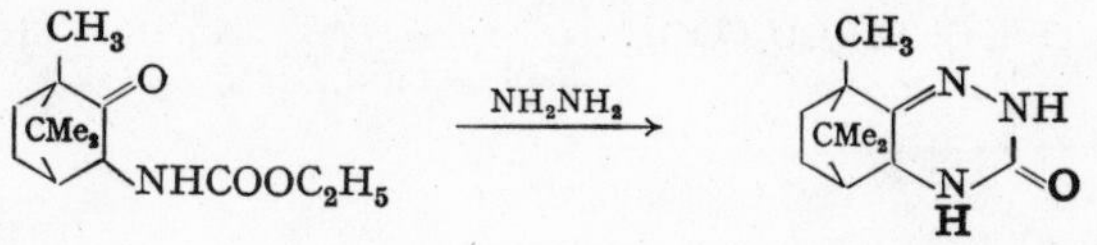

Forster and Zimmerli[95] found that the monothiosemicarbazone of camphorquinone, upon treatment with sodium hydroxide solution, is cyclized to the mercapto compound corresponding to compound LI. The sulfur in this compound cannot be replaced by oxygen by treatment with mercuric oxide. However, when a solution of this mercapto compound in dilute ammonium hydroxide is treated with an ammoniacal solution of silver oxide, the corresponding hydroxy compound, LI, is formed. The mercapto compound reacts with acetic anhydride to form the acetyl derivative of LI.

McRae and Stevens,[119] by treating 4-(3-camphoryl)thiosemicarbazide with dilute hydrochloric acid, cyclized it to a triazine (eq. 89).

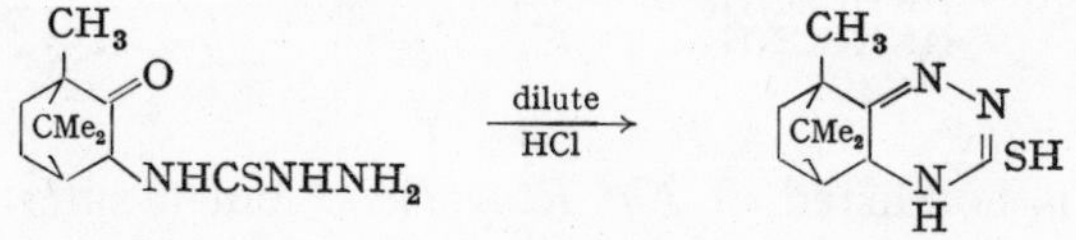

The silver derivative of this compound reacts with methyl iodide to form the S-methyl derivative. Forster and Jackson[93] carried out a similar reaction, using 4-(3-camphoryl)-2-phenylthiosemicarbazide. They did not indicate the method used to bring about ring closure.

(3) Condensed with the Cyclopentaphenanthrene Ring System

Bergström and Haslewood[17] prepared a monosemicarbazone of 11,12-dioxocholanic acid. This, subjected to the conditions of the Wolff-Kishner reaction, gave not a monoöxo acid but rather an as-triazine, the structure of which is probably LII (eq. 90). This ring system is not listed in *The Ring Index*. A suitable name for this compound is 5-(4-carboxy-2-butyl)-5a,13a-dimethyl-3-hydroxy-5,5a,6,7a, 8,8a,9,9a,10,11,12,13,13a,13b-tetradecahydrocyclopenta[f]phenanthro-

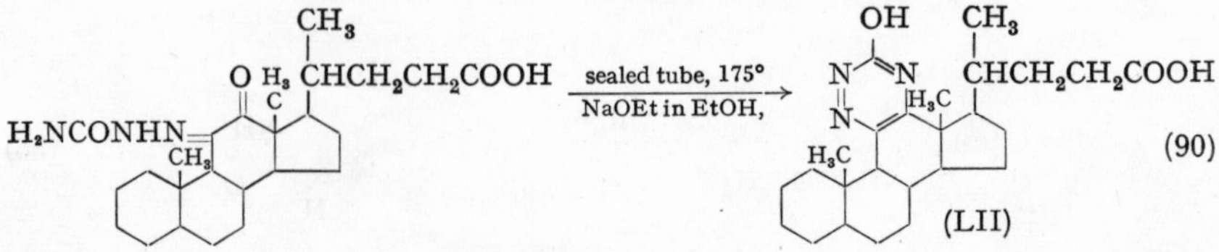

(90)

[3,4-e]-as-triazine. It was obtained as long needles from dilute alcohol, m.p. 292–295° (dec.). When treated with diazomethane, this compound is methylated on both the hydroxyl and the carboxyl group, giving a product, m.p. 142–143°.

(4) Condensed with the Spiro[4.5]decane Ring System

Kon[115] prepared the disemicarbazone of 2,3-dioxospiro[4.5]decane. When it is treated with moderately concentrated mineral acids, it loses semicarbazide and an as-triazine is formed (eq. 91). The parent

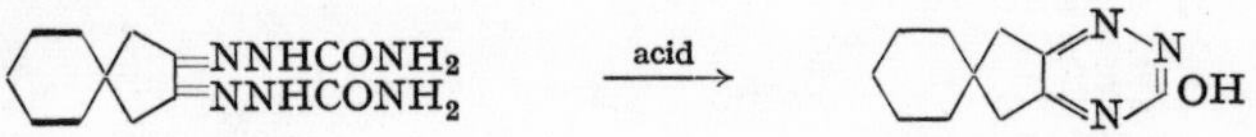

(91)

ring system is not listed in *The Ring Index* but a suitable name for this compound would be 3-hydroxyspiro[4.5]decano[c]-as-triazine. It crystallizes as buff needles from acetic acid, m.p. 295° (dec.), very sparingly soluble in other organic solvents. It is soluble in sodium hydroxide solution and dissolves in concentrated sulfuric acid, giving a deep orange color.

(5) Condensed with the Phenanthridine Ring System

Kondo and Ishiwata[104] oxidized the alkaloid lycoramine first with potassium permanganate and then with chromic oxide, obtaining thereby a dioxo compound (LIII). This reacted with semicarbazide in acetic acid to form an as-triazine, probably LIV (eq. 92). Compound LIV is described as colorless needles from alcohol, m.p. 238° (dec.). Again the ring system is not listed in *The Ring Index*. However, the compound may be named 7-ethyl-9-hydroxy-2-methoxy-6-methyl-5-oxo-5,6,6a,7, 12,12a,-hexahydro-*as*-triazino[6,5-*b*]phenanthridine.

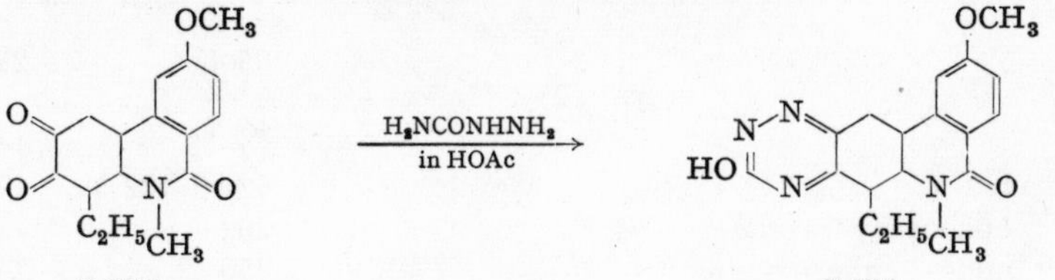

(92)

(LIII) (LIV)

C. Condensed with the Benzene Ring

(1) 1,2,4-Benzotriazine

For many years this ring system (II) was called *α-phentriazine*, following a proposal by Widman.[196] It is No. 934 in *The Ring Index*. Many compounds of this sort have been prepared and are listed in Tables II-8 and II-9.

1,2,4-Benzotriazine was first prepared in 1889 by Bischler,[27] who reduced the *o*-nitrophenylhydrazide of formic acid with sodium amalgam in alcoholic acetic acid. This yielded a dihydro derivative that was not isolated but was oxidized with potassium ferricyanide directly to 1,2,4-benzotriazine (eq. 93). The yield of product is improved by the

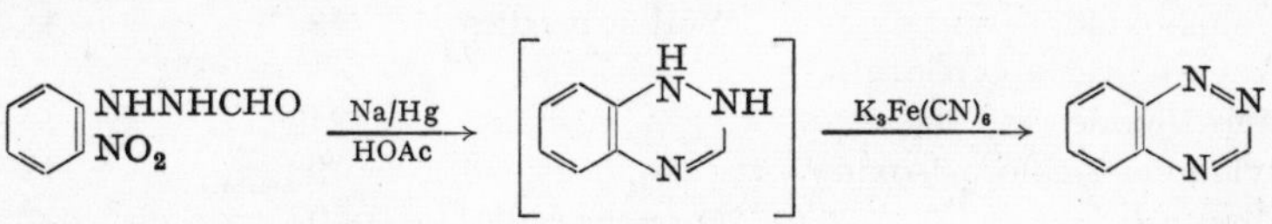

(93)

use of lower temperatures in the reduction step. Use of zinc dust rather than sodium amalgam gave little of the desired product. Substituted 1,2,4-benzotriazines have been prepared by the use of either the 2-nitro-4-bromophenylhydrazide of formic acid or the *o*-nitrophenylhydrazide of acetic acid.[27,28] 2-Methylbenzimidazoles are by-products resulting from reduction to *o*-aminophenylhydrazides, followed by cleavage to *o*-phenylenediamine and subsequent ring closure with acetic acid.

TABLE II-8. 1,2,4-Benzotriazines

Substituents	Color, crystal habit	M.p., °C.	Ref.
None		65–66[a]	27, 111, 175
		74–75	14
3-Acetyl		121.5–122.5	12, 13
3-Acetyl phenylhydrazone		202	12, 13
3-Acetamido-7-chloro-1-oxide		256	148
3-(p-Acetamidophenyl)amino-7-chloro-1-oxide		285–286	147
3-Allylamino-7-chloro-1-oxide		159–160	147
3-Amino		207	2, 3
3-Amino-7-bromo			143
3-Amino-7-bromo-1-oxide		294–295 (dec.)	144
3-Amino-6-chloro		250–251	143
3-Amino-7-chloro			143
3-Amino-5-chloro-1-oxide		258–259 (dec.)	144
3-Amino-6-chloro-1-oxide		293	143, 144
3-Amino-7-chloro-1-oxide		302 (dec.)	144
3-Amino-5,7-dichloro-1-oxide		287 (dec.)	144
3-Amino-7-methoxy		221–222	143
3-Amino-7-methoxy-1-oxide		258–259	143, 144
3-Amino-5-methyl		207–208	143
3-Amino-7-methyl		217–218	143
3-Amino-5-methyl-1-oxide		258–260	143
3-Amino-7-methyl-1-oxide		265–270	143
3-Amino-1-oxide		269	2
		270–271	5
3-Amino-2-oxide	Yellow needles	187	4
3-(5-Amino-5-carboxypentyl)-amino-1-oxide		248	147
3-Amylamino-7-chloro-1-oxide		79	147
3-Anilino	Orange needles	197	4
3-Anilino-1-oxide	Orange-red needles	197	4
3-Anilino-2-oxide	Gleaming yellow leaves	163	4
3-Anilino-7-chloro-1-oxide		210–211	147
3-p-Anisidino-7-chloro-1-oxide	Dark red	210–211	147
3-Benzoyl		114	15, 16
3-Benzoyl phenylhydrazone		185	15, 16
3-Benzylamino-7-bromo		172–173	151

(Table continued)

TABLE II-8 *(continued)*

Substituents	Color, crystal habit	M.p., °C.	Ref.
3-Benzylamino-7-chloro		175	151
3-Benzylamino-7-chloro-1-oxide		186	147
3-Bromo		122	4
6-Bromo			28
5-(or 6-)Bromo-3-(2,4-diamino-phenyl)	Almost colorless plates	180	138
6-Bromo-3-methyl		115	28
3-Butylamino-7-chloro		151–152	151
3-Butylamino-7-chloro-1-oxide	Yellow needles	170	147
3-(4-Carboxyphenyl)amino-7-chloro-1-oxide		300	147
3-β-Carboxypropionylamino-7-chloro-1-oxide	Green platelets	250–251	148
3-p-(γ-Carboxypropyl)phenyl-amino-7-chloro-1-oxide		250–251	147
3-Chloro	Yellow needles	100–101	4
7-Chloro-3-[2-(2-diethylamino-ethylmercapto)ethylamino]-1-oxide		104–105	147
7-Chloro-3-(5-diethylamino-2-pentyl)-amino		—[b]	151
7-Chloro-3-(5-diethylamino-2-pentyl)amino-1-oxide		88–89	147
7-Chloro-3-[2-(3,4-dimethoxy-phenyl)ethylamino]-1-oxide		183–184	147
7-Chloro-3-(5-dimethylamino-2-pentyl)amino-1-oxide		—[c]	147
7-Chloro-3-(di-n-propylamino)		66	151
7-Chloro-3-(di-n-propylamino)-1-oxide		105–106	147
7-Chloro-3-dodecylamino-1-oxide		140	147
7-Chloro-3-guanidino-1-oxide		282 (dec.)	147
7-Chloro-3-hydroxy	Yellow	220–222 (dec.)	149
7-Chloro-3-hydroxy-1-oxide		230–231	145
7-Chloro-3-(1-hydroxy-2-butyl)-amino-1-oxide		138	147
7-Chloro-3-(2-hydroxyethyl)-amino-1-oxide		186	147
7-Chloro-3-(3-hydroxy-5-hydroxymethyl-2-methyl-4-pyridyl)methylamino-1-oxide		213–214 (dec.)	147

(Table continued)

TABLE II-8 *(continued)*

Substituents	Color, crystal habit	M.p., °C.	Ref.
7-Chloro-3-(6-methoxy-8-quinolinyl)-amino-1-oxide	Yellow	254	147
7-Chloro-3-*N*-methylanilino		145–146	151
7-Chloro-3-(4-morpholinyl)-1-oxide		175	147
7-Chloro-3-(4-nitrobenzene sulfonyl)-amino	Yellow	240	152
7-Chloro-3-(2-octylamino)-1-oxide		89–90	147
7-Chloro-3-(2-phenylethyl)-1-oxide		195–196	147
7-Chloro-3-(1-piperidyl)-1-oxide		142	147
7-Chloro-3-sulfanilylamino	Bright yellow	219–220	152
7-Chloro-3-(4-sulfanilylphenyl)-amino-1-oxide		293	147
7-Chloro-3-(2-thienylamino)-1-oxide		142–143	147
3,7-Dichloro		140	150
3,7-Dichloro-1-oxide		153–154	146
3-Dimethylamino-1-oxide	Orange needles	161–161.5	5
3,3'-Dithio-1,1'-dioxide	Yellow	205	4
3-Hydroxy	Yellowish-brown needles	209–210	4
3-Hydroxy-1-oxide		219	2
3-(2-Hydroxyphenyl)		167	87
3-Mercapto		208–209	4
3-Mercapto-1-oxide	Dark red needles	184	4
3-Methoxy		106	84
3-Methoxy-1-oxide		121	84
3-Methyl		88–89[d]	27
3-(3,4-Methylenedioxyphenyl)		154	87
3-Methylmercapto	Yellow leaves	104	3
	Yellow needles	104	4
3-Methylmercapto-1-oxide	Greenish-yellow needles	123	4
6-Methyl-3-phenyl		95–96	192
3-(4-Nitrobenzenesulfonyl)amino	Yellow needles	252–253	152
3-Oxalo-6-sulfonic acid	Brownish-orange		132
3-Phenyl		123	88, 192
3-Sulfanilylamino		216–217	152

[a]B.p. 235–240° (undec.). [b]B.p. 70° (3 μ). [c]B.p. 130° (3 μ).
[d]B.p. 250–255° (sl. dec.).

TABLE II-9. Hydrogenated Derivatives of 1,2,4-Benzotriazines

Substituents	Color, crystal habit	M.p., °C.	Ref.
1-Acetyl-7-methyl-3-oxo-2-*p*-tolyl-1,2,3,4-tetrahydro		190	38
4-Acetyl-3-mercapto-1-phenyl-1,4-dihydro[a]		203–204	108
3-Amino-1,2-dihydro			2
3-Benzoylmercapto-1,2-dihydro[a]		174	107
1-Carbamido-3-methylmercapto-1,2-dihydro-	Colorless	208–210	3
6-Cyanamido-3-imino-2-phenyl-2,3-dihydro)		290	155
6-Cyanamido-3-oxo-2-phenyl-2,3-dihydro		258	155
6-Cyanamido-3-oxo-2-phenyl-1,2,3,4-tetrahydro		210 (dec.)	155
3,3′-Dithiobis(1,2-dihydro)[a]		208–210	107
3,3′-Dithiobis(1-phenyl-1,4-dihydro		>300	108
3,3′-Dithiobis(4-phenyl-1,4-dihydro)	Yellowish needles	175–176	105
3,3′-Dithiobis(4-*p*-tolyl-1,4-dihydro)		97–98 (dec.)	105
3-Mercapto-1,2-dihydro[a]		298–300	107
3-Mercapto-1-phenyl-1,4-dihydro	White	292–293	108
3-Mercapto-4-phenyl-1,4-dihydro	White needles	151	105, 107
3-Mercapto-4-*p*-tolyl-1,4-dihydro	Yellow, rectangular	182	105
3-Mercapto-4-xylyl-1,4-dihydro	White plates	173–174	105
2-Methyl-3-oxo-2,3-dihydro		157–158 (dec.)	84
4-Methyl-3-oxo-3,4-dihydro		202	84
4-Methyl-3-oxo-3,4-dihydro-1-oxide		233	84
2-Methyl-3-oxo-1,2,3,4-tetrahydro		147–152 (dec.)	84
4-Methyl-3-oxo-1,2,3,4-tetrahydro		146–147 (dec.)	84
7-Methyl-3-oxo-2-*p*-tolyl-2,3-dihydro		168	38
7-Methyl-3-oxo-2-*p*-tolyl-1,2,3,4-tetrahydro		146	38
7-Methyl-2-phenyl-3-phenyl-imino-2,3-dihydro		127.5	38
7-Methyl-2-phenyl-3-phenyl-imino-1,2,3,4-tetrahydro		141	38

(Table continued)

TABLE II-9 *(continued)*

Substituents	Color, crystal habit	M.p., °C.	Ref.
7-Methyl-2-*p*-tolyl-3-*m*-nitro-phenylimino-2,3-dihydro		185–190 (dec.)	40
7-Methyl-2-*p*-tolyl-3-*p*-tolyl-imino-2,3-dihydro		147	38
7-Methyl-2-*p*-tolyl-3-*o*-tolyl-imino-2,3-dihydro		167	40
7-Methyl-2-*p*-tolyl-3-*p*-tolyl-imino-1,2,3,4-tetrahydro			38
3-Methylmercapto-1,4-dihydro		199–200	106
3-Oxo-4-phenyl-1,2,3,4-tetrahydro	White prisms	170–171	106
3-Oxo-2-phenyl-6-ureido-2,3-dihydro		> 300	155
3-Oxo-1,2,3,4-tetrahydro	Rectangular plates	310–312	107

[a]One of several possible structures.

Hempel[111] has described an interesting method of cyclization. 1-(*o*-Acetamidophenyl)-1-methylhydrazine, upon standing with phosphorus pentoxide at room temperature, is converted to 1,2,4-benzotriazine, apparently by elimination of the elements of water and ethane

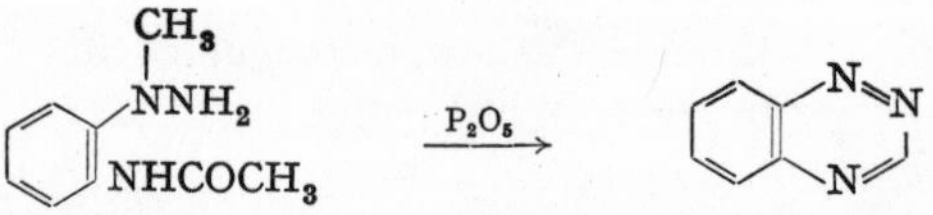

(94)

(eq. 94). Use of 1-(*o*-acetamidophenyl)-1-ethylhydrazine gave the same product. Hempel said that 1-(*o*-acetamidophenyl)-1-methylhydrazine, heated by itself at 140°, yields 1,2-dimethylbenzimidazole rather than 1,2,4-benzotriazine.

Another approach to the preparation of 1,2,4-benzotriazines is through the "formazyl" or phenylhydrazinophenylhydrazono compounds. Thus, Bamberger and Wheelwright[14] converted ethyl acetoacetate to ethyl "formazylacetate" by treating it with benzenediazonium chloride in the presence of base. Ethyl "formazylacetate," when treated with concentrated mineral acids, yields 1,2,4-benzotriazine, as well as other products (eq. 95). The product was purified by sublimation.

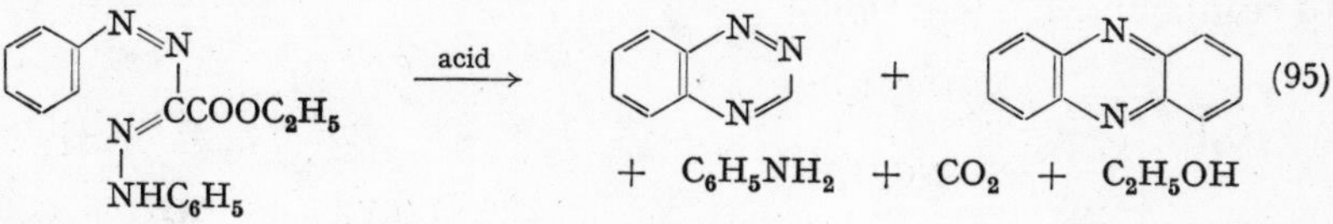

$$+ \ C_6H_5NH_2 \ + \ CO_2 \ + \ C_2H_5OH \qquad (95)$$

The formazyl synthesis has been extended to the preparation of the 3-aryl derivatives of 1,2,4-benzotriazine. Von Pechmann,[192] by treating the phenylhydrazone of benzaldehyde with benzenediazonium chloride and alkali, prepared "formazylbenzene." This, with sulfuric acid in acetic acid, is converted to 3-phenyl-1,2,4-benzotriazine (eq. 96).

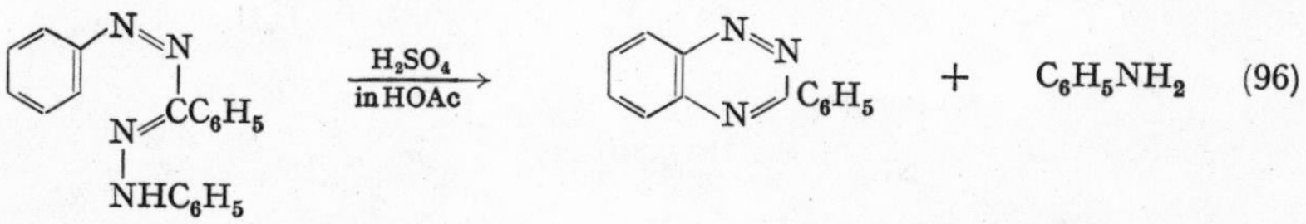

The reaction is very rapid and requires only a minute or so on the steam bath. A similar reaction shows that aniline is eliminated from mixed formazyl compounds exclusively in preference to p-toluidine; only 6-methyl-3-phenyl-1,2,4-benzotriazine and aniline were formed in the cyclization of the formazyl compound from p-toluenediazonium chloride and the phenylhydrazone of benzaldehyde (eq. 97). In another

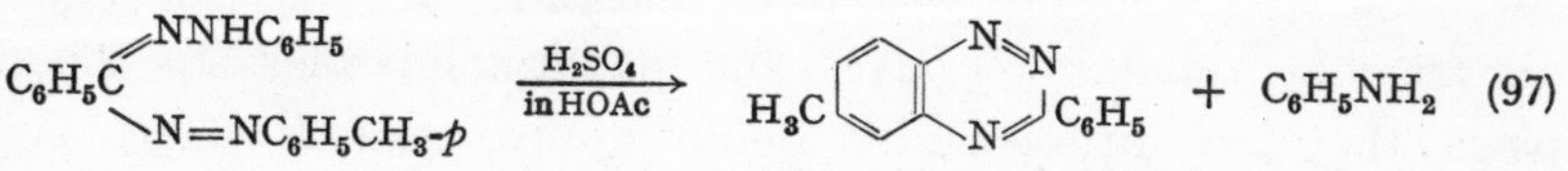

study by Fichter and Schiess,[88] it was shown that sulfanilic acid is eliminated in preference to aniline; the formazylbenzene obtained by reaction of diazotized sulfanilic acid with the phenylhydrazone of benzaldehyde, when treated with sulfuric acid in acetic acid, yielded only 3-phenyl-1,2,4-benzotriazine. Fichter and Frolich[87] applied the formazyl synthesis to the preparation of 3-o-hydroxyphenyl- and 3-(3,4-methylenedioxyphenyl)-1,2,4-benzotriazines. Parkes and Aldis[138] were forced to modify the reaction conditions. In the preparation of compound LV, boiling hydrochloric acid alone had no effect, possibly because of the insolubility of the starting material. However, with hot concentrated hydrochloric acid and tin, they obtained a very low yield of compound LV (eq. 98).

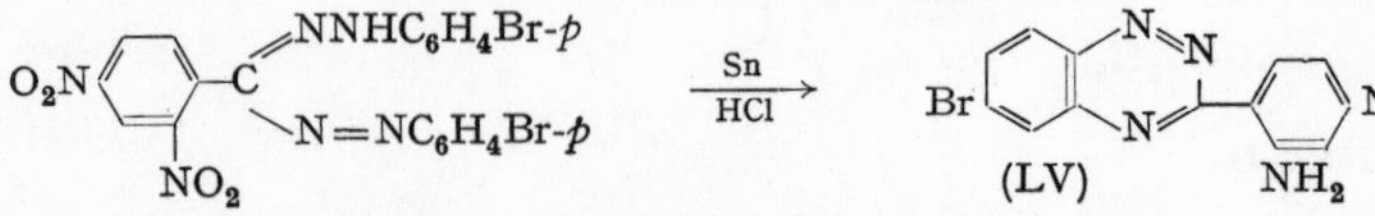

(98)

Goldschmidt and co-workers[101, 102] reported that the action of aldehydes upon o-aminoazo compounds results in the formation of aryl-substituted dihydronaphtho-as-triazines (eq. 99). Following them, other workers[136,154] claimed to have obtained 1,2,4-benzotriazines by similar reactions. Many years later, Fischer[90] reinvestigated the reaction.

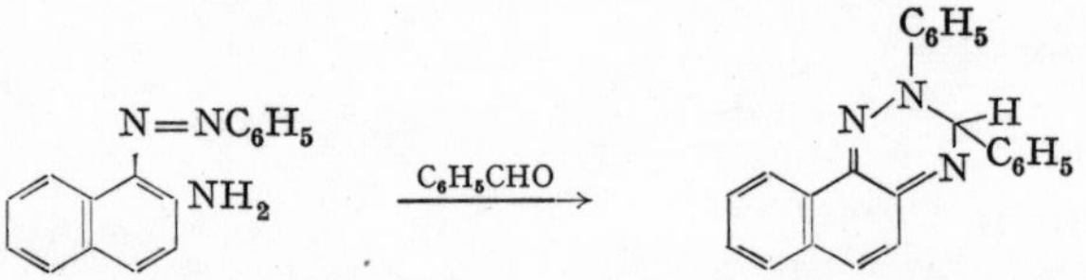

(99)

He found that the action of aromatic aldehydes upon o-aminoazo compounds such as, for example, 2-amino-4-methylazobenzene, gives, first, colored intermediate products that are Schiff bases and that, in some cases, can be isolated in a pure state. These Schiff bases, when treated with such acids as formic acid, acetic acid, or alcoholic hydrogen chloride, or when heated with pyridine, are converted to the colorless, so-called "triazines." Fischer showed that these "triazines" are actually arylaminobenzimidazoles (LVI) and naphthimidazoles. In the first place, they contain secondary amino groups, as well as tertiary nitrogen atoms, for they yield nitrosamines and acetyl derivatives.

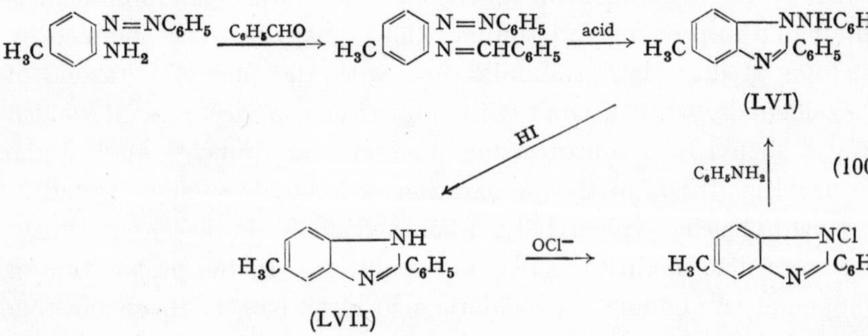

(100)

Further, they can be split with hydriodic acid to give benzimidazoles (LVII) and naphthimidazoles, besides amines, such as aniline (100). Finally, the "triazines" can be synthesized from benzimidazoles and naphthimidazoles by converting these to their N-chloro derivatives with hypochlorite solutions, then treating them with aniline or toluidine (eq. 100).

A compound known as "glucin" (see p. 45) was for a time commercially produced as a sweetening agent.[80] It was prepared by the reaction of benzaldehyde with chrysoidine (2,4-diaminoazobenzene), followed by sulfonation with fuming sulfuric acid.[118] In view of Fischer's work, it seems very probable that "glucin" is not a 1,2,4-benzotriazine, as was once thought.

Amino and Imino Derivatives. Arndt[2] found that o-nitrophenylguanidine, treated with solutions of alkali metal hydroxides, is converted to 3-amino-1,2,4-benzotriazine 1-oxide in nearly quantitative yield (eq. 101). Sodium carbonate, ammonia, or strong acids do not bring about

$$\text{(101)}$$

ring closure. Arndt suggested that the reaction might go through the alkali metal salt of a pseudonitro form, since the mixture is red at the start. 3-Amino-1,2,4-benzotriazine 1-oxide is soluble with difficulty in hot water and alcohol, insoluble in ether and, since it is weakly basic, easily soluble in warm 2 N hydrochloric acid.

Wolf and Pfister[144] prepared a number of 5-, 6-, and 7-substituted derivatives of 3-amino-1,2,4-benzotriazine 1-oxide by the reaction of equation 101 and Arndt and Rosenau[4] obtained 3-anilino-1,2,4-benzotriazine 1-oxide in an analogous manner. The same fundamental reaction is probably involved in work done by Backer and Moed[5]; they found that o-nitrobenzenesulfonylguanidine, heated with sodium hydroxide solution, loses sulfur dioxide and is converted in 85% yield to 3-amino-1,2,4-benzotriazine 1-oxide (eq. 102). o-Nitrophenylguanidine is probably an intermediate in this reaction but it was not isolated.

Backer and Moed also prepared 3-dimethylamino-1,2,4-benzotriazine 1-oxide in 94% yield by the same means.

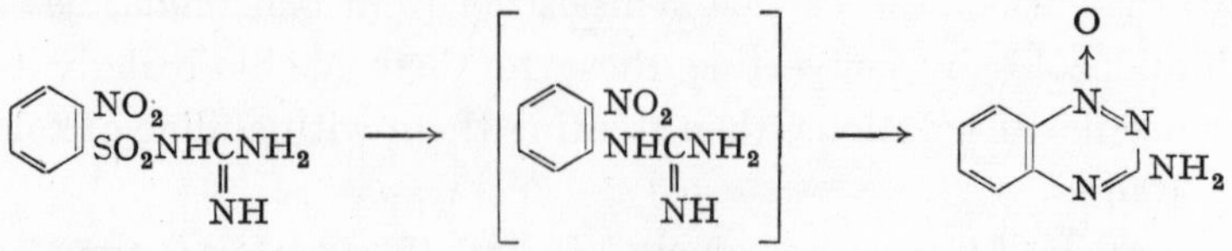

$$
\begin{array}{ccc}
\text{(benzene-}NO_2, SO_2NHCNH_2, NH) & \longrightarrow & \left[\text{(benzene-}NO_2, NHCNH_2, NH)\right] & \longrightarrow & \text{(benzotriazine-}O, N=N, N, NH_2) \qquad (102)
\end{array}
$$

Arndt and Eistert[3] employed another type of ring closure to obtain 3-amino-1,2,4-benzotriazine itself. A substituted phenyl-guanidine (LVIII) was heated at 200° under reduced pressure (eq. 103). The product was obtained as a sublimate. Wolf and Pfister[151]

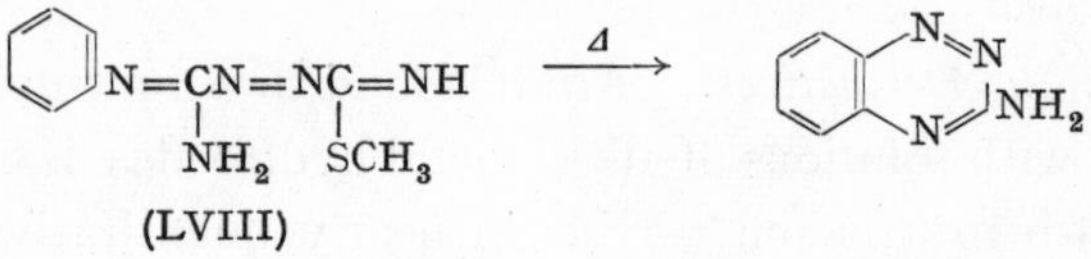

$$
\begin{array}{ccc}
\text{(benzene-}N=CN=NC=NH, NH_2, SCH_3) & \xrightarrow{\Delta} & \text{(benzotriazine-}N=N, N, NH_2) \qquad (103) \\
\text{(LVIII)}
\end{array}
$$

prepared 3-butylamino-7-chloro-1,2,4-benzotriazine by heating 3,7-dichloro-1,2,4-benzotriazine with n-butylamine (eq. 104). They also prepared a large number of substituted 3-amino-7-chloro-1,2,4-benzotriazine 1-oxides from 3,7-dichloro-1,2,4-benzotriazine 1-oxide and various aliphatic, aromatic, and heterocyclic amines.[147]

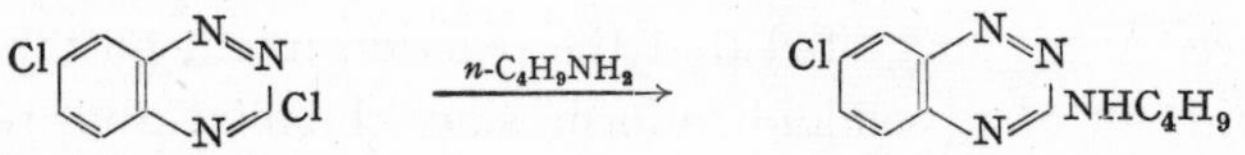

$$
\text{(Cl-benzotriazine-}N=N, N, Cl) \xrightarrow{n\text{-}C_4H_9NH_2} \text{(Cl-benzotriazine-}N=N, N, NHC_4H_9) \qquad (104)
$$

Arndt[2] found that the oxygen in 3-amino-1,2,4-benzotriazine 1-oxide can be removed by warming this compound with zinc and hydrochloric acid. This gives rise to a dihydro form that can be isolated as its nitrate. It is a very strong reducing agent, easily oxidized by air.

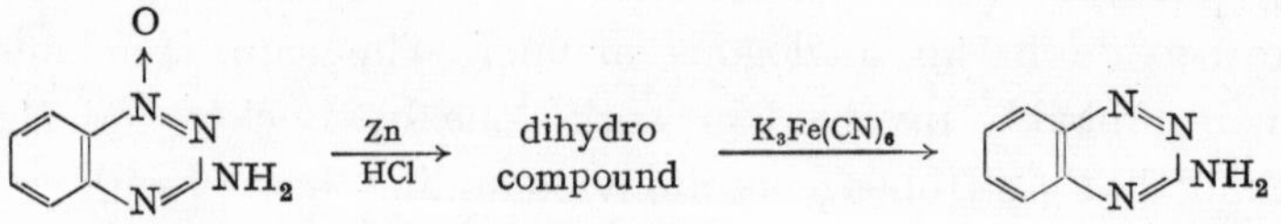

$$
\text{(benzotriazine-}O, N=N, N, NH_2) \xrightarrow[\text{HCl}]{\text{Zn}} \begin{array}{c}\text{dihydro} \\ \text{compound}\end{array} \xrightarrow{K_3Fe(CN)_6} \text{(benzotriazine-}N=N, N, NH_2) \qquad (105)
$$

Arndt used potassium ferricyanide to oxidize it to 3-amino-1,2,4-benzotriazine (eq. 105). Wolf and Pfister[143] removed the oxygen in

3-amino-7-chloro-1,2,4-benzotriazine 1-oxide by hydrogenation in pyridine solution, using hydrogen and Raney nickel. The dihydro compound obtained in this fashion was oxidized to the aromatic form by means of air.

3-Amino-1,2,4-benzotriazine is easily soluble in warm alcohol and not very soluble in ether. It sublimes without decomposition at atmospheric pressure. It was observed to be more strongly basic than its 1-oxide. Hydrogen peroxide easily oxidizes it to the 2-oxide (eq. 106).[4]

$$\text{(structure)} \xrightarrow{\text{H}_2\text{O}_2} \text{(structure)} \tag{106}$$

The 2-oxide is much less basic than the 1-oxide and is more soluble in alcohol. When heated with dilute sodium hydroxide solution, the 2-oxide undergoes some fundamental breakdown and nitrogen is evolved; the 1-oxide is stable towards alkali, as is 3-amino-1,2,4-benzotriazine itself. Like the 1-oxide, the 2-oxide can be reduced to a dihydro derivative and this can be reoxidized to 3-amino-1,2,4-benzotriazine. In similar experiments, 3-anilino-1,2,4-benzotriazine was prepared from its 1-oxide and was then oxidized with hydrogen peroxide to its 2-oxide. 3-Anilino-1,2,4-benzotriazine and its 1-oxide possess the same melting point, 197°, but a mixed melting point shows that the two compounds are quite distinct. 3-Anilino-1,2,4-benzotriazine is soluble in dilute acids, alcohol, and ether, whereas its 1-oxide is insoluble in dilute acids and ether.

3-Amino-1,2,4-benzotriazine shows the normal reaction of an aromatic amine towards nitrous acid; it is converted to 3-hydroxy-1,2,4-benzotriazine in 90% yield (eq. 107).[4] The same type of reaction takes place with 3-amino-7-chloro-1,2,4-benzotriazine,[149] 3-amino-1,2,4-benzotriazine 1-oxide,[2] and 3-amino-7-chloro-1,2,4-benzotriazine 1-oxide.[145] When hydrochloric acid was present, 3-chloro-1,2,4-benzo-

$$\text{(structure)OH} \xleftarrow[\text{H}_2\text{SO}_4]{\text{NaNO}_2} \text{(structure)NH}_2 \xrightarrow[\text{HCl}]{\text{NaNO}_2} \text{(structure)Cl} \tag{107}$$

triazine was obtained in 10% yield (eq. 107). The yield of the 3-chloro compound is increased by the addition of potassium ferrocyanide and potassium ferricyanide.[4] When potassium bromide is added to the reaction mixture of 3-amino-1,2,4-benzotriazine and nitrous acid, 3-bromo-1,2,4-benzotriazine is formed.[4]

Wolf and Pfister[148] have acylated 3-amino-7-chloro-1,2,4-benzotriazine 1-oxide, using acetic anhydride and succinic anhydride. They also prepared sulfonamides from p-nitrobenzenesulfonyl chloride and 3-amino-1,2,4-benzotriazine and its 7-chloro derivative. These sulfonamides were reduced by iron powder and hot alcoholic hydrogen chloride to yield the sulfanilamides.[152]

When 3-amino-7-chloro-1,2,4-benzotriazine is heated with refluxing benzylamine, the amino group is replaced by a benzylamino group.[151] A similar reaction takes place with 3-amino-7-bromo-1,2,4-benzotriazine 1-oxide but in this case the oxide oxygen appears to be lost (eq. 108).

$$\text{Br} \underset{N}{\overset{O\uparrow}{\longrightarrow}} \underset{N}{\overset{N=N}{\bigcirc}} NH_2 \quad \xrightarrow{C_6H_5CH_2NH_2} \quad \text{Br} \underset{N}{\overset{N=N}{\bigcirc}} NHCH_2C_6H_5 \quad (108)$$

Goldschmidt and Rosell[102] found that naphtho-as-triazines can be synthesized by reactions of arylazonaphthylamines with isocyanates. These reactions presumably go through diarylureas as intermediates. Following this earlier work, Busch[38] tried unsuccessfully to prepare 1,2,4-benzotriazines by cyclizations of o-arylazodiarylureas. However, he and Bergmann[38,40] were able to prepare 1,2,4-benzotriazines from the thiourea analogs (eq. 109). Warming with mercuric oxide in benzene

$$\bigcirc \underset{NHCNHAr}{\overset{N=NAr}{\bigcirc}} \quad \xrightarrow[\Delta]{HgO} \quad \bigcirc \underset{N}{\overset{N}{\bigcirc}} \underset{=NAr}{\overset{NAr}{\bigcirc}} \quad (109)$$
$$\qquad\qquad \underset{S}{\overset{\|}{}} \qquad\qquad\qquad\qquad (LIX)$$

was the most effective means of bringing about ring closure but warming with acetic acid alone was sufficient. The products are 2-aryl-3-arylimino-2,3-dihydro-1,2,4-benzotriazines (LIX), listed in Table II-9. Busch assigned his products structure LIX because they are strongly basic (amidine grouping), they are unchanged by boiling aqueous or alcoholic hydrogen chloride, they do not add hydrogen sulfide or ammonia (hence are not the isomeric carbodiimides), and their preparation takes place under conditions in which thioureas in general do not lose hydrogen sulfide. These compounds are reduced by hydrogen sulfide to other products, thought to be 1,4-dihydro derivatives of LIX (eq. 110). They can also be reduced by zinc dust and

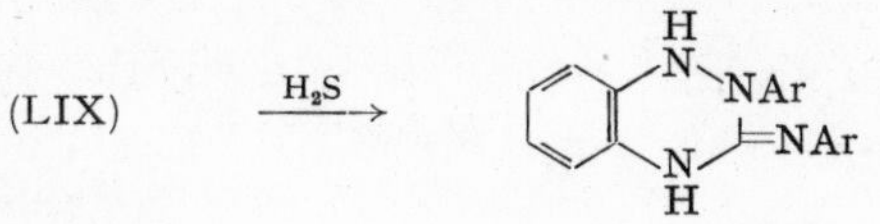

$$(\text{LIX}) \xrightarrow{\text{H}_2\text{S}} \qquad\qquad (110)$$

acetic acid, giving products of undetermined structure. Pierron[155] has prepared a similar product (LX) by a different reaction (eq. 111). Compound LX forms a stable hydrochloride and is only slightly acidic.

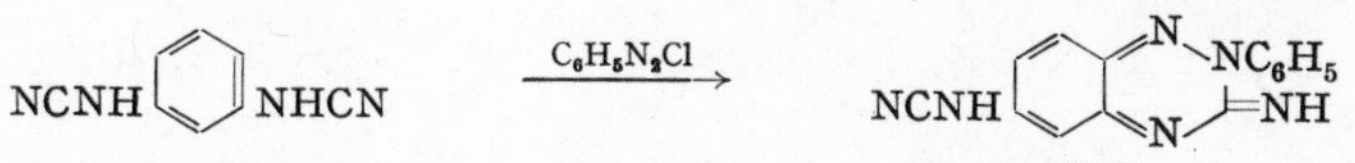

$$\text{NCNH}\underset{}{\bigcirc}\text{NHCN} \xrightarrow{\text{C}_6\text{H}_5\text{N}_2\text{Cl}} \qquad\qquad (111)$$

(LX)

Guha and Ghosh[106] reported that the action of tin and hydrochloric acid upon 1-o-nitrophenylsemicarbazide or 1-o-nitrophenylthiosemicarbazide yields 3-imino-1,2,3,4-tetrahydro-1,2,4-benzotriazine. This statement apparently did not escape unchallenged. Three years later, a paper appeared by Guha and Arndt[104] which showed that the reaction product had actually been impure o-phenylenediamine.

Hydroxy and Oxo Derivatives. The conversion of 3-amino-1,2,4-benzotriazines to 3-hydroxy-1,2,4-benzotriazines, as already discussed, is a direct means of obtaining these compounds. There is one other method used to prepare these compounds. o-Nitrophenylurea, heated with solutions of sodium hydroxide or potassium hydroxide, forms the 1-oxide of 3-hydroxy-1,2,4-benzotriazine (eq. 112).[2,145] As with the amino compounds, the 1-oxide oxygen can be removed by reduction.

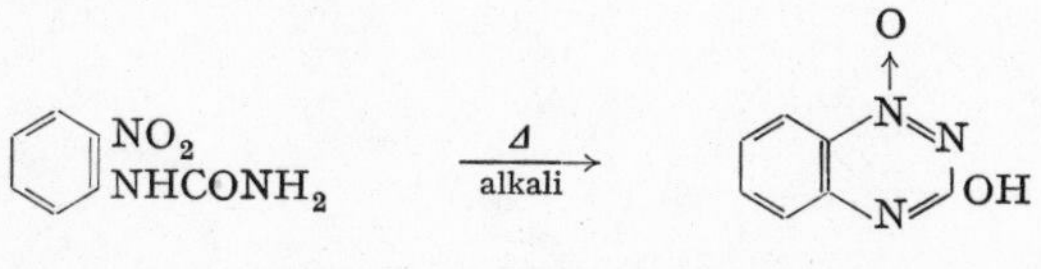

$$\underset{\text{NHCONH}_2}{\overset{\text{NO}_2}{\bigcirc}} \xrightarrow[\text{alkali}]{\Delta} \qquad\qquad (112)$$

Zinc and ammonium chloride have been used for this purpose[149]; an 88% yield was reported.

As with many other hydroxyheterocycles, the hydroxyl group in 3-hydroxy-1,2,4-benzotriazines can be replaced by chlorine rather readily. A mixture of phosphorus oxychloride and dimethylaniline has been used for this purpose and the reaction then proceeds in a straightforward manner (eq. 113).[146,150] When a mixture of phosphorus pentachloride and phosphorus oxychloride is used, the 1-oxide oxygen, if present, is apparently lost (eq. 114).[150]

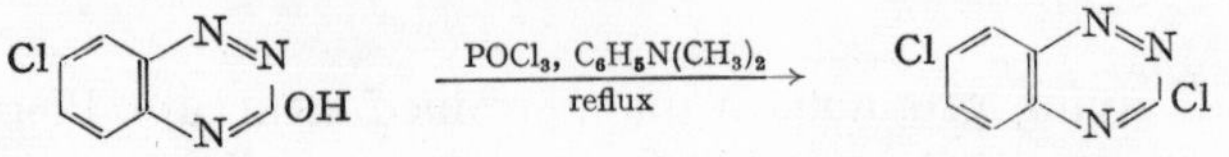

$POCl_3$, $C_6H_5N(CH_3)_2$
reflux

(113)

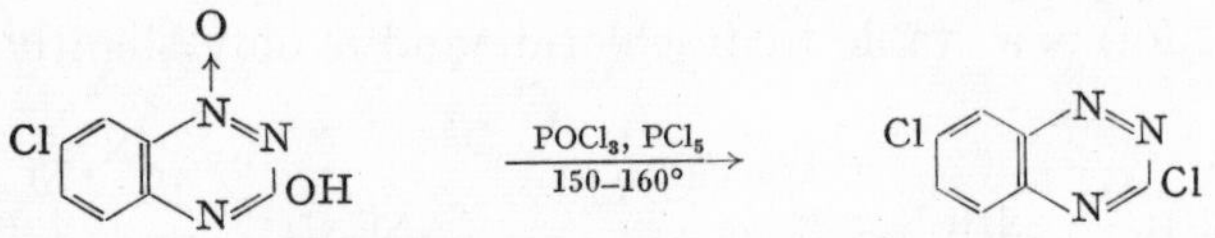

$POCl_3$, PCl_5
150–160°

(114)

According to Ergener,[84] methylation of 3-hydroxy-1,2,4-benzotriazine with diazomethane gives both *N*-methyl and *O*-methyl derivatives. The nature of the product is determined by the order of addition. When diazomethane is slowly added to 3-hydroxy-1,2,4-benzotriazine, or when the triazine is added to a very dilute solution of diazomethane,

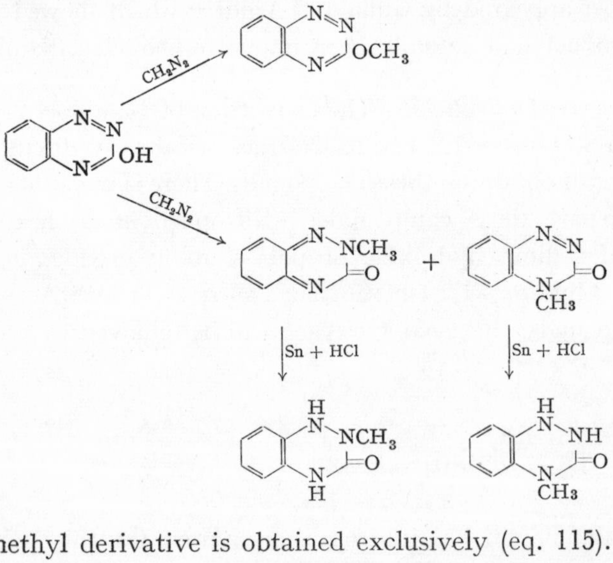

CH_2N_2
CH_2N_2
Sn + HCl
Sn + HCl

(115)

(116)

the *O*-methyl derivative is obtained exclusively (eq. 115). When the triazine is added to a concentrated solution of diazomethane, the two

N-methyl derivatives are formed (eq. 116). These *N*-methyl derivatives are reduced by tin and hydrochloric acid to tetrahydro-1,2,4-benzo-triazines. Methylation of the 1-oxide of 3-hydroxy-1,2,4-benzotriazine follows a somewhat different course; regardless of the order of addition, the *O*-methyl and the 4-methyl derivatives are formed.

Two studies have been made of 2-aryl-3-oxo-2,3-dihydro-1,2,4-benzotriazines. In the first of these, Busch[38] treated *o*-aminoazotoluene with phosgene and obtained 7-methyl-3-oxo-2-*p*-tolyl-2,3-dihydro-1,2,4-benzotriazine (eq. 117). Attempts to prepare this compound by hydrolysis of its imino analog, which has been described already, were not

$$\text{H}_3\text{C} \overset{\text{N}=\text{NC}_7\text{H}_7\text{-}p}{\underset{\text{NH}_2}{\bigcirc}} \xrightarrow{\text{COCl}_2} \text{H}_3\text{C} \bigcirc \overset{\text{N}}{\underset{\text{N}}{\diagdown}} \overset{\text{NC}_7\text{H}_7\text{-}p}{\underset{=\text{O}}{}} \qquad (117)$$

successful. This compound is weakly basic and its salts hydrolyze in water. Its solutions in concentrated sulfuric acid are dark red. Boiling hydrochloric acid has no effect but ammonia, amines, ethanol, and alcoholic potassium hydroxide cleave the ring between positions 2 and 3. Zinc dust and warm acetic acid or tin and hydrochloric acid reduce it to an easily oxidized dihydro derivative. Sodium amalgam merely cleaves the ring. If the reduction is carried out with zinc dust and acetic anhydride, the more stable acetyl derivative of the reduction product is formed.

Pierron[155] treated *m*-bis(cyanamido)benzene with benzenediazonium chloride and isolated a product (80% yield), said to be 6-cyanamido-3-oxo-2-phenyl-2,3-dihydro-1,2,4-benzotriazine (eq. 118). It was probably formed by hydrolysis of the imino analog, which has already

$$\text{NCNH} \bigcirc \text{NHCN} \xrightarrow{\text{C}_6\text{H}_5\text{N}_2\text{Cl}} \text{NCNH} \bigcirc \overset{\text{N}}{\underset{\text{N}}{\diagdown}} \overset{\text{NC}_6\text{H}_5}{\underset{=\text{O}}{}} \qquad (118)$$

been described. The possibility that the phenylazo grouping became attached to the benzene ring at a position *ortho* to each of the cyanoamino groups is not excluded but seems less likely. When treated with aqueous alkali, Pierron's product undergoes ring opening. With concentrated hydrochloric acid, it is converted to the 6-ureido compound.

Reduction with stannous chloride gives a very easily oxidized dihydro derivative, very soluble in base or acid but insoluble in water.

Guha and Ray[107] heated o-aminophenylhydrazine with urea, thereby obtaining 3-oxo-1,2,3,4-tetrahydro-1,2,4-benzotriazine (eq. 119). It is soluble in cold alkali. A rather closely related reaction was

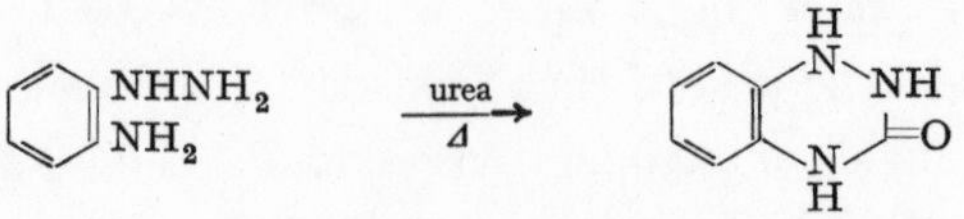

$$\text{(119)}$$

carried out by Guha and Ghosh[106] when they reduced 1-o-nitrophenyl-4-phenylsemicarbazide with tin and hydrochloric acid. One of the products was said to be 3-oxo-4-phenyl-1,2,3,4-tetrahydro-1,2,4-benzotriazine (eq. 120). It too is soluble in cold alkali.

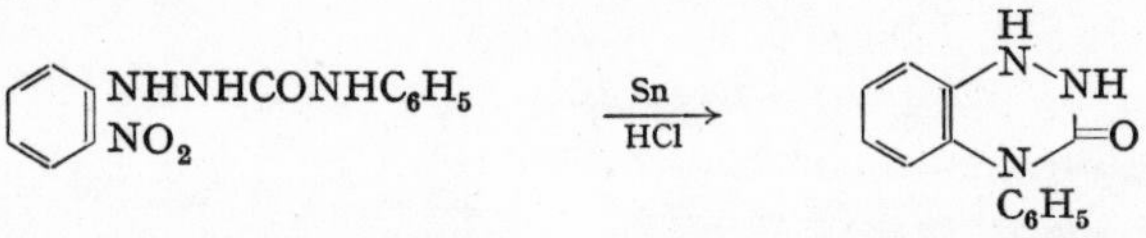

$$\text{(120)}$$

Mercapto and Thioxo Derivatives.   Arndt and Rosenau[4] found that o-nitrophenylthiourea, dissolved in dilute sodium hydroxide solution and heated for several minutes, is converted in 80% yield to the 1-oxide of 3-mercapto-1,2,4-benzotriazine (eq. 121). This compound is insoluble in

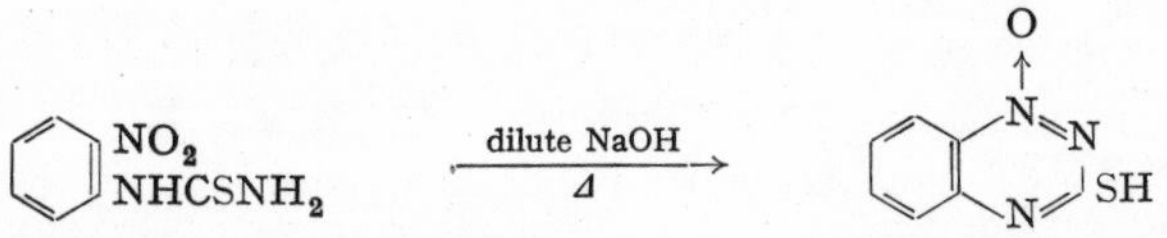

$$\text{(121)}$$

ether and soluble with difficulty in alcohol and acetic acid, but dissolves readily in ammonium hydroxide solution and in alkali to give solutions of a deep red color. It is reduced by zinc dust and sodium hydrox-

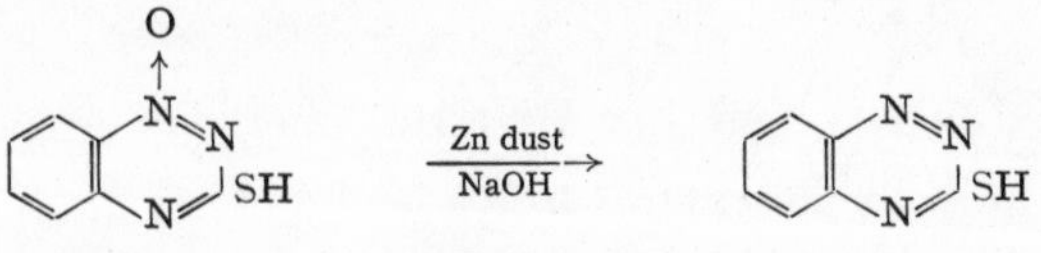

$$\text{(122)}$$

ide solution to 3-mercapto-1,2,4-benzotriazine (eq. 122); this product could not be recrystallized and was purified by heating with hot water and alcohol. The 1-oxide of 3-mercapto-1,2,4-benzotriazine, dissolved in cold ammonium hydroxide solution and treated with potassium ferricyanide, is oxidized to its disulfide (eq. 123), which is soluble in acetic

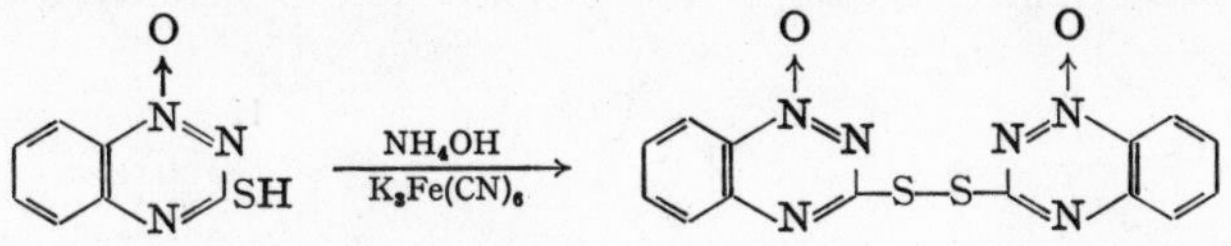

acid and insoluble in alkali. The 1-oxide is methylated with methyl sulfate and alkali; reduction of this methyl derivative with tin and hydrochloric acid yields 3-methylmercapto-1,2,4-benzotriazine (eq. 124), soluble in organic solvents and in concentrated hydrochloric acid but not in 3 N hydrochloric acid. 3-Methylmercapto-1,2,4-benzotriazine has also been obtained by a different series of reactions (eq. 124). The first

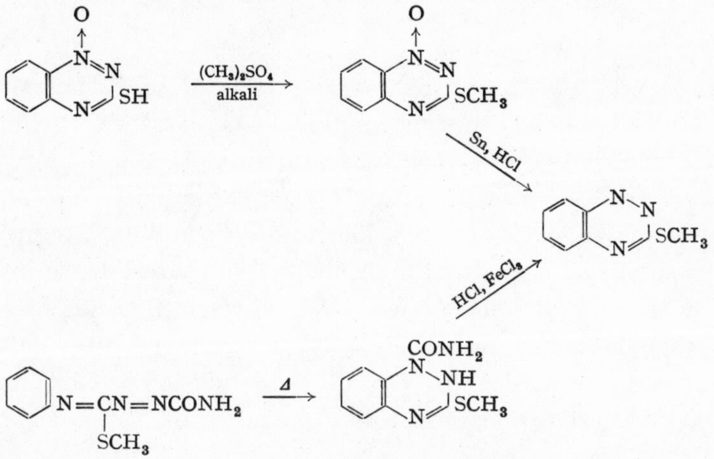

stage, which is carried out in boiling ethyl acetate, is complete in a few minutes and yields 3-methylmercapto-1,2,dihydro-1,2,4-benzotriazine-1-carboxamide. This compound is converted to 3-methylmercapto-1,2,4-benzotriazine in quantitative yield by dissolving in strong hydrochloric acid and adding ferric chloride solution.

Guha and co-workers in India have reported a number of compounds that may contain 1,2,4-benzotriazine ring systems. Potassium xanthate reacts with o-aminophenylhydrazine to yield a product that is probably 3-mercapto-1,2-dihydro-1,2,4-benzotriazine (eq. 125).[107] This structure was favored because the compound is acidic, gives a yellow mercaptide with mercuric chloride, and forms a benzoyl derivative and a disulfide. In another paper the preparation of 3-methylmercapto-

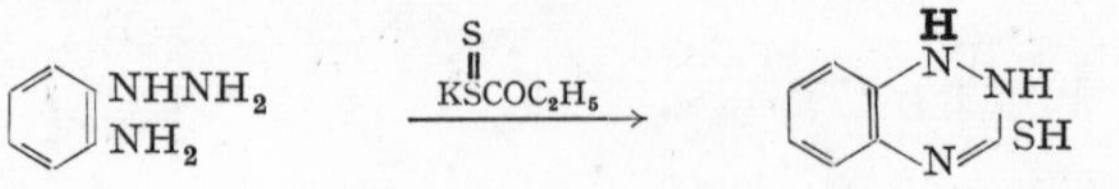

$$\text{(125)}$$

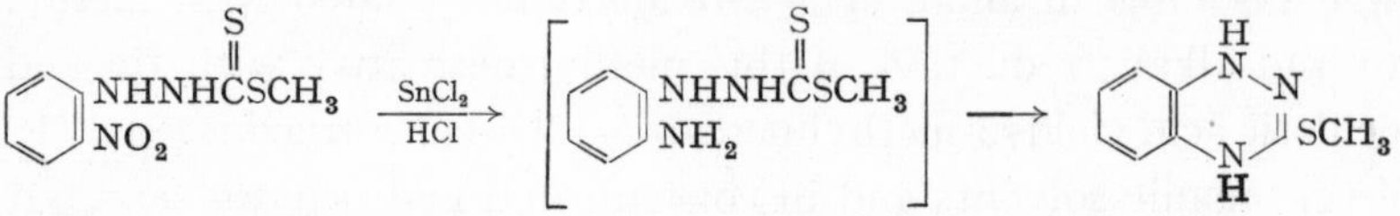

$$\text{(126)}$$

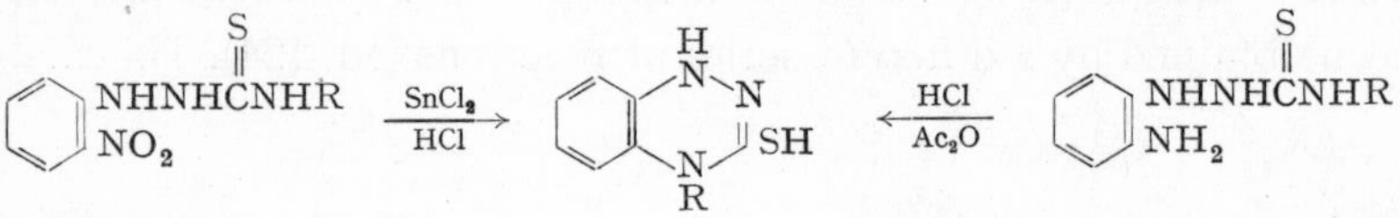

$$\text{(127)}$$

1,4-dihydro-1,2,4-benzotriazine was reported (eq. 126).[106] The reduction of a series of 4-aryl-1-o-nitrophenylthiosemicarbazides with stannous chloride and hydrochloric acid was said to yield 4-aryl-3-mercapto-1,4-dihydro-1,2,4-benzotriazines (eq. 127).[105] The products were assigned this structure because they are acidic, form mercaptides with mercuric chloride, and can be oxidized to disulfides. They are all listed in Table II-9. In the case in which R was allyl, no cyclization was observed. These compounds can also be prepared by warming 1-o-aminophenyl-4-arylthiosemicarbazides with hydrogen chloride and acetic anhydride (eq. 127). An isomeric product was prepared by Guha and Roy-

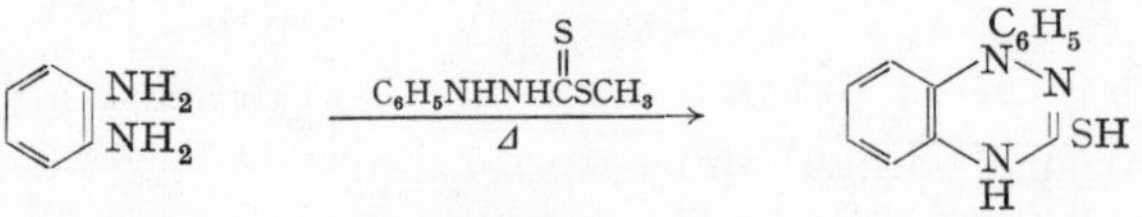

$$\text{(128)}$$

Choudhury (eq. 128).[108] Like these other compounds, it is acidic, can be oxidized to a disulfide, and also forms an acetyl derivative. The acetyl group may possibly be in the 4-position because this derivative is alkali-soluble. Of course, the alkali solubility may also be due to saponification of an S-acetyl grouping.

1,2,4-Benzotriazinyl Ketones. The formazyl synthesis has been applied by Bamberger and associates to the preparation of 1,2,4-benzotriazinyl ketones. Thus, 3-acetyl-1,2,4-benzotriazine was prepared in two steps from acetone, the last step giving a yield of 23% (eq. 129).[12,13] It is

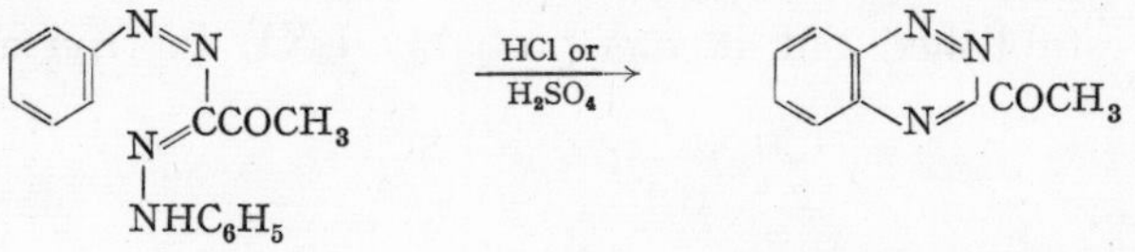

$$(129)$$

soluble in concentrated hydrochloric acid and rather easily soluble in boiling water but much less soluble in cold water. 3-Benzoyl-1,2,4-benzotriazine was obtained in a similar manner but in a better yield.[15,16] The phenylhydrazones of these compounds have been prepared.

Mossini[132] treated sodium pyruvate with diazotized sulfanilamide to obtain a product that, further treated with concentrated sulfuric acid, yields 6-sulfo-1,2,4-benzotriazin-3-ylglyoxylic acid (eq. 130), a brownish-orange material soluble in water and in most organic solvents.

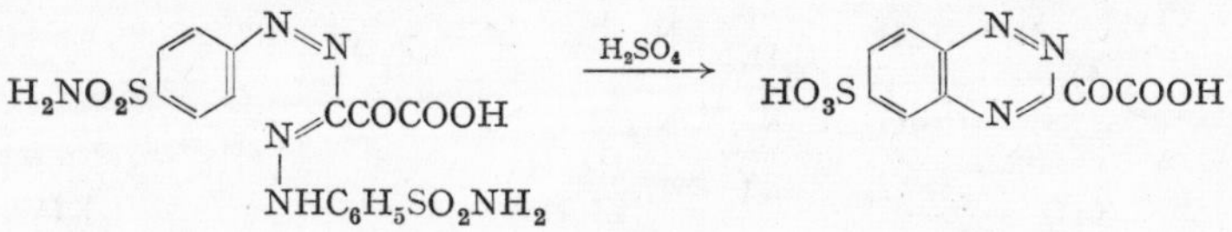

$$(130)$$

(2) Two 1,2,4-Triazine Rings Condensed with One Benzene Ring

Only one compound of this type has ever been reported. Pierron[155] carried out the reaction of benzenediazonium chloride with an alkaline solution of *m*-bis(cyanamido)benzene. This yielded a complex mixture from which he isolated several products (eq. 131), including a compound

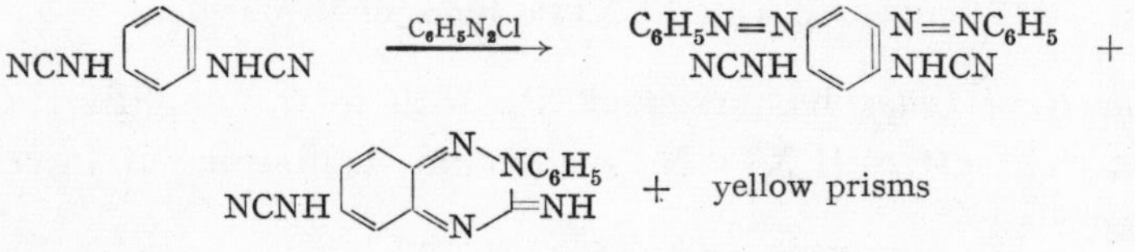

$$(131)$$

characterized as yellow prisms, not melting below 310°, and slightly soluble in the usual organic solvents. Only the nitrogen content was determined. When heated with alcoholic potassium hydroxide, this compound is converted to another, said to be identical with a compound prepared by Griess.[103] The identity was not rigorously proved, however. The structure of Griess's compound, which was obtained by the reaction of benzenediazonium chloride with 2,4-diaminoazobenzene, was not definitely established but it was probably LXI. Pierron apparently

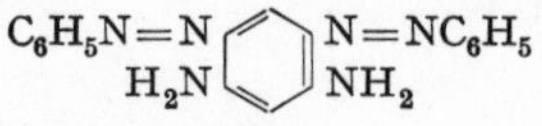

$$C_6H_5N=N \underset{H_2N}{\overset{}{\bigcirc}} \overset{N=NC_6H_5}{\underset{NH_2}{}}$$

(LXI)

accepted structure LXI for the cleavage product from his yellow prisms; on the basis of this result and a nitrogen analysis, he wrote structure LXII for his product. However, this structure cannot be written in such a way as to satisfy valence requirements. A similar structure, LXIII, can be written if we assume that somehow a hydrogenation occurred in the reaction. A more plausible structure is LXIV, which does not require one to assume any reduction reactions.

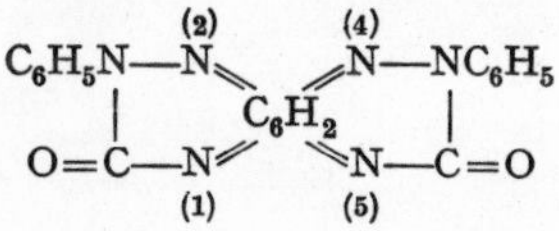

(LXII) 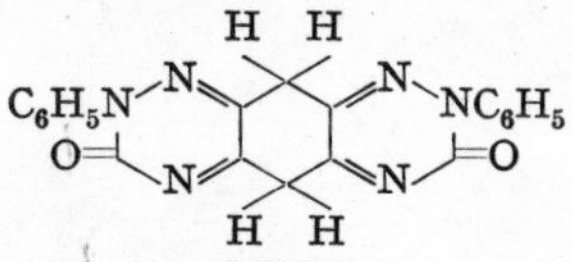   (LXIII) 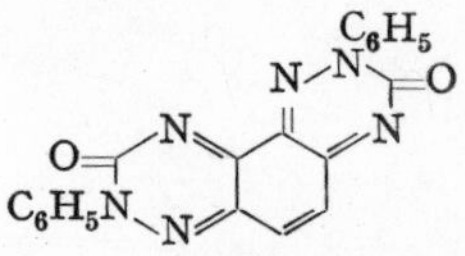   (LXIV)

The Ring Index has assigned No. 1817 to the ring system of LXIII, giving it the name benzo[1,2-e, 5,4-e']bis[1,2,4]-triazine. The ring system of structure LXIV would be called benzo[1,2-e 4,3-e']bis-[1,2,4]triazine.

D. Condensed with Naphthalene

(1) Condensed with the 2,3 Positions of Naphthalene

The Ring Index has assigned No. 1819 to the naphtho[2,3]-as-triazine ring system (LXV). No compounds containing it have ever been reported.

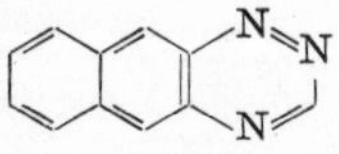

(LXV)

(2) Condensed with the 1,2 Positions of Naphthalene

Compounds containing the naphtho[2,1]-*as*-triazine system (LXVI) (*R.I.* 1820) and the naphtho[1,2]-*as*-triazine system (LXVII) (*R.I.* 1821) are known.

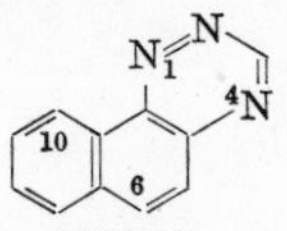

(LXVI) 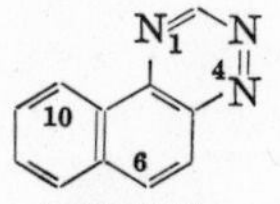   (LXVII)

The known naphtho[2,1]-*as*-triazines are listed in Table II-10. Methods of preparing them are rather limited. Fichter and Schiess[88] prepared 3-phenyl-naphtho[2,1]-*as*-triazine by the formazyl synthesis (eq. 132). No details were given for the procedure. It will be noted that aniline is eliminated in preference to α-naphthylamine.

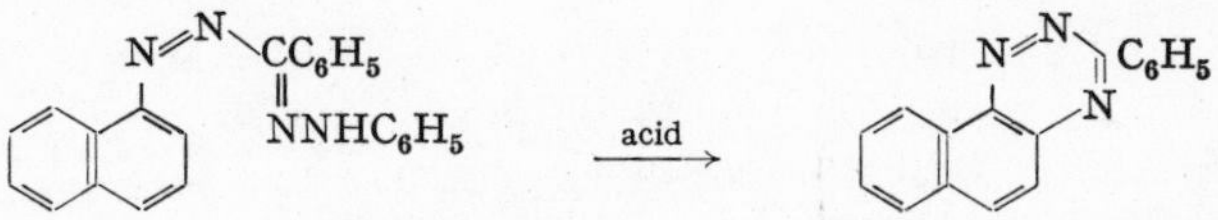

(132)

Goldschmidt and Rosell[102] and, later, Goldschmidt and Poltzer[101] claimed to have prepared naphtho[2,1]-*as*-triazine derivatives by reactions of aromatic aldehydes with *o*-aminoazo compounds (eq. 133).

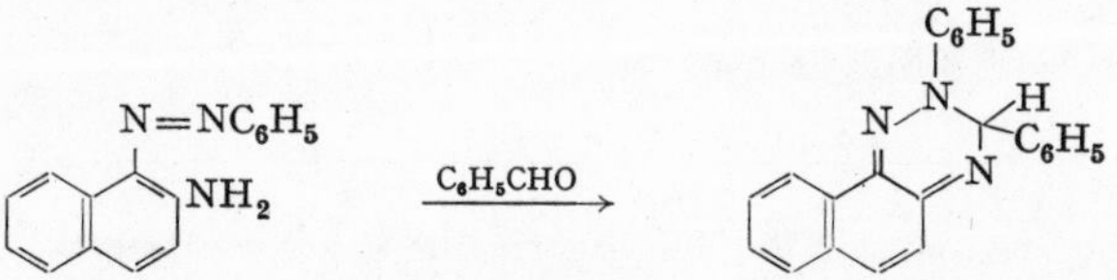

(133)

Following them, other workers (Meldola,[121] Meldola and Forster,[122] Meldola and Hughes,[123] Cassella and Co.,[140] and Woods[199]) described similar reactions. Fischer[90,91] showed in 1922 that the reactions of aromatic aldehydes with *o*-aminoazo compounds lead to the formation of imidazole rings rather than *as*-triazine rings (see page 100). Since that time, several people have claimed to have obtained naphtho[2,1]-*as*-triazines by this method. Cremonini[68] isolated a compound, $C_{25}H_{19}N_3$, from the reaction of 1-phenylazo-2-aminonaphthalene with benzal-

TABLE II-10. Naphtho[2,1]-*as*-triazines

Substituents	Color, crystal habit	M.p., °C.	Ref.
3-Acetamido[a]	Dirty white	208	70
3-Amino[a]	Reddish-yellow needles	240	70
6-Bromo-2-phenyl-3-phenyl-imino-2,3-dihydro		189	40
1-Carbethoxy-3-oxo-1,2,3,4-tetrahydro		265 (dec.)	78
1,2-Dicarbethoxy-3-oxo-1,2,3,4-tetrahydro[b]		180–181	78
6-Ethoxy-2-(4-ethoxy-1-naphthyl)-3-phenylimino-2,3-dihydro		275	40
6-Ethoxy-2-phenyl-3-phenyl-imino-2,3-dihydro		230	40
6-Ethoxy-2-phenyl-3-phenyl-imino-1,2,3,4-tetrahydro		207	40
3-Hydroxy[a]	Yellow		70, 183
3-Imino-2-phenyl-2,3-dihydro		160	155
3-Oxo-2-phenyl-2,3-dihydro	Yellow needles	252	102
		255	38, 155
3-Oxo-1,2,3,4-tetrahydro	Brown prisms	315–320	78
3-Phenyl		145	88
2-Phenyl-3-phenylimino-2,3-dihydro		166	40
2-Phenyl-3-styryl-2,3-dihydro[c]		197	68

[a]Probably has a naphtho[1,2]-*as*-triazine structure but this structure is possible. See text.
[b]Forms a complex, m.p. 127–128°, with acetic acid.
[c]Structure not certain. See the text.

dehyde and pyruvic acid. No structure was shown in the available reference but the compound was described as phenyl-styryl-naphtho-triazine. Presumably, Cremonini thought the reaction went as shown in equation (134). Neri,[133-135] in an extensive study of sweetness in organic compounds, prepared many compounds by means of Goldschmidt's reaction; these were described as "naphthoisotriazines," but, in view of Fischer's work, they are very probably naphthimidazoles.

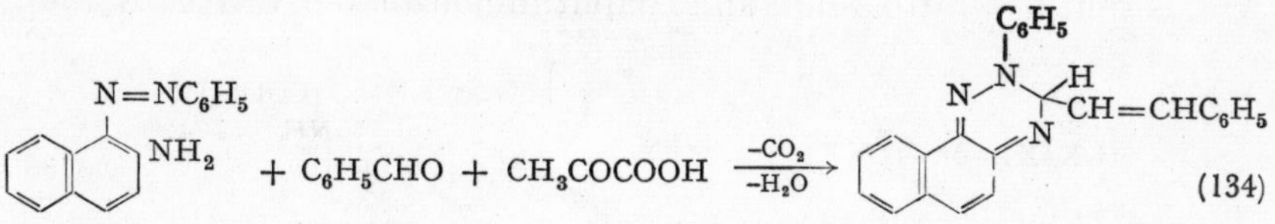

N=NC6H5
NH2
+ C6H5CHO + CH3COCOOH
-CO2
-H2O
C6H5
N
H
CH=CHC6H5
N

(134)

Anderau[142] has described coupling reactions involving compounds such as LXVIII. The method of preparing such compounds was not disclosed. However, they look very much like Goldschmidt's "triazines," written in a somewhat different manner, with a tautomeric shift of

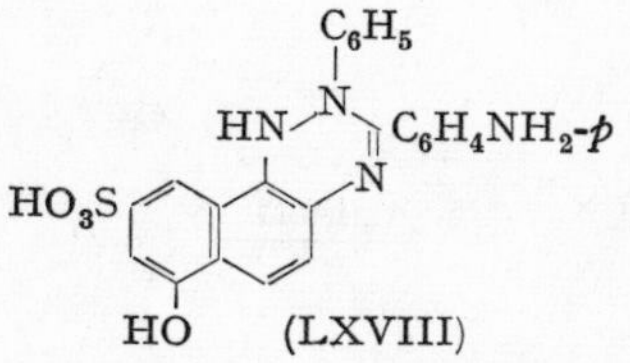

C6H5
HN
N
C6H4NH2-p
N
HO3S
HO

(LXVIII)

hydrogen. Accordingly, they may be regarded with some suspicion since they may in actuality contain imidazole rings rather than *as*-triazine rings. It must be admitted, however, that they may indeed possess the structures claimed for them.

The naphtho[2,1]-*as*-triazine synthesis (eq. 135) reported by Fierz and Sallmann[89] also appears questionable. These workers heated ethyl 1-*p*-nitrophenylazo-2-naphthylaminoacetate in acetic acid, thereby obtaining a product that was given structure LXIX. We believe

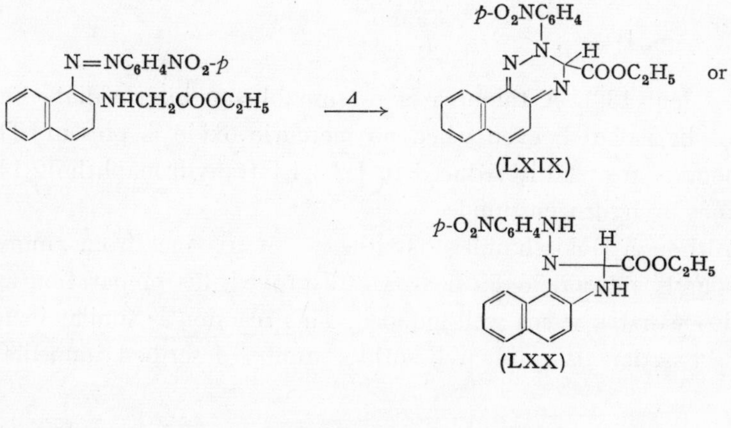

N=NC6H4NO2-p
NHCH2COOC2H5
Δ
p-O2NC6H4
N
H
COOC2H5
N
(LXIX)
or
p-O2NC6H4NH
N
H
COOC2H5
NH
(LXX)

(135)

that stucture LXX is a better one since the compound, treated with hydrogen chloride in ether and then with concentrated hydrochloric acid, is split to *p*-nitroaniline and a naphthimidazole derivative (eq. 136).

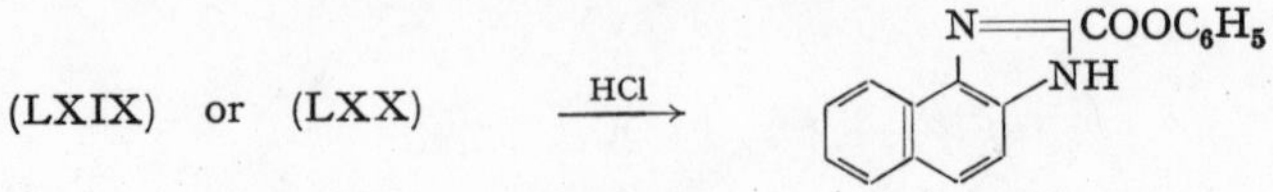

(LXIX) or (LXX)
HCl
N
COOC6H5
NH

(136)

Pierron[155] treated 2-cyanamidonaphthalene with benzenediazonium chloride. Presumably a phenylazo compound was an intermediate but the product isolated was 3-imino-2-phenyl-2,3-dihydronaphtho[2,1]-*as*-triazine (eq. 137). When heated with alcoholic potassium

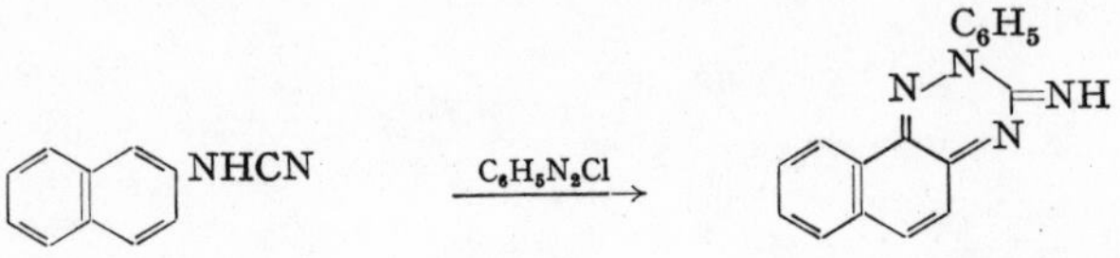

NHCN
C6H5N2Cl
C6H5
N
N
NH
N

(137)

hydroxide or aqueous acetic acid, it is hydrolyzed to the corresponding 3-oxo compound It is easily reduced by stannous chloride to a dihydro derivative; this is readily reoxidized by air.

Busch and Bergmann[40] obtained several 2-phenyl-3-phenylimino-2,3-dihydronaphtho[2,1]-*as*-triazines by heating 2-amino-1-phenylazonaphthalenes with phenyl isothiocyanate and mercuric oxide in

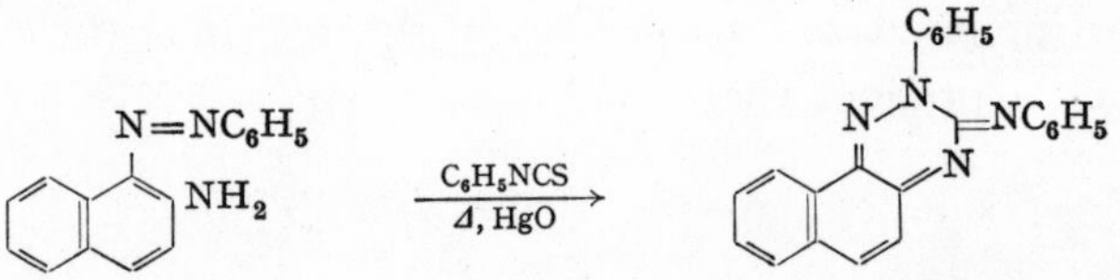

N=NC6H5
NH2
C6H5NCS
Δ, HgO
C6H5
N
N
NC6H5
N

(138)

alcohol (eq. 138). A thiourea is presumably an intermediate but it cannot be isolated, even when no mercuric oxide is present. These compounds are readily reduced to 1,2,3,4-tetrahydronaphtho[2,1]-*as*-triazines by hydrogen sulfide.

Although Goldschmidt's "synthesis" of triazines from aminoazo compounds and aldehydes has been disproved, his preparation using aryl isocyanates seems well-founded. This reaction is similar in form to the reaction using phenyl isothiocyanate, described immediately

above, but it yields different products, namely, 3-oxo-2-phenyl-2,3-
dihydronaphtho[2,1]-*as*-triazines (eq. 139). The reaction is carried out
by heating the aminoazo compound with two moles of phenylisocyanate

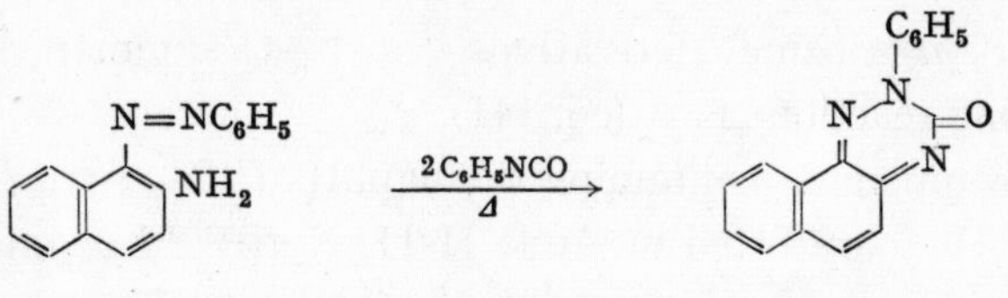

$$\xrightarrow{\underset{\Delta}{2\,C_6H_5NCO}}$$ (139)

at 150°. Busch[38] obtained the same product in two other ways, by the
action of phosgene on the aminoazo compound and by the action of
cold alcoholic potassium hydroxide on ethyl 1-phenylazo-2-naphthyl-
carbamate (eq. 140). Pierron[155] prepared it by the hydrolysis of 3-imino-

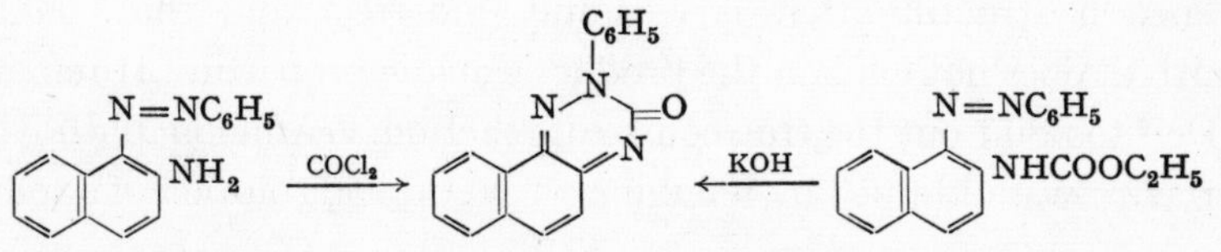

$$\xrightarrow{COCl_2} \qquad \xleftarrow{KOH}$$ (140)

2-phenyl-2,3-dihydronaphtho[2,1]-*as*-triazine (product of reaction 137).
3-Oxo-2-phenyl-2,3-dihydronaphtho[2,1]-*as*-triazine, when heated with
concentrated hydrochloric acid at 160°, is degraded to an unidentified

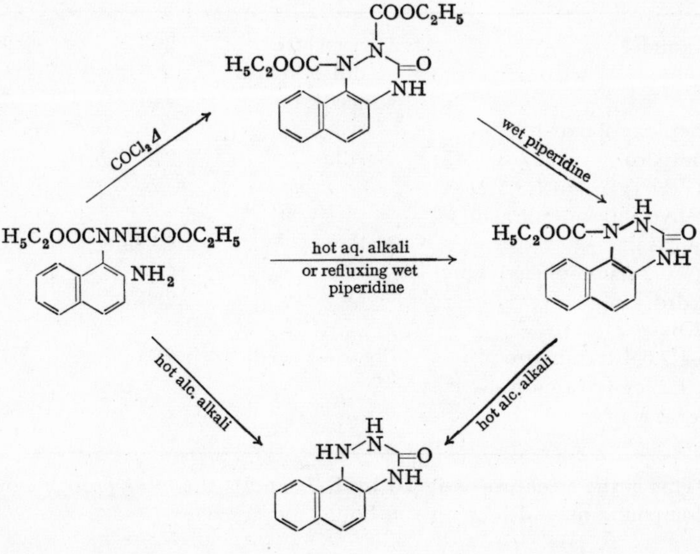

(141)

phenol (possibly phenol itself) and β-naphthylamine; no aniline is obtained.[140]

Diels[78] has studied another approach to the synthesis of naphtho-[2,1]-*as*-triazines. His work, which leads to 3-oxo-1,2,3,4-tetrahydro-naphtho[2,1]-*as*-triazine derivatives, is best summarized in the accompanying reaction chart (eq. 141).

A few compounds containing the naphtho[1,2]-*as*-triazine system are known. They are listed in Table II-11. Neri[133-135] claimed to have prepared many compounds containing this system. Since he employed the discredited Goldschmidt synthesis, his results cannot be accepted.

Thiele and Barlow[183] prepared the β-guanylhydrazone of β-naphthoquinone, then heated it with sodium hydroxide solution to obtain the salt of a compound, $C_{11}H_7N_3O$. To this compound they assigned a structure that is certainly incorrect and that, as they admitted, does not explain the product's acidic properties. It remained for De[70] to point out the true course of reaction. 2-Aminonaphtho[1,2]-*as*-triazine was obtained by refluxing an acetic acid solution of naphtho-

TABLE II-11. Naphtho[1,2]-*as*-triazines

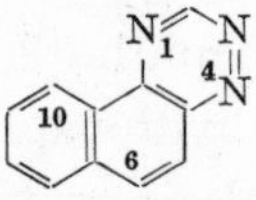

Substituents	Color, crystal habit	M.p., °C.	Ref.
2-Acetamido[a]	Dirty white	208	70
2-Amino[a]	Reddish-yellow needles	240	70
4-Carbethoxy-2-oxo-1,2,3,4-tetrahydro	Needles	272–273	76
4-Carbethoxy-2-oxo-1,2,3,4-tetrahydro-6-sulfonic acid, sodium salt	Yellow	135 (dec.)	76
6-Ethoxy-2-oxo-3-phenyl-2,3-dihydro		236	40
2-Hydroxy[a]			70, 183
2-Oxo-1,2,3,4-tetrahydro	Colorless needles	299	76
2-Oxo-1,2,3,4-tetrahydro-6-sulfonic acid			76

[a]This is the structure assigned by De[70] and is the most probable one. The compound may also be a naphtho[2,1]-*as*-triazine.

quinone and aminoguanidine hydrochloride for four hours (eq. 142). When heated with strong potassium hydroxide solution, this compound

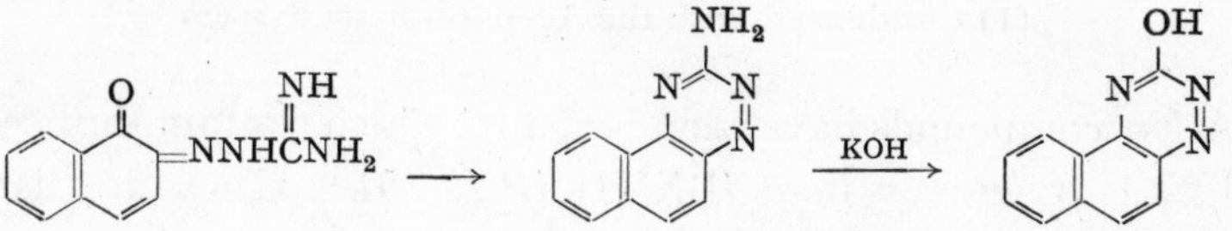

(142)

is converted to 2-hydroxynaphtho[1,2]-as-triazine, the $C_{11}H_7N_3O$ of Thiele and Barlow (eq. 142). It is possible, of course, that naphtho[2,1]-as-triazines might have been obtained through reaction of semicarbazide or aminoguanidine with the α-carbonyl group of β-naphthoquinone rather than with the β-carbonyl group. This seems quite unlikely, however; the β-carbonyl group would be sterically much less hindered for the initial reaction with the carbonyl reagent.

Busch and Bergmann[40] prepared 6-ethoxy-2-oxo-3-phenyl-2,3-dihydronaphtho[1,2]-as-triazine by the reaction of phosgene with 1-amino-4-ethoxy-2-phenylazonaphthalene (eq. 143).

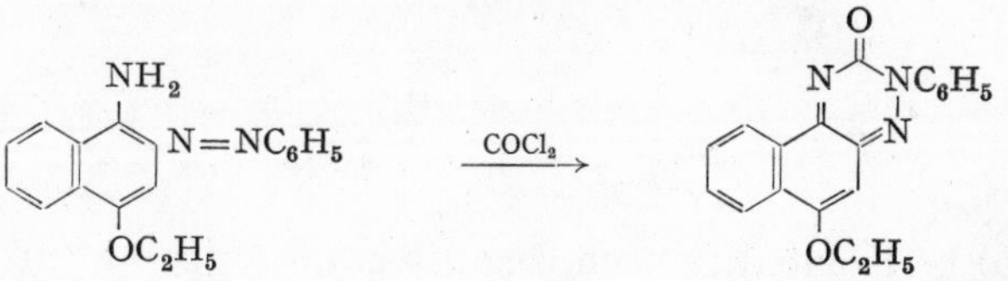

(143)

Diels[76] has prepared several derivatives of 2-oxo-1,2,3,4-tetrahydronaphtho[1,2]-as-triazine. This work is summarized in the accompanying reaction chart (eq. 144).

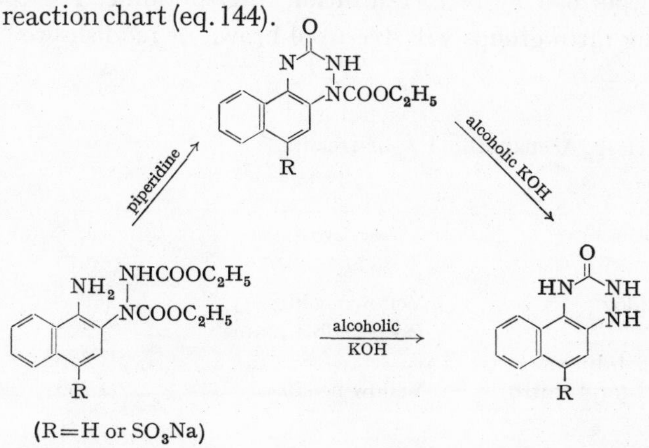

(144)

(R=H or SO_3Na)

E. Condensed with Higher Aromatic Ring Systems

(1) Condensed with the Acenaphthene System

A few compounds have been prepared which contain the acenaphtho[1,2]-*as*-triazine system (**LXXI**) (*R.I.* 2512). They are listed in Table II-12.

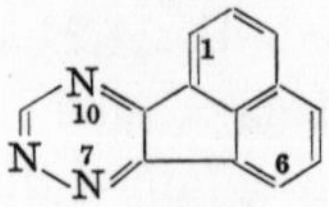

(LXXI)

According to De[70] and De and Dutta,[72] the reactions of acenaphthoquinones with aminoguanidine hydrochloride proceed smoothly in acetic acid solution. The products are 9-aminoacenaphtho[1,2]-*as*-triazines (eq. 145). With unsymmetrically substituted acenaphthoquinones, two products are possible. However, only one product

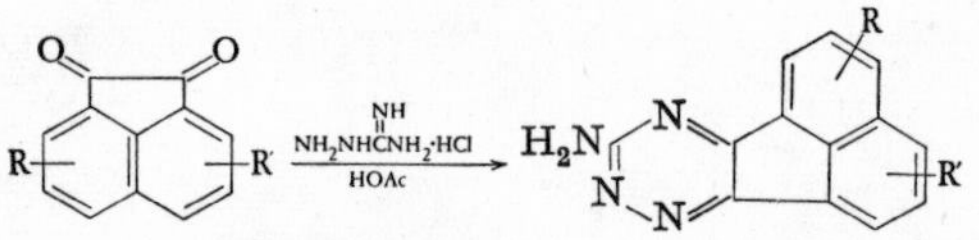

(145)

appears to be isolated in each case; it is not apparent at the present which of the two alternatives is to be preferred. These compounds are colored materials, insoluble in water and in most organic solvents. They are purified by recrystallization from pyridine. The compounds containing nitro groups will dye wool brown or reddish-brown.

TABLE II-12. Acenaphtho[1,2]-*as*-triazines

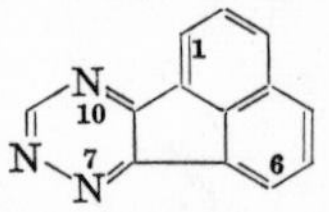

Substituents	Color, crystal habit	M.p., °C.	Ref.
9-Acetamido	Yellow needles	268	70
9-Amino	Deep yellow plates	>305	70
9-Amino-3,4-dinitro		>300	72
9-Amino-3-(or 4-)nitro	Yellow needles	>290	72

(2) Condensed with the Phenanthrene System

Table II-13 lists all reported compounds containing the phe-nanthro[9,10]-*as*-triazine ring system (**LXXII**) (*R.I.* 2597).

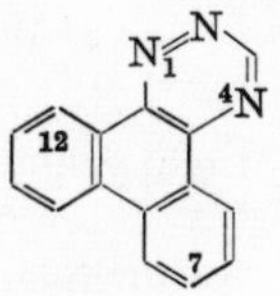

(LXXII)

These compounds have all been prepared by reactions of phenan-thraquinones with aminoguanidine, semicarbazide, and thiosemi-carbazide. It is not possible, in our present state of knowledge, to say which of the two possible products is obtained when an unsymmet-rically substituted phenanthraquinone is used. In general, however, only one product is isolated.

Thiele and Bihan[184] prepared 3-aminophenanthro[9,10]-*as*-triazine by reaction of phenanthraquinone with aminoguanidine dinitrate. De[70] subsequently prepared a number of other 3-aminophenanthro[9,10]-*as*-triazines by reactions of aminoguanidine hydrochloride with sub-stituted phenanthraquinones. He used acetic acid as solvent for the reactions. Schmidt and Bürkert[171] obtained a quantitative yield of product by heating 2,7-dibromophenanthraquinone with amino-guanidine hydrochloride and a slight excess of hydrochloric acid in alcoholic solution for seven hours. This product, treated with ammonia to give the free base, was found to contain two substances. One was a stable yellow material; the other was a labile red substance, which was transformed to the stable form in boiling alcohol and when heated by itself at 200°. The stable form was presumed to be the fully aromatic compound; the labile form was thought to be its imino tautomer (eq. 146). Both forms give the same salts and derivatives, summarized in Table II-13.

It was at first believed that phenanthraquinones would not react with semicarbazide to yield 3-hydroxyphenanthro[9,10]-*as*-triazines. Schmidt, Schairer, and Glatz[173] reported that phenanthraquinone

TABLE II-13. Phenanthro[9,10]-as-triazines

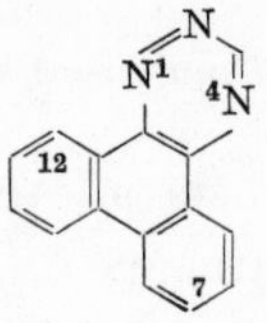

Substituents	Color, crystal habit	M.p., °C.	Ref.
3-Acetamido-6(or 11)-bromo	Light yellow	278	70
3-Acetamido-6,11-dibromo		309	171
3-Acetamido-8,9-dibromo	Rectangular, light yellow	>310	70
3-Acetamido-6,11-dinitro	Yellow needles	>310	70
3-Acetamido-8,9-dinitro	Rectangular, yellow	275	70
3-Acetamido-6(or 11)-nitro	Yellow needles	298	70
3-Acetamido-8(or 9)-nitro	Light yellow needles	270	70
3-Amino		262	184
3-Amino-6(or 11)-bromo	Reddish-yellow needles	235	70
3-Amino-6,11-dibromo	Orange, rectangular	288	70
	Yellow (stable form)	333	171
	Red (labile iminoform)		171
3-Amino-6,11-dibromo, hydrochloride		238	171
3-Amino-8,9-dibromo	Greenish-yellow plates	>305	70
3-Amino-6,11-dinitro	Brown needles	>310	70
3-Amino-8,9-dinitro	Greenish-yellow needles	265	70
3-Amino-6(or 11)-nitro	Yellow needles	280	70
3-Amino-8(or 9)-nitro	Yellow needles	215	70
3-Benzamido-6,11-dibromo		240	171
7(or 10)-Bromo-3-hydroxy		304	173
6(or 11)-Chloro-3-hydroxy		288 (dec.)	173
6,11-Dibromo-3-hydroxy		295	71, 171
6,11-Dinitro-3-mercapto	Brown, rectangular	220	71
3-Hydroxy		285 (dec.)	173
		287	71
3-Hydroxy-7(or 10)-nitro		273–274 (dec.)	173
3-Hydroxy-8(or 9)-nitro		285	173
		286	71
3-Mercapto	Dull red, rectangular	198	71
3-Mercapto-6(or 11)-nitro		>300	71
3-Mercapto-8(or 9)-nitro	Brown, rectangular	230	71

itself, when heated with semicarbazide hydrochloride in alcoholic solution, yielded only the monosemicarbazone. When they employed the

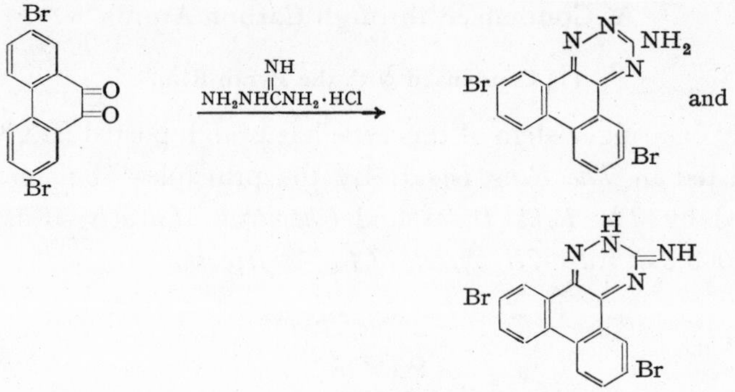

(146)

monoxime, they were successful in closing the triazine ring. This method was used to prepare a series of compounds of this type (eq. 147).[171,173] In one case,[173] reaction of the oxime with semicarbazide hydrochloride yielded the oxime-semicarbazone of the phenanthraquinone and this

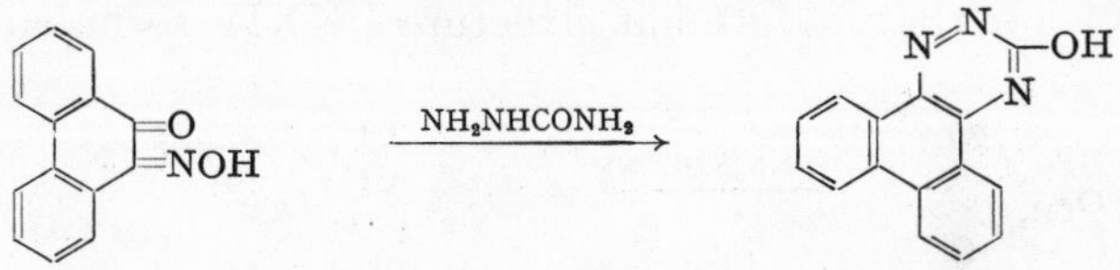

(147)

was subsequently cyclized by treatment with concentrated hydrochloric acid. It was later discovered that use of the monoxime is not necessary, the quinone itself being satisfactory, especially if acetic acid is used as solvent for the reaction.[71,171]

Several 3-mercaptophenanthro[9,10]-as-triazines have been prepared by De,[71] who carried out the reaction of the phenanthraquinones with thiosemicarbazide in two steps, first isolating the thiosemicarbazone and then heating this in acetic acid for 30–35 hours to bring about cyclization. As might be expected, the 4-phenylthiosemicarbazone of phenanthraquinone failed to yield a triazine.

In general, the phenanthro[9,10]-as-triazines are soluble only with difficulty in the usual organic solvents. Pyridine appears to be the best solvent for them and they are ordinarily recrystallized from this solvent.

3. 1,2,4-TRIAZINE RINGS CONDENSED
WITH HETEROCYCLES

A. Condensed through Carbon Atoms

(1) Condensed with the Pyran Ring

Only one ring system of this type has been reported (LXXIII). It is not listed in *The Ring Index*. By the principles of nomenclature employed by *The Ring Index* and *Chemical Abstracts*, it is named *5,8-ethano-5,8-dihydro-7H-pyrano[3,4-e]-as-triazine*.

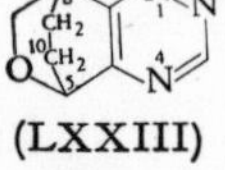

(LXXIII)

Cusmano[69] has reported that dioxocineole reacts with semicarbazide in aqueous-alcohol solution to give a monosemicarbazone. This is cyclized by treatment with sodium ethoxide in ethanol or with 15% potassium hydroxide solution (eq. 148). Cusmano favored structure LXXV for the product but structure LXXIV seems much more

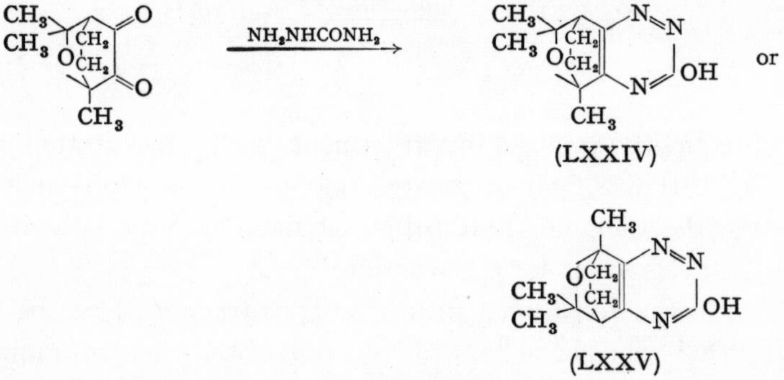

(LXXIV)

or

(LXXV)   (148)

likely. Examination of a molecular model constructed from Fisher-Hirshfelder atomic shows that, while both carbonyl groups in dioxocineole are sterically blocked, the *gem*-dimethyl group apparently has less covering effect than the lone methyl group adjacent to one of the carbonyl groups. Structurally, dioxocineole resembles camphorquinone. It will be recalled (page 89) that in camphorquinone the carbonyl group furthest from the methyl group appears to react first with carbonyl reagents. The existence of effective steric blocking in dioxo-cineole is shown by the fact that Cusmano obtained only a mono-semicarbazone although he used a large excess of semicarbazide. 3-Hydroxy-5,7,7-trimethyl-5,8-ethano-5,8-dihydro-7*H*-pyrano[3,4-*e*]-*as*-triazine (LXXIV), m.p. 202°, is soluble in water. In chloroform it adds two atoms of bromine, forming a precipitate that, slowly loses bromine and reverts to the parent compound, LXXIV.

The reaction of dioxocineole with aminoguanidine gives 3-amino-5,7,7-trimethyl-5,8-ethano-5,8-dihydro-7*H*-pyrano[3,4-*e*]-*as*-triazine as colorless crystals for which no melting point was given in the accessible reference. When treated with nitrous acid, this amino compound is converted to compound LXXIV.

(2) Condensed with the Indole Ring System

The Ring Index has listed such a system (LXXVI) (*R.I.* 1624), calling it *9-as-triazino[6,5-b]indole*. As is shown in the discussion that follows, no compounds of this type have yet been prepared. However,

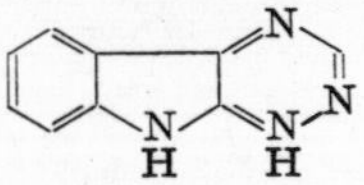

(LXXVI) 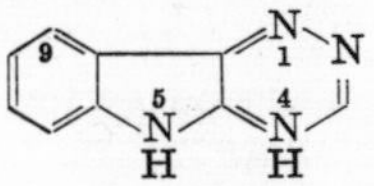   (LXXVII)

compounds containing a similar system (LXXVII) have been synthesized. This system is called *5-as-triazino[5,6-b]-indole*. Compounds of this sort are listed in Table II-14.

TABLE II-14. 5-*as*-Triazino[5,6-*b*]indoles[a]

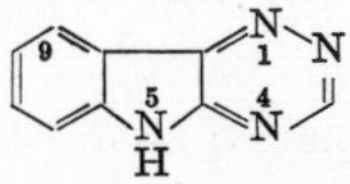

Substituents	Color, crystal habit	M.p., °C.	Ref.
3-(*p*-Acetamidobenzene-sulfonylamino)		261–262	162
5-Acetyl-3-acetamido	Colorless prisms	283[b]	114
3-Acetamido	Yellow	200	70
3-Amino	Colorless needles	350–354 (dec.)	114
	Yellow needles	>296	70
		195–196	162

(Table continued)

TABLE II-14 *(continued)*

Substituents	Colo[a], crystal habit	M.p., °C.	Ref.
3-Amino, hydrochloride	Pale yellow needles	324 (efferv.)	114
3-Amino, nitrate	Pale yellow prisms	228	114
3-Amino-8-bromo	Brownish-yellow needles	>295[c]	72
3-Amino-8-bromo-6-nitro	Yellow needles	268 (dec.)[d]	72
3-Amino-8-chloro	Red needles	184	72
3-Amino-6,8-dibromo	Yellow needles	>295[e]	72
3-Amino-5-methyl	Colorless prisms	314	114
3-Amino-5-methyl, hydrochloride	Pale yellow needles		114
3-Amino-5-methyl, nitrate	Pale yellow nedles	210 (dec.)	114
3-Amino-8-nitro	Thin brown plates	>300[f]	72
3-Amino-8-sulfamyl	Colorless prisms	>320	114
3-Amino-8-sulfonic acid	Yellow needles	>310	114
3-Amino-8-sulfonic acid, sodium salts	Colorless prisms	>300	114
3-Sulfanilylamino		200–201	161, 162

[a]Some of the structures and properties reported below are open to doubt. See text.
[b]Can be sublimed under vacuum.
[c]Colors wool yellow.
[d]Colors wool orange.
[e]Colors wool dark yellow.
[f]Colors wool brown.

For some time an incorrect view prevailed as to the course of the reaction between isatin and aminoguanidine. Thus, De,[70] who heated isatin with aminoguanidine hydrochloride in acetic acid, believed that reaction took place first on the α-carbonyl group (eq. 149). The final

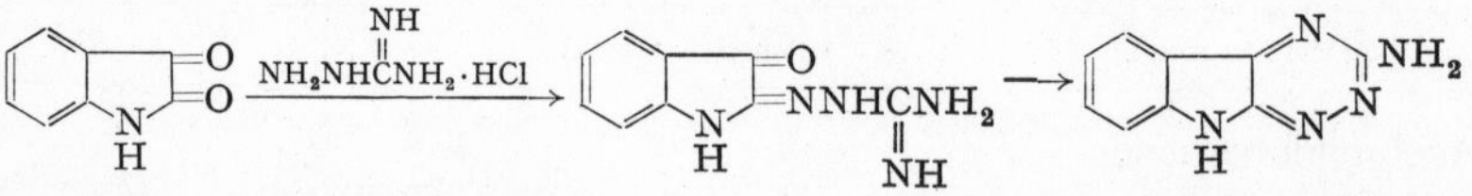

(LXXVIII)

product, then, would have structure LXXVIII. De described his product as yellow needles, not melting below 296°. Rajagopalan,[162] who also heated isatin with aminoguanidine in acetic acid, obtained a material, m.p. 195–196°, that was also assigned structure LXXVIII.

One may well question the validity of Rajagopalan's work, for his experimental results indicate a 122% yield of product. Using conventional methods, Rajagopalan[161,162] converted his material to a sulfanilamide.

De and Dutta[72] heated several substituted isatins with aminoguanidine hydrochloride in acetic acid. The products have colors ranging from yellow through red to brown and will readily dye wool. Nitrogen analyses of these products clearly indicate that cyclization took place. In assigning the structures of these compounds, De and Dutta assumed that α-guanylhydrazones were first formed, then converted to products similar to LXXVIII.

It is well known[181] that carbonyl reagents react with the β-oxo group in isatin rather than with the α-oxo group. King and Wright[114] have pointed out that aminoguanidine is not an exception. They repeated Rajagopalan's work and obtained, not the triazine compound, but rather isatin *syn* β-guanylhydrazone (LXXIX). Digestion of this *syn* form with sodium hydroxide solution converts it to the *anti* form. Cyclization of this guanylhydrazone (eq. 150) was brought about by

$$\text{(LXXIX)} \longrightarrow \text{(LXXX)} \qquad (150)$$

(LXXIX)   (LXXX)

heating the hydrochloride of the *syn* form with excess ammonium hydroxide solution or by heating the *anti* form at 250° under very low pressure. 3-Amino-5H-*as*-triazino[5,6-*b*]indole (LXXX), formed in this manner, was obtained as colorless needles from pyridine, m.p. 350–354° (dec.). It was converted to its hydrochloride and its nitrate. Heating compound LXXX with acetic anhydride yields the diacetyl derivative (acetyl groups on both amino group and the 5-nitrogen). When heated with sulfuric acid, compound LXXX forms its 8-sulfonic

$$\text{(LXXX)} \xrightarrow{\text{H}_2\text{SO}_4} \qquad (151)$$

acid (eq. 151); this, treated with chlorosulfonic acid and then ammonia, gives the 8-sulfamyl derivative. 3-Amino-5-methyl-5H-*as*-triazino-

[5,6-*b*]indole was prepared from *N*-methylisatin and aminoguanidine or by direct methylation of LXXX with sodium methoxide and methyl sulfate (eq. 152). This methyl derivative, unlike LXXX, is not soluble in

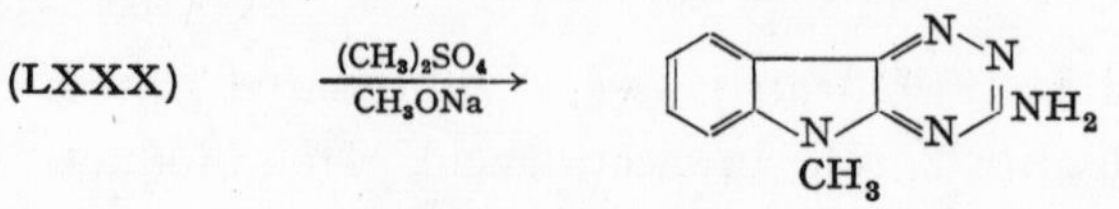

$$(LXXX) \quad \xrightarrow[\text{CH}_3\text{ONa}]{(\text{CH}_3)_2\text{SO}_4} \quad \text{(structure)} \quad (152)$$

hot dilute sodium hydroxide solution. It is unexpected that the amino group was not also methylated. Compound LXXX does not react with acrylonitrile, ethylene chlorohydrin, ethylene bromohydrin, or dicyandiamide under a variety of conditions.

It is fairly clear that Rajagopalan did not obtain a triazine. De[70] and De and Dutta[72] almost certainly obtained triazines, since the nitrogen analyses of their products agree closely with those calculated for ring closure. Their assigned structures, however, should be amended so as to conform with the structure (LXXX) put forth by King and Wright.[114] It appears that ring closure results when isatins are heated with aminoguanidine hydrochloride in acetic acid but not when they are heated with aminoguanidine itself in the same solvent.

B. Condensed through a Carbon Atom and a Nitrogen Atom

(1) Condensed with the Pyrazole Ring

A ring system of this type is known. It is called *pyrazolo[3,2-c]-[1,2,4]benzotriazine* (LXXXI) (*R.I.* 1556). Compounds containing it are listed in Table II-15.

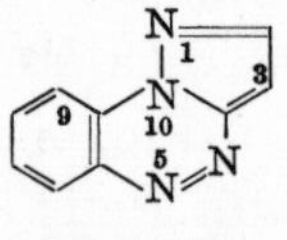

(LXXXI)

Mohr[131] noted that, when certain phenylpyrazolediazonium sulfates are added to boiling dilute sulfuric acid, precipitates appear but no evolution of gas is observed. Because of this failure to evolve nitrogen, and in view of analyses and molecular weight determinations, the reaction was considered to be an intramolecular cyclization involving the diazonium grouping (eq. 153). The simplest assumption

TABLE II-15. Pyrazolo[3,2-*c*][1,2,4]benzotriazines

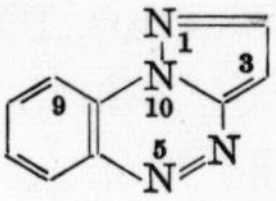

Substituents	Color, crystal habit	M.p., °C.	Ref.
4-Anilino-5-hydroxy-2-methyl-7-nitro-4,5-dihydro-5-oxide	Lemon yellow	216 (dec.)	164
3-Benzyl-2-methyl		128–130	131
3-Benzyl-2-methyl, silver salt		169–170	131
2,3-Dimethyl		145[a]	131
3-Ethyl-2-methyl		106[b]	131
4-Formyl-5-hydroxy-2-methyl-7-nitro-4,5-dihydro-5-oxide	Yellow, rectangular	286	164
5-Hydroxy-2-methyl-7-nitro-4,5-dihydro-5-oxide	Yellow	197–200	164
5-Hydroxy-2-methyl-7-nitro-4-4-phenyl-4,5-dihydro-5-oxide	Yellow leaves	Stable form, 190	164
		Labile form, 156	164
5-Hydroxy-2-methyl-7-nitro-4-*p*-tolyl-4,5-dihydro-5-oxide	Yellow leaves	166	164

[a]B.p. 208–215° (15–17 mm.), 350–352° (753 mm.).   [b]B.p. 210° (14 mm.).

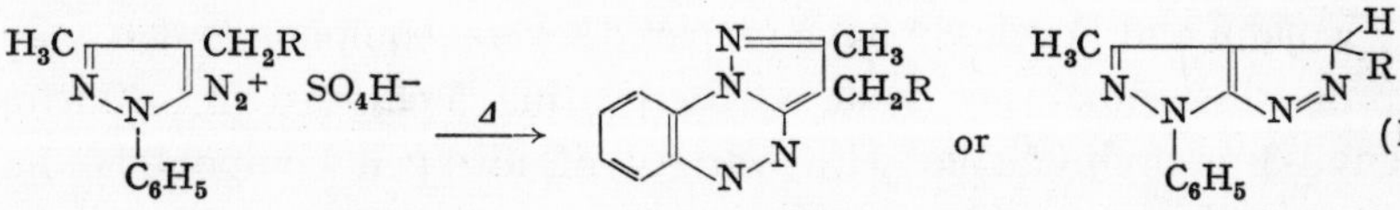

(R=H, CH$_3$ or C$_6$H$_5$)   (LXXXII)   or   (LXXXIII)   (153)

regarding the binding of the nitrogen is that the diazonium grouping reacts either with the neighboring phenyl group or with the RCH$_2$ group; that is, that either LXXXII or LXXXIII is formed. The product obtained, wherein R is a phenyl group, is quite different in its chemical and physical properties from a compound prepared by Michaelis and Bender[125] (eq. 154). Because of this difference, Mohr

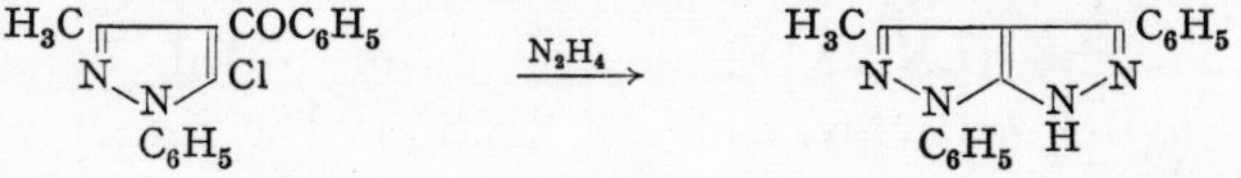

(154)

preferred structure LXXXII for his products. It is unfortunate that treatment of 3-amino-5-methyl-2-phenylpyrazole with nitrous acid gave only an isonitroso derivative. Otherwise the matter could have been settled definitely; this compound, had it formed a diazonium compound, could have cyclized only to give a structure similar to LXXXII. Despite the failure of this reaction, it is very probable that Mohr assigned the correct structures to his products.

2,3-Dimethylpyrazolo[3,2-c][1,2,4]benzotriazine (LXXXII, R = H) was obtained in a crude yield of 80–90%. It boils almost undecomposed under reduced pressure or with considerable decomposition at atmospheric pressure. The molten material, upon cooling, throws up thick clouds of yellow dust with surprising force and noise. This effect was thought to be due to a change in crystalline state. The compound is easily soluble in the usual organic solvents but it is very weakly basic and is insoluble in alkali. It is not affected by sodium amalgam or zinc and hydrochloric acid, nitrous acid, or nitric acid. It is oxidized by alkaline permanganate solution or chromic acid but no products were isolated. The molten 3-ethyl-2-methyl derivative (LXXXII, R = CH_3), upon cooling, does not behave like the dimethyl compound. Ammonia is evolved when the 3-benzyl-2-methyl derivative (LXXX, R = C_6H_5) is heated with zinc dust and sodium hydroxide. Treated with silver nitrate in alcohol, it forms a silver salt.

Rojahn and Fegeler[164] have prepared several compounds that may contain this same ring system. By heating 5-chloro-1-(2,4-dinitrophenyl)-3-methylpyrazole with variety of nitrogen compounds, including aniline, p-toluidine, ammonia, formamide and phenylhydrazine (eq. 155) they obtained compounds that might be either 4-subsitituted

(LXXXIV)   (LXXXV)   (155)

5-hydroxy-2-methyl-7-nitro-4 5-dihydropyrazolo[3.2-c][1,2,4]benzotriazine 5-oxides (LXXXIV) or amino-substituted 5-amino-1-(2,4-dinitrophenyl)-3-methylpyrazoles (LXXXV). The rather remarkable structure, **LXXXIV**, was preferred because the compound obtained from ammonia (**LXXXIV** or **LXXXV**, R = H) forms neither picrate nor hydrochloride and cannot be acetylated or benzoylated. These compounds dissolve with gentle warming in alcoholic potassium hydroxide to give red colors; they are reprecipitated by the addition of acid. This behavior might be explained by assuming structure **LXXXV**. Heating with aqueous or alcoholic alkali was said to open the triazine ring; at any rate, 1-(2,4-dinitrophenyl)-5-hydroxy-3-methylpyrazole was formed in all cases.

(2) Condensed with the Indazole Ring System

In the course of his work with indazole, Bamberger[11] coupled diazotized 3-aminoindazole with β-naphthol. The coupling product when heated, preferably in a hydroxylated solvent, lost water, forming indazolo[3,2-c]naphtho[2,1-e]triazine (*R.I.* 3037) (eq. 156). This com-

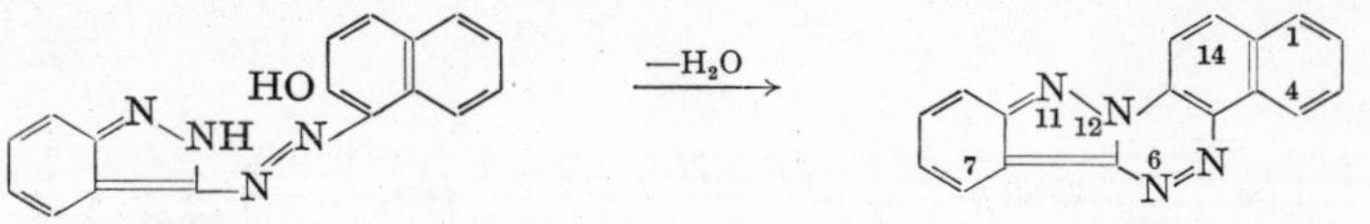

$$(156)$$

pound was isolated in almost quantitative yield as golden crystals, m.p. 249°, soluble in concentrated sulfuric acid or hydrochloric acid, insoluble in alkali, and soluble with difficulty in most organic solvents except chloroform. The 8,10 dimethyl derivative, m.p. 267°, was obtained in a similar manner from 3-amino-5,7-dimethylindazole. Von Auwers, Bahr, and Frese[191] obtained a tetrahydro derivative (golden needles, m.p. 152–154°) by coupling diazotized 3-amino-4,5,6,7-tetrahydroindazole with β-naphthol and cyclizing the product in hot alcohol (eq. 157). This tetrahydro derivative is reduced by zinc dust and

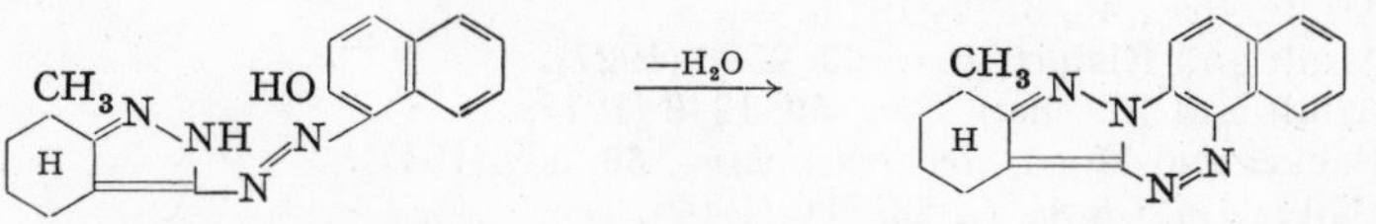

$$(157)$$

hot acetic acid to a colorless solution, easily reoxidized to a colored product by air.

(3) Condensed with the 1,2,4-Triazole Ring

The simplest compounds of this type were prepared by Hoggarth.[112] By heating 3,4-diamino-5-phenyl-1,2,4-triazole with benzil, he obtained 3,6,7-triphenyl-s-triazolo[4,3-b]-as-triazine (LXXXVI, R = C_6H_5) as deep yellow square plates, m.p. 250° (eq. 158). The use of biacetyl

$$\begin{array}{ccc}
\text{H}_2\text{N}\,\fbox{}\,\text{N} & & R\,\overset{\text{N}}{\underset{8}{\bigcirc}}\,\fbox{}\,\text{N} \\
\text{H}_2\text{NN}\,\diagdown\,\diagup\text{N} & \xrightarrow{\text{RCOCOR}} & R\,\diagdown\,\underset{\text{N}}{\underset{\text{N}^4}{\diagup}}\,\diagup\text{N} \\
C_6H_5 & & C_6H_5
\end{array} \tag{158}$$

(LXXXVI)

gives 6,7-dimethyl-3-phenyl-s-triazolo[4,3-b]-as-triazine (LXXXVI, R = CH_3), long deep yellow needles, m.p. 203°.

Stollé and Dietrich[180] treated guanazole with bleaching powder solution to obtain a product, thought to be a bis(chloroimino) compound. This reacts with β-naphthylamine in hot alcoholic solution to form a dyestuff that was considered to be 9-aminonaphtho[1,2-e]-s-triazolo[4,3-b]-as-triazine (R.I. 2344) (eq. 159). It was obtained as brown-

$$\begin{array}{ccc}
\text{N}\!=\!\!=\!\!\text{N} & & \\
\text{ClN}\!=\!\!\Big\langle\,\underset{\text{N}}{}\,\Big\rangle\!=\!\text{NCl} & \xrightarrow{\beta\text{-C}_{10}\text{H}_7\text{NH}_2} & \text{H}_2\text{N} \\
\text{H} & &
\end{array} \tag{159}$$

red prisms, m.p. 285°, insoluble in water and slightly soluble in ether and in hot alcohol. Its solution in concentrated hydrochloric acid, treated with sodium nitrite, gives a diazonium compound that can be coupled with R-salt or with β-naphthol in alkaline solution. It is upon this fact, together with elementary analysis, that the structure assigned this compound is based. Other and similar structures are also possible.

Bibliography

1. Adickes, Ber., 58, 211 (1925).
2. Arndt, Ber., 46, 3522 (1913).
3. Arndt and Eistert, Ber., 60, 2598 (1927).
4. Arndt and Rosenau, Ber., 50, 1248 (1917).
5. Backer and Moed, Rec. trav. chim., 66, 689 (1947).
6. Baily, Am. Chem. J., 28, 386 (1902).
7. Baily and Knox, J. Am. Chem. Soc., 29, 881 (1907).
8. Bailey and Read, J. Am. Chem. Soc., 36, 1747 (1914).
9. Baker, Ollis and Poole, J. Chem. Soc., 1949, 307.
10. Bamberger, Ann., 305, 332, 354 (1899).

11. Bamberger, *Ber.*, **32**, 1797 (1899).
12. Bamberger and de Gruyter, *J. prakt. Chem.*, **64**, 222 (1901).
13. Bamberger and Lorenzen, Ber., **25**, 3539 (1892).
14. Bamberger and Wheelwright, *Ber.*, **25**, 3201 (1892).
15. Bamberger and Witter, *Ber.*, **26**, 2786 (1893).
16. Bamberger and Witter, *J. prakt. Chem.*, **65**, 146 (1902).
17. Bergström and Haslewood, *J. Chem. Soc.*, **1939**, 540.
18. Biltz, *Ber.*, **38**, 1417 (1905).
19. Biltz, *Ber.*, **40**, 2630 (1907).
20. Biltz, *Ber.*, **41**, 1880 (1908).
21. Biltz, *Ber.*, **43**, 1815 (1910).
22. Biltz and Arnd, *Ann.*, **339**, 267 (1905).
23. Biltz and Arnd, *Ber.*, **35**, 344 (1902).
24. Biltz, Arnd, and Stellbaum, *Ann.*, **339**, 243 (1905).
25. Biltz and Stellbaum, *Ann.*, **339**, 275 (1905).
26. Biquard, *Bull. soc. chim. France*, [5], **3**, 656 (1936).
27. Bischler, *Ber.*, **22**, 2801 (1889).
28. Bischler and Brodsky, *Ber.*, **22**, 2809 (1889).
29. Bougalt, *Ann. chim.*, [9], **5**, 317 (1916).
30. Bougalt, *Compt. rend.*, **159**, 83 (1914).
31. Bougalt, *Compt. rend.*, **159**, 631 (1914).
32. Bougalt, *Compt. rend.*, **160**, 625 (1915).
33. Bougalt, Cattelain and Chabrier, *Compt. rend.*, **208**, 657 (1939).
34. Bougalt and Chabrier, *Compt. rend.*, **213**, 400 (1941).
35. Bougalt and Daniel, *Compt. rend.*, **186**, 151 (1928).
36. Bougalt and Daniel, *Compt. rend.*, **186**, 1216 (1928).
37. Bougalt and Popovici, *Compt. rend.*, **190**, 1019 (1930).
38. Busch, *Ber.*, **32**, 2959 (1899).
39. Busch, *Ber.*, **36**, 3877 (1903).
40. Busch and Bergmann, *Z. Farben-Textilchemie*, **4**, 105; through *Chem. Zentr.*, **1905**, I, 1102.
41. Busch, Foerst, and Stengel, *J. prakt. Chem.*, **119**, 287 (1928).
42. Busch, Friedenberger, and Tischbein, *Ber.*, **57**, 1783 (1924).
43. Busch and Hefele, *J. prakt. Chem.*, **83**, 425 (1911).
44. Busch and Küspert, *J. prakt. Chem.*, **144**, 273 (1936).
45. Busch and Meussdörfer, *Ber.*, **40**, 1021 (1907).
46. Cattelain, *Ann. chem. analyt. appl.*, **24**, 150 (1942); through *Chem. Abstracts*, **38**, 1971 (1944).
47. Cattelain, *Bull. soc. chim. France, Mém.*, **9**, 907 (1942).
48. Cattelain, *Bull. soc. chim. France, Mém.*, **11**, 18 (1944).
49. Cattelain, *Bull. soc. chim. France, Mém.*, **11**, 249 (1944).
50. Cattelain, *Bull. soc. chim. France, Mém.*, **11**, 256 (1944).
51. Cattelain, *Bull. soc. chim. France, Mém.*, **11**, 273 (1944).
52. Cattelain, *Bull. soc. chim. France, Mém.*, **12**, 39 (1945).
53. Cattelain, *Bull. soc. chim. France, Mém.*, **12**, 47 (1945).
54. Cattelain, *Bull. soc. chim. France, Mèm.*, **12**, 53 (1945).
55. Cattelain, *Bull. soc. chim. France, Mém.*, **12**, 59 (1945).
56. Cattelain, *Compt. rend.*, **207**, 998 (1938).
57. Cattelain, *Compt. rend.*, **208**, 1656 (1939).
58. Cattelain, *Compt. rend.*, **208**, 1912 (1939).
59. Cattelain, *Compt. rend.*, **210**, 301 (1940).
60. Cattelain, *Compt. rend.*, **210**, 763 (1940).

61. Cattelain, *Compt. rend.*, **212**, 551 (1941).
62. Cattelain, *Compt. rend.*, **214**, 429 (1942).
63. Cattelain, *Compt. rend.*, **215**, 257 (1942).
64. Cattelain and Chabrier, *Bull. soc. chim. France, Mém.*, **1947**, 1098.
65. Cattelain and Chabrier, *Bull. soc. chim. France, Mém.*, **1948**, 700.
66. Cattelain and Chabrier, *Compt. rend.*, **224**, 1571 (1947).
67. Chabrier (de la Saulniere), *Ann. chim.*, **17**, 353 (1942).
68. Cremonini, *Gazz. chim. ital.*, **58**, 127 (1928).
69. Cusmàno, *Annales real. acad farm.*, **9**, 307 (1943); through *Chem. Abstr.*, **43**, 7926 (1949).
70. De, *J. Indian Chem. Soc.*, **4**, 183 (1927).
71. De, *J. Indian Chem. Soc.*, **7**, 361 (1930).
72. De and Dutta, *Ber.*, **64**, 2604 (1931).
73. Dedichen, *Avhandl. Norske Videnskaps-Akad.*, I, *Mat.-Naturv. Klasse*, **1936**, No. 5, 42 pp.; through *Chem. Abstracts.* **31**, 4985 (1937) and *Chem. Zentr.*, **1937**, I, 86.
74. Delaby, *Ann. chim.*, **20**, 73 (1923).
75. Delaby, *Compt. rend.*, **176**, 1153 (1923).
76. Diels, *Ann.*, **429**, 1 (1922).
77. Diels, *Ber.*, **35**, 347 (1902).
78. Diels, *Ber.*, **54**, 213 (1921).
79. Diels and vom Dorp, *Ber.*, **36**, 3183 (1903).
80. Dyson, *A Manual of Organic Chemistry*, Longmans, Green, New York, 1950, p. 868.
81. Ekeley, Carlson, and Ronzio, *Rec. trav. chim.*, **59**, 496 (1940).
82. Ekeley and O'Kelly, *J. Am. Chem. Soc.*, **50**, 2731 (1928).
83. Elvidge and Spring, *J. Chem. Soc.*, **1949**, S135.
84. Ergener, *Rev. fac. sci. univ. Istanbul*, **15 A**, No. 2, 91–107 (1950); through *Chem. Abstracts*, **44**, 10718 (1950).
85. Erickson, *J. Am. Chem. Soc.*, **74**, 4706 (1952).
86. Fawcett, *Chem. Revs.*, **47**, 219 (1950).
87. Fichter and Fröhlich, *Z. Farben-Textilchemie*, **2**, 251; through *Chem. Zentr.*, **1903**, II, 426.
88. Fichter and Schiess, *Ber.*, **33**, 747 (1900).
89. Fierz and Sallmann, *Helv. Chim. Acta*, **5**, 560 (1922).
90. Fischer, *J. prakt. Chem.*, **104**, 102 (1922).
91. Fischer, *J. prakt. Chem.*, **107**, 16 (1924).
92. Fodor, *Acta Lit. Sci. Regiae Univ. Hung. Francisco-Josephinae, Sect. Chem. Mineral Phys.*, **6**, 1 (1937); through *Chem. Abstracts*, **32**, 2124 (1938).
93. Forster and Jackson, *J. Chem. Soc.*, **91**, 1890 (1907).
94. Forster and Zimmerli, *J. Chem. Soc.*, **97**, 2156 (1910).
95. Forster and Zimmerli, *J. Chem. Soc.*, **99**, 489 (1911).
96. Frerichs and Beckurts, *Arch. Pharm.*, **237**, 346 (1899); through *Chem. Zentr.*, **1899**, II, 421.
97. Fusco and Romani, *Gazz. chim. ital.*, **78**, 332 (1948); through *Chem. Abstracts*, **43**, 4259 (1949).
98. Girard, *Ann. chim.*, **16**, 326 (1941).
99. Girard, *Compt. rend.*, **206**, 1303 (1938).
100. Godfrin, *J. pharm. chim.*, **30**, 321 (1939); through *Chem. Abstracts*, **34**, 5087 (1940).
101. Goldschmidt and Poltzer, *Ber.*, **24**, 1000 (1891).
102. Goldschmidt and Rosell, *Ber.*, **23**, 487 (1890).

103. Griess, *Ber.*, **16**, 2028 (1883).
104. Guha and Arndt, *J. Indian Chem. Soc.*, **8**, 199 (1931).
105. Guha and Ghosh, *J. Indian Chem. Soc.*, **4**, 561 (1927).
106. Guha and Ghosh, *J. Indian Chem. Soc.*, **5**, 439 (1928).
107. Guha and Ray, *J. Indian Chem. Soc.*, **2**, 83 (1925).
108. Guha and Roy-Choudhury, *J. Indian Chem. Soc.*, **5**, 163 (1928).
109. Harries, *Ber.*, **28**, 1223 (1895).
110. Harries and Kaiser, *Ber.*, **32**, 1338 (1899).
111. Hempel, *J. prakt. Chem.*, **41**, 161 (1890).
112. Hoggarth, *J. Chem. Soc.*, **1950**, 614.
113. Hopper, *J. Roy. Techn. College*, **2**, 52 (1929); through *Chem. Zentr.*, **1937**, I, 4088.
114. King and Wright, *J. Chem. Soc.*, **1948**, 2314.
115. Kon. *J. Chem. Soc.*, **121**, 522 (1922).
116. Kondo and Ishiwata, *Ber.*, **70**, 2427 (1937).
117. Locquin, *Bull. soc. chim. France*, [3], **35**, 962 (1906).
118. Lorges, *Rev. chim. ind.*, **35**, 113 (1926).
119. McRae and Stevens, *Can. J. Research*, **22B**, No. 2, 45 (1944).
120. Maccoll, *J. Chem. Soc.*, **1946**, 670.
121. Meldola, *J. Chem. Soc.*, **57**, 328 (1890).
122. Meldola and Forster, *J. Chem. Soc.*, **59**, 678 (1891).
123. Meldola and Hughes, *J. Chem. Soc.*, **59**, 381 (1891).
124. Michael, *J. prakt. Chem.*, **60**, 456 (1899).
125. Michaelis and Bender, *Ber.*, **36**, 523 (1903).
126. Michaelis and Brust, *Ann.*, **339**, 138 (1905).
127. Michaelis and Klappert, *Ann.*, **397**, 149 (1913).
128. Michaelis and Schäfer, *Ann.*, **397**, 119 (1913).
129. Michaelis and Schäfer, *Ann.*, **407**, 234 (1915).
130. Mohr, *J. prakt. Chem.*, **90**, 232 (1914).
131. Mohr, *J. prakt. Chem.*, **90**, 509 (1914).
132. Mossini, *Ann. chim. farm.* (suppl. to *Farm. ital.*), May **1940**, 23; through *Chem. Abstracts*, **34**, 7916 (1940).
133. Neri, *Gazz. chim. ital.*, **67**, 282, 289, 448, 473, 477, 513 (1937); **70**, 311, 317, 323 (1940); **71**, 201 (1941); through *Chem. Abstracts*, **32**, 173–175, 1265–69 (1938); **35**, 3260 (1941); **36**, 2865 (1942).
134. Neri, *Chimica e industria* (*Italy*), **23**, 11 (1941); through *Chem. Abstracts*, **35**, 3261 (1941).
135. Neri and Grimaldi, *Gazz. chim. ital.*, **67**, 273, 453, 468 (1937); through *Chem. Abstracts*, **32**, 173, 1266–1267 (1938).
136. Noelting and Wegelin, *Ber.*, **30**, 2595 (1897).
137. Ohta, *J. Pharm. Soc. Japan*, **66**, 11 (1946); through *Chem. Abstracts*, **45**, 6577 (1951).
138. Parkes and Aldis, *J. Chem. Soc.*, **1938**, 1841.
139. French Patent 876,296; through *Chem. Zentr.*, **1943**, I, 1822.
140. German Patent 180,031 (to Leopold Cassella & Co.); *Frdl.*, **8**, 183 (1908).
141. U.S. Patent 2,160,293 (May 30, 1939), to Shoemaker and Loane, assignors to Standard Oil Co. (Indiana).
142. U.S. Patent 2,411,646 (Nov. 26, 1946), to Anderau, assignor to Society of Chemical Industry.
143. U.S. Patent 2,489,351 (Nov. 29, 1949), to Wolf and Pfister, assignors to Merck & Co., Inc.
144. U.S. Patent 2,489,352 (Nov. 29, 1949), to Wolf and Pfister, assignors to Merck & Co., Inc.

145. U.S. Patent 2,489,353 (Nov. 29, 1949), to Wolf and Pfister, assignors to Merck & Co., Inc.
146. U.S. Patsnt 2,489,354 (Nov. 29, 1949), to Wolf and Pfister, assignors to Merck & Co., Inc.
147. U.S. Patent 2,489,355 (Nov. 29, 1949), to Wolf and Pfister, assignors to Merck & Co., Inc.
148. U.S. Patent 2,489,356 (Nov. 29, 1949), to Wolf and Pfister, assignors to Merck & Co., Inc.
149. U.S. Patent 2,489,357 (Nov. 29, 1949), to Wolf and Pfister, assignors to Merck & Co., Inc.
150. U.S. Patent 2,489,358 (Nov. 29, 1949), to Wolf and Pfister, assignors to Merck & Co., Inc.
151. U.S. Patent 2,489,359 (Nov. 29, 1949), to Wolf and Pfister, assignors to Merck & Co., Inc.
152. U.S. Patent 2,496,364 (Feb. 7, 1950), to Wolf and Pfister, assignors to Merck & Co., Inc.
153. Patterson and Capell, *The Ring Index*, Reinhold, New York, 1940.
154. Perucchetti, *Chem.-Ztg.*, **26**, 28 (1902).
155. Pierron, *Ann. chim. phys.*, [8], **15**, 239 (1908).
156. Pinner, *Ann.*, **297**, 247 (1897).
157. Popovici, *Ann. chim.*, **18**, 183 (1932).
158. Popovici, *Compt. rend.*, **191**, 210 (1930).
159. Pummerer and Gump, *Ber.*, **56**, 999 (1923).
160. Raiziss, Clemence, and Freifelder, *J. Am. Chem. Soc.*, **63**, 2739 (1941).
161. Rajagopalan, *Current Sci.*, **11**, 146 (1942); through *Chem. Abstracts*, **36**, 6511 (1942).
162. Rajagopalan, *Proc. Indian Acad. Sci.*, **18A**, 100 (1943).
163. Ramart-Lucas, Hoch and Grumez, *Bull. soc. chim. France, Mém.*, **1949,** 447.
164. Rojahn and Fegeler, *Ber.*, **63**, 2510 (1930).
165. Rolla, *Gazz. chim. ital.*, **38**, I, 342 (1908).
166. Rupe and Buxtorf, *Helv. Chim. Acta*, **13**, 444 (1930).
167. Rupe and Heberlein, *Ann.*, **301**, 68 (1898).
168. Rupe and Kessler, *Ber.*, **42**, 4503 (1909).
169. Rupe and Schlochoff, *Ber.*, **36**, 4377 (1903).
170. Rupe, Werder, and Takagi, *Helv. Chim. Acta*, **1**, 311, 335 (1918).
171. Schmidt and Bürkert, *Ber.*, **60**, 1356 (1927).
172. Schmidt and Sauer, *Ber.*, **44**, 3250 (1911).
173. Schmidt, Schairer, and Glatz, *Ber.*, **44**, 276 (1911).
174. Scholtz, *Ber.*, **29**, 610 (1896).
175. Searles, private communication.
176. Seibert, *Chem. Ber.*, **80**, 494 (1947).
177. Sen, *J. Indian Chem. Soc.*, **6**, 1001 (1929).
178. Simonsen, *The Terpenes*, Cambridge Univ. Press, 1932, Vol. II, pp. 345–6.
179. Speck and Bost, *J. Org. Chem.*, **11**, 788 (1946).
180. Stolle and Dietrich, *J. prakt. Chem.*, **139**, 197 (1934).
181. Sumpter, *Chem. Revs.*, **34**, 393 (1944).
182. Thiele and Bailey, *Ann.*, **303**, 75 (1898).
183. Thiele and Barlow, *Ann.*, **302**, 311 (1898).
184. Thiele and Bihan, *Ann.*, **302**, 299 (1898).
185. Thiele and Dralle, *Ann.*, **302**, 275 (1898).
186. Thiele and Stange, *Ann.*, **283**, 1 (1894).
187. Tingle and Bates, *J. Am. Chem. Soc.*, **32**, 1510 (1910).

188. Venus-Danilova, *J. Gen. Chem. (U.S.S.R.)*, **6**, 1784 (1936).
189. Venus-Danilova,*J. Gen. Chem. (U.S.S.R.)*, **6**, 1863 (1936).
190. Venus-Danilova, *J. Gen. Chem. (U.S.S.R.)*, **8**, 1179 (1938).
191. von Auwers, Bahr and Frese, *Ann.* **441**, 80 (1925).
192. von Pechmann, *Ber.*, **27**, 1679 (1894).
193. von Walther and Hübner, *J. prakt. Chem.*, **93**, 134 (1916).
194. Whiteley and Yapp, *J. Chem. Soc.*, **1927**, 521.
195. Widman, *Ber.*, **26**, 2612 (1893).
196. Widman, *J. prakt. Chem.*, **38**, 192 (1888).
197. Wolff, *Ann.*, **325**, 129 (1902).
198. Wolff and Lindenhayn, *Ber.*, **36**, 4126 (1903).
199. Woods, *J. Soc. Chem. Ind. London*, **24**, 1284 (1905).
200. Zakutskaya, *J. Gen. Chem. (U.S.S.R.)*, **10**, 1553 (1940); through *Chem. Abstracts*, **35**, 3230 (1941).

CHAPTER III

The 1,2,3,4-Tetrazines

Introduction

In the older literature, monocyclic or uncondensed 1,2,3,4-tetrazines (I) are called osotetrazines, the prefix *oso-* denoting their derivation from the oxidation of the osazones of α,β-diketones.[50] Osotetrazine implies the 2,3-dihydro derivatives. Von Pechmann, their discoverer, had originally named them *osotetrazones*, but he used this term for only a short time.[48] *Chemical Abstracts* has indexed 1,2,3,4-tetrazines variously under *Osotetrazine* or *v-Tetrazine*. From 1928 to 1938 they were indexed at *v-Tetrazine* with no cross reference to *Osotetrazine*. From 1938 to the present *Osotetrazine* has been preferred, undoubtedly because the 1,2,3,4-tetrazine structure assigned certain compounds is questionable.* *The Ring Index* prefers the name *v-tetrazine* (*R.I.* 133).[36]

As in the nomenclature of the triazines, the prefixes *v*, *as-*, and *s-* may be used to advantage in designating the isomeric 1,2,3,4-, 1,2,3,5-, and 1,2,4,5-tetrazines, respectively. In this chapter *v-tetrazine* is used to name specific 1,2,3,4- or "vicinal" tetrazines when the structure appears to be correct. When the structure is not certain, as in the case of the 2,3-diaryl compounds, the osotetrazine nomenclature is used.

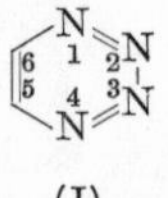

(I)	(II)
v-Tetrazine	Benzotetrazine
1,2,3,4-Tetrazine	1,2,3,4-Benzotetrazine
Osotetrazine (2,3-dihydro)	

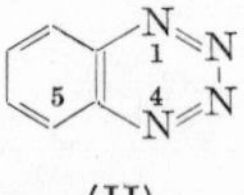

* "Osotriazoles," triazoles derived from osotetrazines or osazones, are indexed in *Chemical Abstracts* at 1,2,3-, 1,2,5-, or 2,1,3-Triazole, less frequently at *v*-Triazole or Osotriazole.

The most important of the condensed v-tetrazines are those which contain the *benzotetrazine* or *1,2,3,4-benzotetrazine* nucleus (II). Both *Chemical Abstracts* and *The Ring Index* (*R.I.* 910) prefer the former name. Neither the v- nor the 1,2,3,4-locants are necessary because no ambiguity exists.

Neither the syntheses nor the reactions of compounds containing the 1,2,3,4-tetrazine ring have been studied very extensively. About forty individual compounds have been prepared and described, although the tetrazine structures proposed for most of them are doubtful. No naturally occurring derivative of 1,2,3,4-tetrazine has been reported. A single reference to the practical application of a 1,2,3,4-tetrazine is disclosed in the broad claims of a U.S. Patent on corrosion inhibitors for lubricating oils.[35] There are no sulfonamide type antibiotics derived from 1,2,3,4-tetrazine rings listed in the compilation of Northey.[33]

Almost all of the published literature on the 1,2,3,4-tetrazines deals with their preparation. Relatively little study has been made of the reactivity of this heterocyclic ring aside from that incidental to its preparation. More than half of the papers published on this class of compounds predate World War I, and only a few important ones have appeared since 1940.

The principal reaction employed for the synthesis of the 1,2,3,4-tetrazine ring is the oxidation of the dihydrazones (or osazones) of α,β-diketones, a reaction first described in 1888 by H. von Pechmann.[48] Most of the uncondensed tetrazines have been prepared by some modification of this reaction, the usual variation being in the choice of

$$
\begin{array}{l}
\text{RC}=\text{NNHR}'' \\
\quad | \\
\text{R}'\text{C}=\text{NNHR}''
\end{array}
\xrightarrow{\text{[O]}}
\begin{array}{c}
\text{R} \\
\text{R}'
\end{array}
\begin{array}{c}
\text{N} \diagdown \text{NR}'' \\
\quad | \\
\text{N} \diagup \text{NR}''
\end{array}
\; + \; \text{H}_2\text{O}
\qquad (1)
$$

(III)

$$
\begin{array}{l}
\text{R}''\text{N}=\text{N}-\text{C}=\text{C}-\text{N}=\text{NR}'' \\
\qquad\qquad | \quad | \\
\qquad\qquad \text{R} \quad \text{R}'
\end{array}
$$

(IIIa)

R = H, alkyl, eryl
R' = H, alkyl, aryl
R'' = aryl, acyl

oxidizing agent. Recent spectral evidence indicates that, when R'' = aryl, the products are not dihydro-v-tetrazines (III) but rather have the isomeric bis(phenylazo)ethylene structure (IIIa).[7,16,54] This possibility was already recognized by Bucherer and Stickel[9] and advanced by Stollé[43] in the middle 1920's.

The oxidation of osazones has been limited to those containing simple alkyl, aryl, and acyl groups, and their positions on the tetrazine nucleus are predetermined. The 5-and 6-positions are occupied by radicals from the original α,β-diketone, and the 2- and 3- positions hold radicals from the original hydrazine molecules. The tetrazines produced are the 2,3-dihydro derivatives, generally of the form III in equation 1.

Benzotetrazine and naphthotetrazine systems have been prepared most commonly by the diazotization of o-aminoarylhydrazines followed by reduction[59] or neutralization with alkali.[21]

Other reactions which have been used to prepare 1,2,3,4-tetrazines are more specialized and diversified, and are not conveniently grouped together. They will be discussed under the specific compounds for which they were employed.

Aside from oxidation, reduction, and the hydrolysis of substituents, the reaction of 1,2,3,4-tetrazines that has been investigated most extensively is their rather easy conversion into 1,2,3-triazoles by the action of acids, bases, and heat.[45,48,50] This important transformation is discussed in greater detail as part of the historical development of the monocyclic 1,2,3,4-tetrazines.

Substitution reactions on the 1,2,3,4-tetrazine ring have been limited to acylations; bromination of phenyl-v-tetrazines introduces a bromo group on the aromatic nucleus, rather than the heterocyclic ring. Of the substituted 1,2,3,4-tetrazines reported in the literature, the substituents resulting from ring closure or introduced as an integral part of the reactants have been acyl, carbethoxy, cyano, and keto groups.

1. UNCONDENSED 1,2,3,4-TETRAZINES

A. 1,2,3,4-Tetrazine

1,2,3,4-Tetrazine itself has not been described in the literature. H. von Pechmann and his students at Tübingen considered the possibility of its synthesis and embarked on a rather extensive but unsuccessful program to secure it.[3,5,33] The intermediates they prepared during this work are of greater importance in other connections, and the results of these experiments are discussed elsewhere in this chapter. The only recent reference to 1,2,3,4-tetrazine concerns its hypothetical structure. By means of the valence-bond method, Maccoll[30] predicted the first absorption maximum of 1,2,3,4-tetrazine to be 5300 A., and its resonance energy 10 kilocalories per mole. Of the two possible nonequivalent Kekulé structures that can be drawn for this substance, the one containing the =N–N=N–N= sequence is considered to be more stable than the other, which has the –N=N–N=N– arrangement of double bonds.

B. Dihydro-1,2,3,4-Tetrazines

Completely unsaturated 1,2,3,4-tetrazines also have never been prepared; practically all of the compounds that have been reported are the dihydro derivatives. The apparent nonexistence of true tetrazines is doubtless associated with the rather easy rearrangement of the 2,3-dihydro derivatives into aminotriazoles.

The chemistry of the 1,2,3,4-tetrazines may be more clearly presented by grouping certain of the specific compounds into two genera: (1) those substituted in the 2- and 3- positions with phenyl groups and (2) those substituted in the 2- and 3- positions with benzoyl groups. The former are derived from the bis(phenylhydrazones) of α,β-diketones and the latter from the bis(benzoylhydrazones) of α,β-diketones. The two types have strikingly different properties.

All of the dihydro-v-tetrazines of the first type are colored, some of them intensely; those of the second type are white or colorless. Compounds of the first may be reduced to the original osazone with phenylhydrazine or alcoholic hydrogen sulfide; those of the second type are stable toward these reagents.

Using these two experimental facts as his basis, Stollé[43] suggested that the 2,3-diaryl-2,3-dihydro-v-tetrazines may not be tetrazines at all, but may exist in an open-chain azo structure (IIIa). On the other hand, the lack of color and the stability toward reducing agents of the benzoyl compounds prompted Stollé to accept them as derivatives of v-tetrazine.

Recent studies of visible and ultraviolet spectra by Bodforss[7] and Grammaticakis[16] offer additional evidence for the linear structure of the osotetrazines. Grammaticakis suggested that the oxidation of osazones may take the course shown in reaction 2, and proposed the intermediate formation of a tautomer of the osazone.

$$
\begin{array}{ccccc}
RC{=}NNHC_6H_5 & & RC{-}N{=}NC_6H_5 & & RC{-}N{=}NC_6H_5 \\
| & \longrightarrow & \| & \xrightarrow{[O]} & \| \\
R'C{=}NNHC_6H_5 & & R'C{-}NHNHC_6H_5 & & R'C{-}N{=}NC_6H_5
\end{array} \qquad (2)
$$

The ingenious experiments of Vorländer and co-workers[54] lend considerable support to Stollé's contention that the highly colored 2,3-diaryl derivatives, obtained by the oxidation of osazones, are indeed azo compounds. They investigated the liquid crystal properties of a series of osazones and their oxidation products, the osotetrazines. Osotetrazines might be expected to form liquid crystals on melting if they exist in the linear azo form (IV), but not if they have the cyclic tetrazine structure (IVa). The oxidation products obtained were actually found to pass into a liquid crystal state and characteristically exhibited two melting points. Accordingly Vorländer concluded that structure IV is the correct one.

$$
\begin{array}{cc}
p\text{-}ROC_6H_4N{=}N{-}C{=}C{-}N{=}NC_6H_4OR\text{-}p & \\
\qquad\qquad\qquad\quad | \;\; | & \\
\qquad\qquad\qquad\;\; R \;\; R'' & \\
\end{array}
$$

(IV)   (IVa)

$$
\begin{array}{l}
R \;\,= CH_3,\, C_2H_5 \\
R' = H,\, CH_3 \\
R'' = H,\, CH_3
\end{array}
$$

The evidence in favor of the azo structure for the oxidation products of the osazones is steadily mounting. However, in the absence of more rigorous structure proof, the osotetrazines are still treated as heterocyclic compounds in this chapter. The potential importance of extensive spectroscopic study and the application of other physical techniques to structure proofs in this field is quite apparent.

(1) Substituted in the 2- and 3-Positions with Aryl Groups

A discussion of the individual 1,2,3,4-tetrazines might best begin with those substituted in the 2- and 3-positions by aromatic nuclei. Structurally simpler species are known, but the 2,3-diaryl derivatives offer a better introduction to the subject from the standpoints of chronology of development and simplicity of presentation.

In his earliest researches, von Pechmann treated the phenyl-osazones of glyoxal, pyruvaldehyde, and biacetyl with potassium dichromate in dilute acetic acid, and got neutral, colored products. They contained two hydrogen atoms less than the original osazone. Because of this, and since osazones without hydrogens on their sec-ondary nitrogen atoms do not readily oxidize, von Pechmann concluded that the products isolated were cyclic compounds. He regarded them as diphenyl-2,3-dihydro-v-tetrazines and called them osotetrazines[50] (originally osotetrazones[48]), to differentiate them from the 1,2,4,5- or s-tetrazines, which were already known and called "tetrazines."

2,3-Diphenylosotetrazine (VI), prepared by the oxidation of glyoxal phenylosazone, is described as dark red plates of m.p. 152° (dec.) from alcohol, but no experimental details are given for its preparation. A second preparation by the same method is reported[49]; however, again the experimental part in this paper is sketchy, but a satisfactory analysis is included. Dieckmann and Platz[13] obtained VI in 70% yield by treating the phenylosazone of glyoxylyl chloride (V) with potassium hydroxide in alcohol (eq. 3). In this novel reaction, the result was

$$
\begin{array}{ccc}
\begin{array}{l} ClC{=}NNHC_6H_5 \\ | \\ HC{=}NNHC_6H_5 \end{array}
& \xrightarrow[-HCl]{KOH}
& \begin{array}{l} {-}N{\diagdown}NC_6H_5 \\ | \\ {\diagup}N{-}NC_6H_5 \end{array}
\end{array}
\qquad (3)
$$

$$\text{(V)} \qquad\qquad\qquad \text{(VI)}$$

accomplished by dehydrochlorination rather than oxidation. By this process the formation of the linear azo compound (VIa) is more readily conceivable, especially if the glyoxylyl chloride phenylosazone is considered in the form of the tautomer (Va).

$$
\begin{array}{ccccc}
\begin{array}{l} ClC{=}NNHC_6H_5 \\ | \\ HC{=}NNHC_6H_5 \end{array}
& \rightleftharpoons
& \begin{array}{l} ClCH{-}N{=}NC_6H_5 \\ | \\ HCH{-}N{=}NC_6H_5 \end{array}
& \longrightarrow
& \begin{array}{l} HC{-}N{=}NC_6H_5 \\ \| \\ HC{-}N{=}NC_6H_5 \end{array}
\end{array}
\qquad (4)
$$

$$\text{(V)} \qquad\qquad \text{(Va)} \qquad\qquad \text{(VIa)}$$

Experimental details are presented by von Pechmann for the preparation of 5,6-dimethyl-2,3-diphenylosotetrazine by the oxidation of biacetyl phenylosazone with potassium dichromate in dilute acetic acid solution.[48] Oxidation of biacetyl phenylosazone may be performed with either alkaline or acidic oxidizing agents. The reaction is reported to be quantitative in the absence of strong acid.

5,6-Dimethyl-2,3-diphenylosotetrazine, recrystallized from hot acetone and then alcohol, forms dark red needles of m.p. 169° (dec.). It is soluble in chloroform, benzene, and ether, slightly soluble in acetone and alcohol, and insoluble in water and acetic acid. Solutions of it are reddish-brown, and a brown color develops when it is dissolved in concentrated sulfuric acid. On warming with phenylhydrazine, it is reduced to the original osazone of m.p. 245°.

5-Methyl-2,3-diphenylosotetrazine, likewise obtained by the dichromate oxidation of pyruvaldehyde phenylosazone, melts at 106–7° and decomposes at 124°. Its reactions with sulfuric acid and phenylhydrazine are similar to those of the dimethyl homolog.[48]

Other 2,3-diarylosotetrazines described in the literature are included in Table III-1 and discussed in greater detail in the following paragraphs.

TABLE III-1. 2,3-Dihydro-v-tetrazines

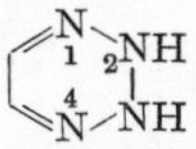

Substituents	Color, crystal habit	M.p., °C.	Ref.
2-Benzoyl-5,6-dimethyl[a]	White crystals	95	50
2-Benzoyl-5,6-diphenyl[a]	Colorless fine needles	248	46
5,6-Bis(carbethoxy)-2,3-diphenyl[b]	Violet black needles or flat red prisms	143 (dec. pt.)	2, 43
2,3-Bis(2,4-dichloro-phenyl)5,6-diphenyl[b,c]	Lemon yellow needles	217	10
2,3-Bis(4-ethoxyphe-nyl)-5-methyl[b]	Red needles	116	3, 50, 54
5,6-Bis(2-indolyl)-2,3-diphenyl[b]	Colored solution only		40
5,6-Bis(2-methoxy-phenyl)[a]	Colorless needles	138	56
2,3-Bis(2-nitrophenyl)-5,6-diphenyl[a]	White powder	200 (dec.)	17

(Table continued)

TABLE III-1 *(continued)*

Substituents	Color, crystal habit	M.p., °C.	Ref.
5-Cyano-2,3-diphenyl[b]	Reddish-brown needles	137 (dec. pt.)	53
2,3-Dibenzoyl-5,6-dimethyl	White needles	140	45, 50, 51
2,3-Dibenzoyl-5,6-diphenyl	White voluminous powder	189	32, 44, 45, 46
5,6-Dibenzoyl-2,3-diphenyl[b]	Small red-brown needles	200–201	29
2,3-Dibenzoyl-5-methyl	Small white needles	124	43
5,6-Dimethyl[a]	Colorless plates	95	50
5,6-Dimethyl-2,3-diphenyl[b]	Dark red needles	169 (dec.)	48
2,3-Diphenyl[b]	Dark red plates	152	7, 13, 48, 49
5,6-Diphenyl[a]	Colorless stout needles	135	8, 29, 31, 44, 46
2,3-Diphenyl-5-methyl[b]	(Not described)	106–107 124 (dec. pt.)	48

[a] May be an aminotriazole.
[b] May have linear structure; called osotetrazines in text.
[c] 1,2,3,4-Tetrahydro derivative.

In the course of his work on the synthesis of v-tetrazine, Auden prepared 5-methyl-2,3-bis(p-ethoxyphenyl)osotetrazine, as red needles of m.p. 116°, by oxidizing the corresponding osazone.[3, 50] It could not be reconverted to the osazone, presumably by phenylhydrazine reduction. This osotetrazine was also prepared by Vorländer, Zeh, and Enderlein[54] (Compound IVa, $R'' = H$, $R' = CH_3$, and $R = C_2H_5$) for their study of the liquid crystal properties of osazone oxidation products. They report that the lower melting point, 116° in this case, is not the true melting point but rather the transition temperature at which the substance passes into the liquid crystal phase. The true melting point is actually about 210° (dec.). In Table III-2 are listed the osotetrazines studied by Vorländer and co-workers. The lower melting points (transition temperatures) are those observed by the ordinary capillary tube method. The higher melting points were determined by the Seger cone method. Between these two temperatures the substances are birefringent.

TABLE III-2. Osazone Oxidation Products (Osotetrazines)
of Vorländer, Zeh, and Enderlein[54]

$$R''{-}\mathrm{N}{=}\!\!\overset{\displaystyle N C_6 H_4 OR\text{-}p}{\underset{\displaystyle N C_6 H_4 OR\text{-}p}{\Big|}}\ \ \text{or}\ \ p\text{-}ROC_6H_4N{=}N{-}\overset{\displaystyle C}{\underset{\displaystyle R'}{|}}{=}\overset{\displaystyle C}{\underset{\displaystyle R''}{|}}{-}N{=}NC_6H_4OR\text{-}p$$

| | | | | Melting point, °C. ||
R	R'	R''	Color	Lower	Upper
CH₃	H	H	Garnet red	158	ca. 200
C₂H₅	H	H	Garnet red	167	ca. 220
CH₃	CH₃	H	Yellow-red	123	ca. 200
C₂H₅	CH₃	H	Red-violet	115	ca. 210
CH₃	CH₃	CH₃	Red-violet	171.5	ca. 188
C₂H₅	CH₃	CH₃	Brown-violet	170	ca. 187

Auden[3] produced the osazones (VII) and (VIII) by reacting 5-hydrazinosalicylic acid with pyruvaldehyde and 2,3-pentanedione, respectively. Neither of these could be oxidized to the corresponding osotetrazine in the usual manner. Stollé[43] attributed this failure to the formation of quinoneimines, perhaps of the type illustrated by compound IX, which could not cyclize to the desired tetrazine (eq. 5).

$$
\begin{array}{ccc}
\overset{\textstyle COOH}{RC{=}NNH{-}\!\!\!\bigcirc\!\!\!{-}OH} & & \overset{\textstyle COOH}{RC{=}N{-}N{=}\!\!\!\bigcirc\!\!\!{=}O}\\[2pt]
\overset{}{R'C{=}NNH{-}\!\!\!\bigcirc\!\!\!{-}OH} & \xrightarrow{\ [O]\ } & \overset{}{R'C{=}N{-}N{=}\!\!\!\bigcirc\!\!\!{=}O}\\[-2pt]
\underset{\textstyle COOH}{} & & \underset{\textstyle COOH}{}
\end{array}
\qquad (5)
$$

(VII) R=CH₃, R'=H   (IX)
(VIII) R=CH₃, R'=C₂H₅

Benzil bis(o-nitrophenylhydrazone) forms a white powder of m.p. 200° (dec.) on exposure to air. This osazone is apparently readily oxidized by air, and Guha and De[17] tentatively assigned the dihydro-v-tetrazine structure to the product. The white color of the product is consistent with the v-tetrazine structure, but the possibility of its being an aminotriazole ought not to be excluded.

Oxidation of the phenylosazone of cyanoglyoxal[52] with ferric chloride or potassium dichromate in dilute acetic acid gives 5-cyano. 2,3-diphenylosotetrazine,[53] reddish brown needles, m.p. 137° (dec.). This compound forms 4-cyano-2-phenyl-1,2,3-triazole (colorless needles) on heating with hydrochloric acid.

Anschütz and Pauly[2] obtained three isomeric phenylosazones from diethyl dioxosuccinate and phenylhydrazine: α-, m.p. 120–1°; β-, m.p. 136–7°; and γ-, m.p. 173–5°. Only the α-isomer could be oxidized to the corresponding osotetrazine (X) with potassium per-

$$
\begin{array}{c}
C_2H_5OCOC{=}NNHC_6H_5 \\
| \\
C_2H_5OCOC{=}NNHC_6H_5
\end{array}
\xrightarrow{\ KMnO_4\ }
\begin{array}{c}
C_2H_5OCO \\
C_2H_5OCO
\end{array}
\left\langle
\begin{array}{c}
N{\diagdown}NC_6H_5 \\
| \\
N{\diagup}NC_6H_5
\end{array}
\right.
\tag{6}
$$

$$(X)$$

$$
C_6H_5N{=}N{-}C{=\!\!=}C{-}N{=}NC_6H_5 \\
\;\;\;\;\;\;\;\;\;\;\;\; |\;\;\;\;\;\; | \\
\;\;\;\;\;\;\; C_2H_5OCO\;\; OCOC_2H_5
$$

$$(Xa)$$

manganate and hydrochloric acid in ether solution (eq. 6). The product is dimorphic, occurring as violet black needles, or flat red prisms. Both forms melt at 143° with decomposition. This is another of the tetrazines that Stollé[43] suggested as possibly existing in the linear azo form. Accordingly he felt the compound could be the isomeric α,β-bis-(phenylazo)maleic ester (Xa).

A unique reaction that apparently produced an osotetrazine analogous to X is reported by Krollpfeiffer and Hartmann.[29] They obtained 5,6-dibenzoyl-2,3-diphenylosotetrazine by the reaction of benzenediazonium salts with certain phenacylsulfonium salts according to equation 6a. The primary coupling product is not stable and elim-

$$
2\left[\,C_6H_5COCH_2S\diagup^{\textstyle CH_3}_{\diagdown R}\,\right]^{+}Br^{-}\; +\; 2\,[C_6H_5N_2]^{+}HSO_4^{-}\;\longrightarrow
$$

$$
\begin{array}{c}
C_6H_5CO \\
C_6H_5CO
\end{array}
\left\langle
\begin{array}{c}
N{\diagdown}NC_6H_5 \\
| \\
N{\diagup}NC_6H_5
\end{array}
\right.
\;+\; 2CH_3SR + 2HBr + 2H_2SO_4
\tag{6a}
$$

$$R{=}CH_3,\, C_3H_5,\, C_6H_5CH_2$$

inates the sulfide and hydrogen bromide. The osotetrazine apparently arises by the dimerization of the diazophenacyl intermediate. When R is methyl, allyl or benzyl, the reaction proceeds as shown in equation 6a, but, when R is phenyl, the tetrazine does not form; only methyl phenyl sulfide is eliminated and ω-phenyl-azo-ω-bromoacetophenone is obtained in good yield.

In a typical experiment dimethylphenacylsulfonium bromide is reacted with benzenediazonium sulfate in a solution buffered with sodium acetate. After standing overnight the crude product is isolated and purified by being boiled with methanol and recrystallized from acetic acid. 5,6-Dibenzoyl-2,3-diphenylosotetrazine occurs as small needles that possess the typical red-brown color of the osotetrazines, m.p. 200–201°.

Sanna[40] reported a typical osazone-osotetrazine transformation in the oxidation of α,α- or β,β-biindoxyl bis(phenylhydrazone) with ferric chloride in alcohol or ether. However, in neither case did he isolate the product. He merely reported the formation of the "red color" characteristic of osotetrazines.

The production of the intense osotetrazine color is useful for the qualitative detection of phenylosazones.[48] The osazone is moistened with alcohol, gently warmed with ferric chloride solution, and shaken with ether. The formation of the red to brown-red color of the resulting osotetrazine is indicative of an osazone. According to von Pechmann, only the osazones of simple aliphatic diketones, or those containing only one aromatic radical, respond to this test; tartrazine, and the osazones of benzil, acetylglyoxylic acid, dioxosuccinic acid, and glucose do not give the reaction.

Recent studies have disclosed that the osazones of sugars are nevertheless affected by mild oxidizing reagents, although the final products are not osotetrazines. A brief discussion of this phase of the chemistry of osazones in not out of order, because of its close relationship to the chemistry of the 1,2,3,4-tetrazines.

Diels and co-workers[14,15] have oxidized (dehydrogenated) the osazones of several sugars, especially glucose, to compounds similar to the original osazones but containing two hydrogen atoms less. The oxidation is readily accomplished by bubbling air through a solution of the osazone in alcoholic potassium hydroxide. They contended that their "dehydroösazones" were not osotetrazines because the osazones could not be regenerated by mild reduction. The possibility that the dehydrogenation has occurred elsewhere in the sugar molecule is excluded on the basis that osazones prepared from 1-methyl-1-phenyl-hydrazine are not dehydrogenated.

Diels suggests that the "dehydroösazones" are aminotriazoles of the type XIa and that the reaction proceeds with the intermediate formation of a dihydroösotetrazine (XI) as in reaction 7.

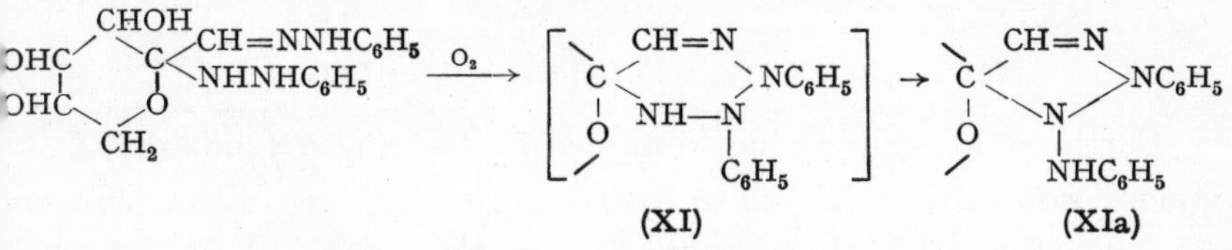

$$(7)$$

More recently C.S. Hudson and his collaborators[18] have discovered that the treatment of sugar osazones with aqueous copper sulfate produces 1,2,3,2H-triazoles with the elimination of aniline (eq. 8). The role of the copper sulfate is not understood; however, it is not primarily an oxidizing agent. The reaction is a general one, and the products, called osotriazoles (for example, phenyl-D-glucosotriazole, XII), have become very popular derivatives for the characterization of sugars.[19, 20, 39] Experiments by Weygand, Grisebach, and Schmeiser, using glucose-p-bromophenylosazone, made from p-bromophenylhydrazine tagged with Br,[82] show that the aniline molecule eliminated is the one from the phenylhydrazono group attached to the first carbon atom as indicated in equation 8.[55]

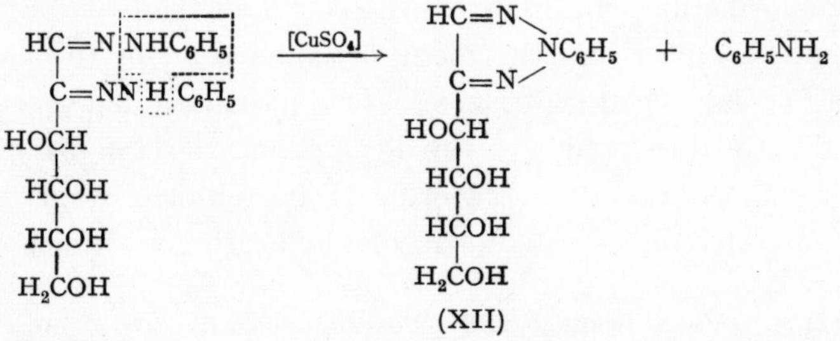

$$(8)$$

Under the influence of moderately strong mineral acids, oso-tetrazines likewise form osotriazoles. They are oily, neutral substances that von Pechmann described as non-volatile and very stable.[48] He identified them as triazoles and proved their structures by alternative syntheses. For example, the reaction of 2,3-diphenylosotetrazine (VI) with hot ferric chloride and hydrochloric acid solution (eq. 9) yielded 2-phenyl-1,2,3-triazole (XIII), which was identical with a sample prepared by the decarboxylation of the silver salt of 2-phenyl-1,2,3-triazole-4-carboxylic acid (XIV).[23]

$$
\underset{\text{(VI)}}{\begin{array}{c}\text{N}\\ \text{NC}_6\text{H}_5\\ \text{N-NC}_6\text{H}_5\end{array}} \xrightarrow[\text{HCl}]{\text{FeCl}_3} \underset{\text{(XIII)}}{\begin{array}{c}\text{N}\\ \text{NC}_6\text{H}_5\\ \text{N}\end{array}} \qquad \underset{\text{(XIV)}}{\text{HOOC}\begin{array}{c}\text{N}\\ \text{NC}_6\text{H}_5\\ \text{N}\end{array}} \qquad (9)
$$

Furthermore, the product obtained by treating 5,6-dimethyl-2,3-diphenylosotetrazine (XV) with hydrochloric acid (eq. 10) was shown to be identical with that resulting from the action of phosphorus pentachloride on the phenylhydrazone oxime of biacetyl (XVI), *viz.*, 5,6-dimethyl-2-phenyl-1,2,3-triazole (XVII).[48]

$$
\underset{\text{(XV)}}{\begin{array}{c}\text{CH}_3\\ \text{CH}_3\end{array}\begin{array}{c}\text{N}\\ \text{NC}_6\text{H}_5\\ \text{N-NC}_6\text{H}_5\end{array}} \xrightarrow[\text{HCl}]{\text{H}_2\text{O}} \underset{\text{(XVII)}}{\begin{array}{c}\text{CH}_3\\ \text{CH}_3\end{array}\begin{array}{c}\text{N}\\ \text{NC}_6\text{H}_5\\ \text{N}\end{array}} \qquad (10)
$$
$$
+ [\text{C}_6\text{H}_5\text{NH}_2]
$$

$$
\underset{\text{(XVI)}}{\begin{array}{c}\text{CH}_3\text{C}=\text{NOH}\\ |\\ \text{CH}_3\text{C}=\text{NNHC}_6\text{H}_5\end{array}}
$$

It is difficult to conceive how aniline, reported to be a product of the reaction, could arise in equation 10; reducing conditons are absent and only the elements of C_6H_5N are lost in the over-all reaction. Because compound XVII was obtained in only 20% yield and considerable tar formation had occurred, the course of the reaction appears to be quite complex and the mode of elimination of the aniline is obscure. The subject of osotriazoles, their formation and reactions, is discussed more thoroughly by von Pechmann in a later paper.[47]

It should be mentioned, in order to be complete, that osazones may be converted directly to osotriazoles by heating in alcohol at 200°.[4]

(2) Substituted in the 2- and 3-Positions with Benzoyl Groups

The second important class of uncondensed *v*-tetrazines comprises the 2,3-dibenzoyl-2,3-dihydro-*v*-tetrazines (XVIII), usually obtained by the oxidation of the bis(benzoylhydrazones) of α,β-diketones. They

differ markedly from osotetrazines in that they are colorless, cannot
be reduced to the original osazone, and rearrange to aminotriazoles
upon heating or treatment with strong acids. Stollé [3] maintains that
compounds of type XVIII actually contain the 1,2,3,4-tetrazine ring.

$$\begin{array}{c} R \\ R' \end{array} \diagdown \begin{array}{c} N \diagdown NCOC_6H_5 \\ | \\ N \diagup NCOC_6H_5 \end{array}$$

(XVIII)

R and R′=H, alkyl, or aryl

In an early attempt to obtain dihydro-v-tetrazine (XXI), Bauer[5]
followed the general procedure for the production of osotetrazines[48, 50]
and oxidized the bis(benzoylhydrazone) of glyoxal (XIX) with alkaline
potassium ferricyanide (eq. 11). He obtained a crystalline compound
of m.p. 151°, and assumed that it was 2-benzoyl-2,3-dihydro-v-
tetrazine (XX). It is surprising that one of the benzoyl groups should
have been eliminated in the reaction, particularly if it simply involved
the oxidation to the tetrazine. Acid hydrolysis (eq. 12) gave a debenzoylated product, at first reported to be the desired tetrazine (XXI).
It was obtained as a very hygroscopic, colorless, crystalline mass of
m.p. 51°, which upon treatment with nitrogen trioxide gave 1,2,3-
triazole (XXII).

$$\begin{array}{c} HC=NNHCOC_6H_5 \\ | \\ HC=NNHCOC_6H_5 \end{array} \xrightarrow{K_3Fe(CN)_6} \begin{array}{c} N \diagdown NCOC_6H_5 \\ | \\ N \diagup NH \end{array} \xrightarrow[HCl]{H_2O} \begin{array}{c} N \diagdown NH \\ | \\ N \diagup NH \end{array} \quad (11, 12)$$

(XIX)   (XX)   (XXI)

Subsequently von Pechmann and Bauer[51] recognized compound
XX to be a triazole and assigned to it structure XXa. According to
Stollé's later findings,[43] however, the correct structure is XXb, and
therefore the supposed dihydro-v-tetrazine is actually 1-amino-1,2,3-
triazole (XXIa). Compound XXIa should be expected to give 1,2,3-
triazole with nitrogen trioxide. Stollé claimed priority over von Pechmann and Bauer in suggesting that certain 2,3-dihydro-v-tetrazines
are in reality aminotriazoles.[42]

$$\begin{array}{c} HC=N \\ | \quad\quad NNHCOC_6H_5 \\ HC=N \end{array} \quad \begin{array}{c} HC-N \diagdown NHCOC_6H_5 \\ \| \quad N \\ HC-N \end{array} \quad \begin{array}{c} HC-N \diagdown NH_2 \\ \| \quad N \\ HC-N \end{array} \quad \begin{array}{c} HC=N \\ | \quad\quad NH \\ HC=N \end{array}$$

(XXa)   (XXb)   (XXIa)   (XXII)

Münch[32] attempted to procure 2,3-dibenzoyl-2,3-dihydro-v-tetrazine by oxidizing the silver salt of glyoxal bis(benzoylhydrazone) with iodine (eq. 13). Instead, the free osazone (XIX) was regenerated and 5,5′-diphenyl-2,2′-bi-1,3,4-oxadiazole (XXIII) resulted as a side product.

$$
\begin{array}{c}
\text{HC}{=}\text{NN}{=}\text{C}{<}^{C_6H_5}_{OAg} \\
| \\
\text{HC}{=}\text{NN}{=}\text{C}{<}^{C_6H_5}_{OAg}
\end{array}
\;\xrightarrow{I_2}\;
\begin{array}{c}
\text{HC}{=}\text{NNHCOC}_6\text{H}_5 \\
| \\
\text{HC}{=}\text{NNHCOC}_6\text{H}_5
\end{array}
\;+\;
C_6H_5\text{-(oxadiazole)-}C_6H_5
\qquad (13)
$$

(XIX)   (XXIII)

Stollé oxidized the bis(benzoylhydrazone) of pyruvaldehyde (XXIV) with mercuric oxide and iodine in the presence of magnesium oxide in dry ether (eq. 14).[43] The product of this reaction appears to be the desired 2,3-dibenzoyl-5-methyl-2,3-dihydro-v-tetrazine (XXV). However, oxidation of XXIV with alkaline potassium ferricyanide

$$
\begin{array}{c}
\text{CH}_3\text{C}{=}\text{NNHCOC}_6\text{H}_5 \\
| \\
\text{HC}{=}\text{NNHCOC}_6\text{H}_5
\end{array}
\;\xrightarrow[\text{(MgO)}]{\text{HgO}+I_2}\;
\begin{array}{c}
\text{CH}_3\text{-}\overset{\text{N}}{\underset{\text{N}}{\big\langle}}\text{-NCOC}_6\text{H}_5 \\
\text{-NCOC}_6\text{H}_5
\end{array}
\qquad (14)
$$

(XXIV)   (XXV)

$$
\xrightarrow{\;K_3Fe(CN)_6\;}
\quad
\text{CH}_3\text{-triazole-NHCOC}_6\text{H}_5 \quad \text{and} \quad \text{CH}_3\text{-triazole-NHCOC}_6\text{H}_5
\qquad (15)
$$

(XXVIa)   (XXVIb)

does not give rise to the dihydro-v-tetrazine (XXV), but gives a mixture of 1-benzamido-4-methyl- and 1-benzamido-5-methyl-1,2,3-triazoles (XXVIa) and (XXVIb).[43] The result obtained in reaction 15 is identical with the experience of von Pechmann and Bauer shown in reaction 11. Choosing the proper oxidizing agent appears to be a critical factor in preparing dihydro-v-tetrazines of type XVIII, particularly where R or R and R′ are hydrogen.

2,3-Dibenzoyl-5-methyl-2,3-dihydro-v-tetrazine (XXV) crystallizes from ethanol in small white needles, m.p. 124°. It is insoluble in water and alkalis, and moderately soluble in ether. It is soluble in hot, but not in cold, ethanol. When finely divided, it is slowly dissolved by hot aqueous sodium carbonate. This behavior is strange in view of the absence of an acidic hydrogen atom in **XXV**.

When **XXV** is refluxed for twenty-four hours with ethanolic hydrochloric acid, it is debenzoylated with the formation of 1-amino-5-methyl-1,2,3-triazole (**XXVII**), m.p. 135° (dec.), and not 5-methyl-2,3-dihydro-*v*-tetrazine (**XXVIIa**). The triazole (**XXVII**) is identical with a sample prepared by the method of Wolff and Hall[57] from compound **XXVIII**, the reaction product of semicarbazide and the diazoanhydride of ethyl acetoacetate (**XXIX**). Although the oxadiazole structure of ethyl acetoacetate diazoanhydride (**XXIX**) is considered to be improbable,[41] the structure of **XXVIII** is nevertheless reasonable, and **XXVII** is probably correct.

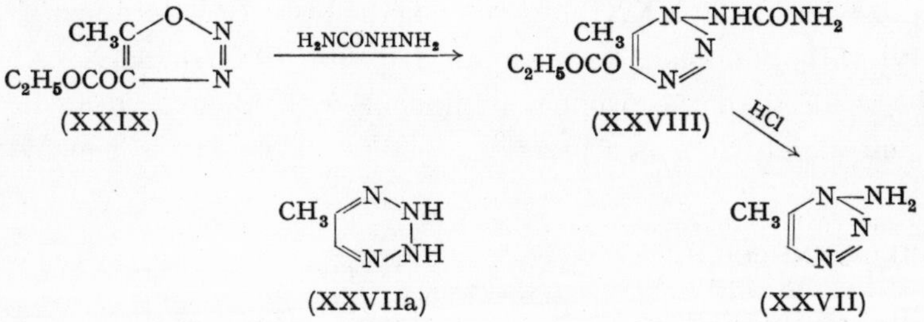

$$\text{(XXIX)} \xrightarrow{\text{H}_2\text{NCONHNH}_2} \text{(XXVIII)} \xrightarrow{\text{HCl}} \quad (16)$$

(XXIX)   (XXVIII)

(XXVIIa)   (XXVII)

Heating tetrazine **XXV**, m.p. 124°, for two hours at 140° results in its rearrangement exclusively to 1-dibenzoylamino-4-methyl-1,2,3-triazole (**XXVa**), m.p. 152° (eq. 17). Compound **XXVa** is identical with the product obtained by benzoylating 1-amino-4-methyl-1,2,3-triazole with benzoyl chloride and calcined sodium carbonate in benzene. The other isomer in this series, 1-dibenzoylamino-5-methyl-1,2,3-triazole, melts at 202°

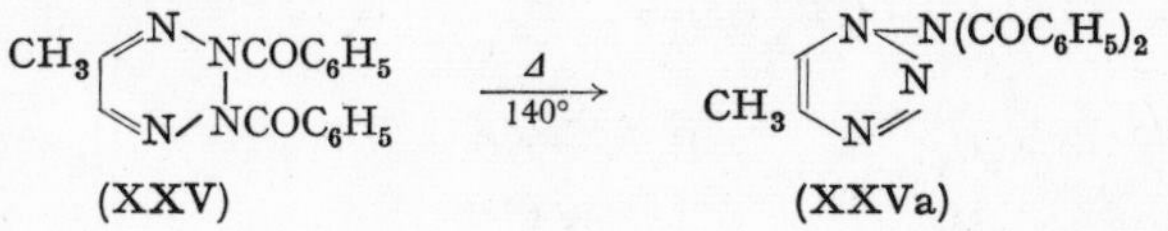

$$\text{(XXV)} \xrightarrow[140°]{\Delta} \text{(XXVa)} \quad (17)$$

(XXV)   (XXVa)

Stollé offered the foregoing reactions as partial proof that 1-amino-1,2,3-triazoles and not 2-amino-1,2,3-triazoles are the products resulting from both the acid catalyzed and thermal isomerizations of 2,3-dibenzoyl-2,3-dihydro-*v*-tetrazines.

In the course of his attempts to obtain v-tetrazine, Auden[3] tried to prepare 5-methyl-2,3-dihydro-v-tetrazine (**XXVIIa**). 5-Methyl-2,3-bis(p-ethoxyphenyl)osotetrazine (**XXX**), prepared by the mild oxidation of the corresponding osazone, was further oxidized by an undisclosed means (eq. 18) in an attempt to eliminate the 2,3-aryl substituents and thus obtain **XXVIIa**. This approach, however, was reported as unsuccessful.[50]

$$CH_3 \underset{\text{(XXX)}}{\overset{N-NC_6H_4OC_2H_5\text{-}p}{\underset{N-NC_6H_4OC_2H_5\text{-}p}{\bigsqcup}}} \xrightarrow[//]{[O]} CH_3 \underset{\text{(XXVIIa)}}{\overset{N-NH}{\underset{N-NH}{\bigsqcup}}} \tag{18}$$

von Pechmann and Bauer[50] prepared 2,3-dibenzoyl-5,6-dimethyl-2,3-dihydro-v-tetrazine (**XXXI**) by oxidizing the bis(benzoylhydrazone) of biacetyl with potassium ferricyanide (eq. 19). Compound **XXXI** cannot be reduced to the original hydrazone with phenylhydrazine. This reagent merely acts as a base and cleaves off one of the benzoyl groups.

$$\begin{array}{c} CH_3C=NNHCOC_6H_5 \\ | \\ CH_3C=NNHCOC_6H_5 \end{array} \xrightarrow{K_3Fe(CN)_6} CH_3 \underset{\text{(XXXI)}}{\overset{N-NCOC_6H_5}{\underset{N-NCOC_6H_5}{\bigsqcup}}} CH_3 \tag{19}$$

Stepwise hydrolysis of the benzoyl groups of **XXXI** with dilute hydrochloric acid (eq. 20) gives first the monobenzoyl compound (**XXXII**), m.p. 140°, and finally 5,6-dimethyl-2,3-dihydro-v-tetrazine (**XXXIII**), m.p. 95°. Treatment of **XXXII** or **XXXIII** with benzoyl chloride and sodium hydroxide regenerates the dibenzoyl derivative (**XXXI**). The beautifully crystalline hydrochloride of **XXXIII** can be readily converted to the free base with silver oxide.

$$CH_3 \underset{\text{(XXXI)}}{\overset{N-NCOC_6H_5}{\underset{N-NCOC_6H_5}{\bigsqcup}}} CH_3 \xrightarrow[HCl]{H_2O} CH_3 \underset{\text{(XXXII)}}{\overset{N-NCOC_6H_5}{\underset{N-NH}{\bigsqcup}}} CH_3 \xrightarrow[HCl]{H_2O} CH_3 \underset{\text{(XXXIII)}}{\overset{N-NH}{\underset{N-NH}{\bigsqcup}}} CH_3 \tag{20}$$

5,6-Dimethyl-2,3-dihydro-v-tetrazine (**XXXIII**) is soluble in the ordinary organic solvents, and it forms neutral aqueous solutions. In contrast to the osotetrazines, it is very stable toward dilute mineral acids. With mercuric chloride, **XXXIII** forms a white precipitate, which crystallizes from hot water in needles of m.p. 146–7°. Silver nitrate slowly produces a precipitate and ferric chloride gives a red-yellow solution with **XXXIII**. It reduces Fehling's and alkaline silver solutions, and is vigorously oxidized by potassium dichromate and sulfuric acid in the cold. However, none of the fully aromatic tetrazine is obtained with any of these reagents. Rapid heating leads to an explosion and the formation of a weakly alkaline vapor.

In a subsequent paper von Pechmann and Bauer[51] reported the treatment of 2,3-dibenzoyl-5,6-dimethyl-2,3-dihydro-v-tetrazine with one equivalent of concentrated hydrochloric acid (eq. 21). They obtained a product in 90% yield which they thought was 2-benzamido-4,5-dimethyl-1,2,3-triazole (**XXXIV**). Benzoyl chloride was isolated as a side product. Stollé's work discussed elsewhere in this chapter, indicates that **XXXIV**a, the 1-benzamido isomer, is the compound actually obtained.

$$CH_3 \quad \underset{(\textbf{XXXI})}{\overset{N\text{-}NCOC_6H_5}{\underset{N\text{-}NCOC_6H_5}{\bigcirc}}} \xrightarrow{\text{HCl}} CH_3 \quad \underset{(\textbf{XXXIV})}{\overset{N}{\underset{N}{\bigcirc}}} NNHCOC_6H_5 + C_6H_5COCl \quad (21)$$

$$CH_3 \quad \underset{(\textbf{XXXIV}a)}{\overset{N\text{-}NHCOC_6H_5}{\underset{N}{\bigcirc}}} N$$

Heating 2,3-dibenzoyl-5,6-dimethyl-2,3-dihydro-v-tetrazine, m.p. 140°, at 150° isomerizes it to 1-(N,N-dibenzoylamino)-4,5-dimethyl-1,2,3-triazole, m.p. 114°. This thermal rearrangement appears to be generally characteristic of 2,3-diacyl-v-tetrazines.[43]

Stollé, Münch, and Kind[46] prepared 2,3-dibenzoyl-5,6-diphenyl-2,3-dihydro-v-tetrazine (**XXXV**) in 75% yield by suspending the chloromercuric derivative of benzil bis(benzoylhydrazone) in ether and shaking it with the calculated amount of iodine until the color disappeared (eq. 22). The reaction mixture was treated with aqueous potassium iodide to remove the mercury salts, and the residue of practically pure dihydrotetrazine was recrystallized from ethanol giving a white voluminous powder, m.p. 189°.

$$
\begin{array}{c}
\text{HgCl} \\
|
\end{array}
$$

$$
\underset{\underset{\text{HgCl}}{\overset{\displaystyle C_6H_5C=N-NCOC_6H_5}{|}}}{\overset{\displaystyle C_6H_5C=N-NCOC_6H_5}{|}} + I_2 \longrightarrow \underset{C_6H_5}{\overset{C_6H_5}{}}\overset{N}{\underset{N}{\diagdown}}\overset{NCOC_6H_5}{\underset{NCOC_6H_5}{}} + HgCl_2 + HgI_2 \quad (22)
$$

(XXXV)

A less satifactory method for preparing **XXXV** is from the monosilver salt of benzil bis(benzoylhydrazone) and iodine in carbon tetrachloride solution. Small yields of **XXXV** may also be obtained by oxidizing the bis(benzoylhydrazone) with potassium ferricyanide in aqueous sodium hydroxide solution.

2,3-Dibenzoyl-5,6-diphenyl-2,3-dihydro-*v*-tetrazine (**XXXV**) is soluble in ethanol and carbon tetrachloride, sparingly soluble in ether, and insoluble in water. When recrystallized from carbon tetrachloride, the product contains one molecule of carbon tetrachloride of crystallization that is lost on heating at 100°.

Treatment of **XXXV** with boiling dilute hydrochloric acid in alcohol for one and one-half days produces a monobenzoyl derivative in good yield but many days' refluxing with concentrated hydrochloric acid in alcohol is necessary to remove the second benzoyl group.[44,46] The monobenzoyl derivative occurs as fine colorless needles which melt at 248°. This product is apparently no longer a *v*-tetrazine however but rather 1-benzamido-4,5-diphenyl-1,2,3-triazole (**XXXVI**). Treatment of **XXXVI** with benzoyl chloride and sodium carbonate produces a dibenzoyl derivative (**XXXVa**) of m.p. 151°, and not the original 2,3-dibenzoyl isomer (**XXXV**) of m.p. 189°.[45]

The completely debenzoylated product although reported to be 5,6-diphenyl-2,3-dihydro-*v*-tetrazine, is undoubtedly 1-amino-4,5- diphenyl-1,2,3-triazole (**XXXVII**). It crystallizes as stout needles from ethanol, m.p. 135°.[46] It is stable to dilute hydrochloric acid, even in a sealed tube at 125°, and attempts to decompose it with hot acids have only yielded small amounts of hydrazine. Compound **XXXVII** forms a benzaldehyde condensation product, m.p. 184°, and, with oxides of nitrogen in cold ether, 4,5-diphenyl-1,2,3-triazole is produced.

Heating 2,3-dibenzoyl-5,6-diphenyl-2,3-dihydro-*v*-tetrazine at 190° also produces the isomer which melts at 151°.[45] It is identical with the dibenzoyl derivative that forms when the monobenzoyl derivative, from the acid hydrolysis of **XXXV**, is rebenzoylated with benzoyl chloride and sodium carbonate. Without presenting any experimental details, Stollé stated that the following reactions occurred. (The triazole products are written as 1-amino-1,2,3-triazole derivatives in accordance with Stollé's revised version.[43])

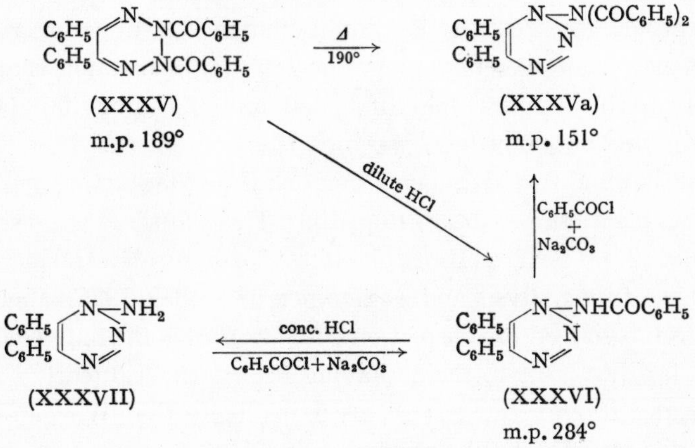

$$
\begin{array}{ccc}
\underset{\substack{\text{(XXXV)}\\ \text{m.p. 189°}}}{
\begin{array}{l}
C_6H_5 \\ C_6H_5
\end{array}
\!\!\!\!
\left\langle
\begin{array}{c}
N-NCOC_6H_5 \\
N-NCOC_6H_5
\end{array}
\right.
}
&
\xrightarrow[190°]{\Delta}
&
\underset{\substack{\text{(XXXVa)}\\ \text{m.p. 151°}}}{
\begin{array}{l}
C_6H_5 \\ C_6H_5
\end{array}
\!\!\!\!
\left\langle
\begin{array}{c}
N-N(COC_6H_5)_2 \\
N
\end{array}
\right.
}
\end{array}
$$

dilute HCl

C_6H_5COCl + Na_2CO_3

$$
\begin{array}{ccc}
\underset{\text{(XXXVII)}}{
\begin{array}{l}
C_6H_5 \\ C_6H_5
\end{array}
\!\!\!\!
\left\langle
\begin{array}{c}
N-NH_2 \\
N
\end{array}
\right.
}
&
\underset{C_6H_5COCl + Na_2CO_3}{\xleftarrow{\text{conc. HCl}}}
&
\underset{\substack{\text{(XXXVI)}\\ \text{m.p. 284°}}}{
\begin{array}{l}
C_6H_5 \\ C_6H_5
\end{array}
\!\!\!\!
\left\langle
\begin{array}{c}
N-NHCOC_6H_5 \\
N
\end{array}
\right.
}
\end{array}
$$

By this scheme, Stollé advanced an explanation for the difference in stability towards hydrolysis of the first and second benzoyl groups of **XXXV**. In addition, he pointed out that the reactions of the end product, 1-amino-4,5-diphenyl-1,2,3-triazole (**XXXVII**), are in complete agreement with those of the 4-amino-1,2,4-triazoles (**XXXVIII**, *R.I.* 78). Neither class reduces Fehling's or ammoniacal silver solutions;

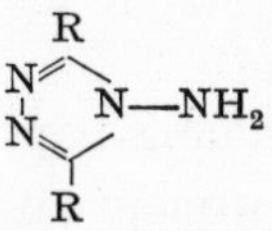

$$
\underset{\text{(XXXVIII)}}{
\begin{array}{c}
R \\
N \\
N \\
R
\end{array}
\!\!\!
N-NH_2
}
\qquad
\underset{\text{(XXXIX)}}{
\begin{array}{l}
C_6H_5 \\ C_6H_5
\end{array}
\!\!\!\!
\left\langle
\begin{array}{c}
N-N=CHC_6H_5 \\
N
\end{array}
\right.
}
$$

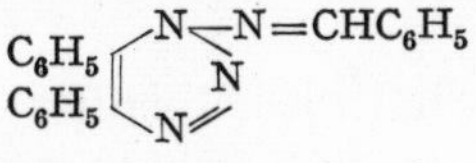

both yield stable aldehyde condensation products (*e.g.*, **XXXIX**), and are deaminated by nitrous acid. The formation of the benzaldehyde condensation products lends support to the contention that the final hydrolysis products of 2,3-diacyl-2,3-dihydro-*v*-tetrazines are actually 1-amino-1,2,3-triazoles.

Although the investigations of Stollé discussed in the preceding paragraphs have established that the existence of 2,3-dihydro-*v*-tetrazines unsubstituted in the 2- and 3-positions is unlikely, a few reactions involving such compounds have been reported since that time. They are of little value as synthetic methods, but are included to make the discussion complete.

Weygand and Siebenmark[56] attempted to prepare bis(2-methoxyphenyl)acetylene by treating the dihydrazone of 2,2′-dimethoxybenzil with mercuric oxide in refluxing xylene (eq. 23), a reaction that was successful on the dihydrazones of benzil and 4,4′-dimethoxybenzil. Their main product, however, was not the desired acetylene, but a compound that had two hydrogen atoms less than the starting material. It occurs as colorless needles of m.p. 138°. These authors suggest that the product is 5,6-bis(2-methoxyphenyl)-2,3-dihydro-*v*-tetrazine (XL) on the basis of its analysis and a reference to Stollé's 1926 paper.[43] If structure XL is indeed the correct one, reaction 23 is the only recorded instance of a dihydro-*v*-tetrazine having been formed directly by the oxidation of a dihydrazone. It seems more likely that Weygand and Siebenmark's product is the aminotriazole (XLa).

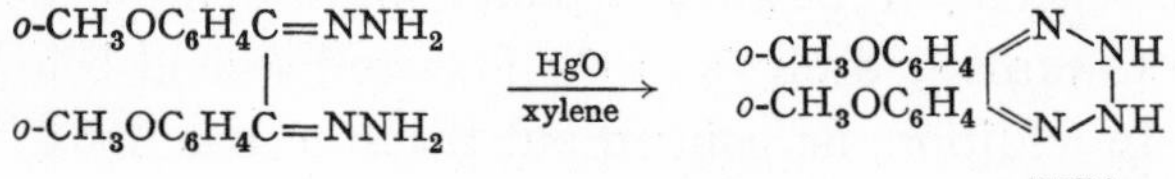

o-CH3OC6H4C=NNH2
o-CH3OC6H4C=NNH2
HgO
xylene
o-CH3OC6H4
o-CH3OC6H4
N
NH
N
NH
(23)

(XL)

o-CH3OC6H4
o-CH3OC6H4
N
NH2
N
N

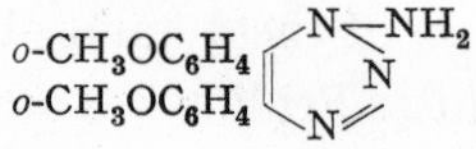

(XLa)

In a footnote to Krollpfeiffer and Hartmann's paper on phenacylsulfonium salts,[29] it was disclosed that treatment of 5,6-diaryl-2,3-dihydro-*v*-tetrazines with sodium ethylate solution transforms them smoothly into arylcyanamides (eq. 23a).[8]

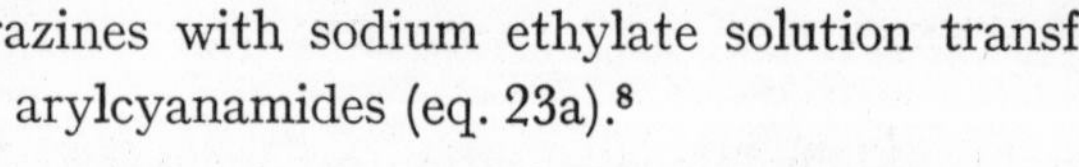

Ar
Ar
N
NH
N
NH
NaOC2H5
2ArNHC≡N
(23a)

Müller and Disselhoff[31] obtained 4,5-diphenylosotriazole from the reaction of phenyldiazomethane with the disodium derivative of 4-phenylbenzophenone. Its formation is explained by postulating a dihydro-v-tetrazine intermediate (eq. 23b).

$$2C_6H_5CHN_2 + C_6H_5\overset{Na}{\underset{ONa}{C}} \underbrace{\hspace{1cm}} \longrightarrow 2C_6H_5CN_2 + C_6H_5\overset{O}{\overset{\|}{C}} \underbrace{\hspace{1cm}}$$

$$\begin{array}{l} [C_6H_5C{=}N{-}N]Na \\ \quad + \\ C_6H_5CH{=}N{\equiv}N \end{array} \rightarrow \begin{array}{c} C_6H_5 \\ C_6H_5 \end{array}\!\!\overset{N\diagdown NNa}{\underset{\underset{H}{|}\,N{=}N}{\diagdown}} \xrightarrow{H_2O} \begin{array}{c} C_6H_5 \\ C_6H_5 \end{array}\!\!\overset{N\diagup NH}{\underset{N\diagdown NH}{\diagdown}} \rightarrow \begin{array}{c} C_6H_5 \\ C_6H_5 \end{array}\!\!\overset{N\diagdown}{\underset{N\diagup}{\diagdown}}NH \quad (23b)$$

(3) 1,2- and 2,5-Dihydro-1,2,3,4-Tetrazines

Perusal of this chapter discloses that practically all of the v-tetrazines described in the literature have been derivatives of 2,3-dihydro-v-tetrazine (XXI). Kleinfeller and Bönig[24, 25] have reported some derivatives of 2-phenyl-2,5-dihydro-v-tetrazine (XLI) and 2-phenyl-1,2-dihydro-v-tetrazine (XLII). They are obtained by the reaction of acetylene bis(magnesium bromide) with phenylazides.

(XXI)   (XLI)   (XLII)

In the mixture produced by reacting two moles of phenylazide with acetylene bis(magnesium bromide) relatively large amounts of aniline, phenol, and biphenyl are found along with small quantities of bis(phenyltriaza)acetylene (XLIII), an isomer of the latter thought to have the structure XLIV, and 2-phenyl-2,5-dihydro-v-tetrazine (XLI). Compound XLI may also be obtained by the action of cold sulfuric acid on compound XLIV. Treatment of the latter with alkali isomerizes it to the acetylene (XLIII).

The 2,5-dihydro structure was assigned to XLI because in contrast to the 1,2-isomer to be described later, it could not be acylated with acetic or formic acids, indicating the absence of an –NH– grouping in the ring. In addition it is not identical with the known isomeric phenyl-amino-1,2,3-triazoles.

2-Phenyl-2,5-dihydro-*v*-tetrazine (XLI) occurs as pearly white platelets m.p. 172°. It forms a very easily hydrolyzed hydrochloride. Bromination of XLI in chloroform produces a 2-(bromophenyl)-2,5-dihydro-*v*-tetrazine, m.p. 150° (dec.) of undetermined orientation, although other brominations in this paper indicate that it is the *o*-bromophenyl isomer.

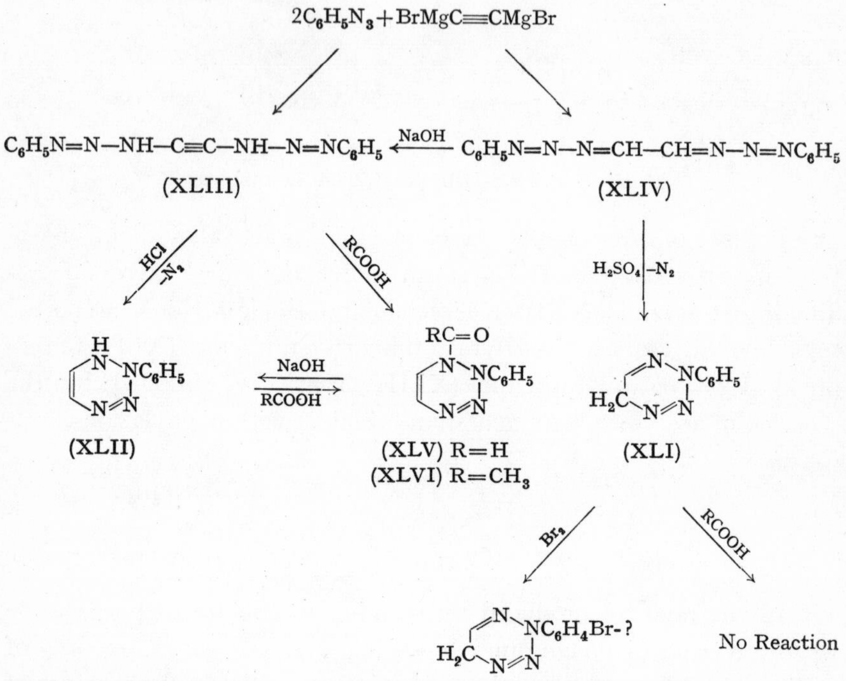

$2C_6H_5N_3 + BrMgC{\equiv}CMgBr$
$C_6H_5N{=}N{-}NH{-}C{\equiv}C{-}NH{-}N{=}NC_6H_5$
NaOH
$C_6H_5N{=}N{-}N{=}CH{-}CH{=}N{-}N{=}NC_6H_5$
(XLIII)
(XLIV)
HCl
$-N_2$
RCOOH
H_2SO_4 $-N_2$
NaOH
RCOOH
(XLII)
(XLV) R=H
(XLVI) R=CH_3
(XLI)
Br_2
RCOOH
NC_6H_4Br-?
No Reaction

Derivatives of 2-phenyl-1,2-dihydro-*v*-tetrazine (XLII) are obtained in two ways from bis(phenyltriaza)acetylene (XLIII): treatment with hydrochloric acid produces XLII directly, whereas cleavage of XLIII by organic acids gives XLII *via* the 1-acyl derivatives (XLV or XLVI). Nitrosation of XLII with nitrogen oxides (As + HNO_3) yields 1-nitroso-2-phenyl-1,2-dihydro-*v*-tetrazine, which on treatment with sodium hydroxide forms a sodium derivative, $C_8H_8N_5O_2Na$. The latter crystallizes from water as small violet needles which decompose at 175°. The yellow nitroso compound can be regenerated by the action of acid on the sodium derivative. It explodes at *ca.* 120°.

No direct proof of structure is offered for this series of compounds by Kleinfeller and Bönig, and it is not clear why the 1,2-dihydro structure is preferred to the equally reasonable 2,3-dihydro form.

Kleinfeller and Bönig also reacted acetylene bis(magnesium bromide) with p-bromophenylazide. The products obtained included 1,2-bis(4-bromophenyltriaza)acetylene (XLVII) but not 2-(4-bromophenyl)-2,5-dihydro-v-tetrazine or the isomer of XLVII corresponding to compound XLIV of the unbrominated series described above.

The behavior of 1,2-bis(4-bromophenyltriaza)acetylene (XLVII) towards acetic anhydride is normal; it gives 1-acetyl-2-(4-bromophenyl)-1,2-dihydro-v-tetrazine (XLVIII), m.p. 265°. The isomer, 1-acetyl-2-(2-bromophenyl)-1,2-dihydro-v-tetrazine (XLIX), m.p. 148°, is obtained by brominating 2-phenyl-1,2-dihydro-v-tetrazine (XLII) with bromine in chloroform, followed by acetylation. The acetylene (XLVII) rca be debrominated to XLIII with hydrogen and a palladium-calcium canbonate catalyst by the method of Busch and Stöve.[12] A sample of XLIII obtained this way, when acetylated and brominated with bromine in dilute sulfuric acid, yields the o-bromo isomer (XLIX). The inter-relation of these products is outlined in the following scheme.

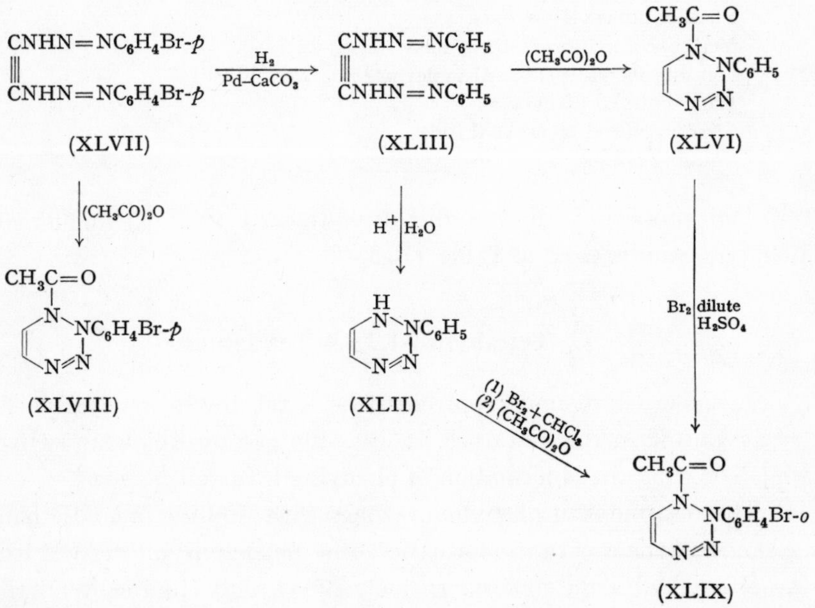

TABLE III-3. Dihydro-*v*-tetrazines of Kleinfeller and Bönig[25]

R	Parent	Melting point, °C.		
		1-Acetyl deriv.	1-Fromyl deriv.	Hydrochloride

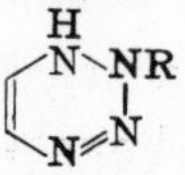

1,2-Dihydro-*v*-tetrazine

2-(2-Bromophenyl)-	135[a]	148[b]		
2-(4-Bromophenyl)-		265 (dec.)		
1-Nitroso-phenyl-[e]	*ca.* 120 (expl.)[d]			
2-Phenyl-	107	219[f]	172[g]	185[h]

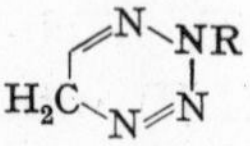

2,5-Dihydro-*v*-tetrazine

2-(2-Bromophenyl)-	150 (dec.)			
2-Phenyl-	172	(Did not form)	(Did not form)	(Stable conc. HCl)

[a] Colorless quadratic leaflets.
[b] White needles.
[c] Small golden-yellow rods.
[d] Yellow-colored crystalline mass.
[e] Sodium derivative, small violet needles, dec. 175°.
[f] Ivory-colored leaflets.
[g] Cream-colored tetragonal rods.
[h] Square leaflets.

The properties of the dihydro-*v*-tetrazines of Kleinfeller and Bönig are summarized in Table 1II-3.

C. Tetrahydro-1,2,3,4-Tetrazines

A single compound reported to be a tetrahydro-*v*-tetrazine has been reported in the literature. It was obtained by Bülow and Huss[10] while studying the chlorination of phenylhydrazones.

The treatment of phenylhydrazones with chlorine in cold ethanol decomposes them with the formation of a diazonium salt derived from the phenylhydrazine moiety. In fact, Bülow and Huss contend that nonformation of a diazonium salt is strong presumptive evidence that a compound is not a phenylhydrazone. For example, they found that, with 2,4-dichlorophenylhydrazine, benzil gave a compound that was indifferent to chlorine (eq. 24). Analysis showed that it had the same composition as the expected osazone, and they concluded that it was probably 2,3-bis(2,4-dichlorophenyl)-5,6-diphenyl-1,2,3,4-tetrahydro-v-tetrazine (L). In addition it was not deeply colored like the osotetrazines, so they excluded that possibility.

$$C_6H_5C=O \atop C_6H_5C=O \quad + \quad Cl\!-\!\!\!\bigcirc\!\!\!\!-NHNH_2 \quad \longrightarrow \quad C_6H_5 \atop C_6H_5 \!\!\! \begin{matrix} H \\ N\!-\!NC_6H_3Cl_2\text{-}2,4 \\ | \\ N\!-\!NC_6H_3Cl_2\text{-}2,4 \\ H \end{matrix} \quad + \quad 2H_2O \qquad (24)$$

$$(L)$$

Compound L forms pale lemon yellow needles, m.p. 217°, when crystallized from ligroin or alcohol and benzene. It is easily soluble in hot pyridine, benzene, and chloroform, soluble with difficulty in ethyl acetate, still less soluble in ether, acetone, ethanol, and cold acetic acid, and insoluble in ligroin. Cold concentrated sulfuric acid decomposes it.

D. Hexahydro-1,2,3,4-Tetrazines

Two hexahydro-v-tetrazines have been described by Ingold and Weaver.[22] They are produced by a unique synthesis, which may be pictured as a "cotrimerization" of two unsaturated species. Equimolar quantities of 1,1-diphenylethylene and diethyl azodiformate are mixed and allowed to stand at room temperature for four days (eq. 25). The color of the azo compound is discharged and the solution becomes viscous. Trituration with ether yields a solid which crystallizes from a chloroform-ligroin solution in colorless prisms, m.p. 164–166°. Ingold and Weaver assigned the structure, tetraethyl 5,5-diphenyl-1...-6-hexahydro-v-tetrazine-1,2,3,4-tetracarboxylate (LI), to their product. The ester is not attacked by cold potassium permanganate or boiling

$$\begin{matrix} R \\ R' \end{matrix}\!\!C=CH_2 \;+\; 2\; \begin{matrix} NCOOC_2H_5 \\ \| \\ NCOOC_2H_5 \end{matrix} \quad \xrightarrow{\text{4 days}} \quad \begin{matrix} & & COOC_2H_5 \\ R & & | \\ R' \!\!\!\! & \!\!\!\! \begin{matrix} N\!-\!N \\ \end{matrix} \!\!\!\! & \!\!NCOOC_2H_5 \\ H_2C & \!\!\!\! N\!-\!N \!\!\!\! & \!\!NCOOC_2H_5 \\ & & COOC_2H_5 \end{matrix} \qquad (25)$$

(LI) R=R′=C_6H_5
(LII) R=C_6H_5, R′=H

acetyl chloride. It could not be successfully hydrolyzed to the free acid; complete decomposition occurred.

By the same procedure tetraethyl 5-phenyl-1...6-hexahydro-v-tetrazine-1,2,3,4-tetracarboxylate (LII) was prepared from diethyl azodiformate and styrene. The colorless prisms of m.p. 133–134° (from chloroform and ligroin) had properties similar to those described for the diphenyl compound (LI).

E. 1,2,3,4-Tetrazines with Valence Bridges

The existence of 1,2,3,4-tetrazines that contain valence bridges is very doubtful. Only one such uncondensed v-tetrazine has been reported in the literature. It is the final product of a series of not-well-understood reactions carried out by W. H. Perkin.[38] He suggested a valence bridge structure for his product only because it agreed well with the empirical formula determined by analysis.

Oxidation of methyl dimethylacetoacetate with concentrated nitric acid (eq. 26) gives a product called a "glyoximeperoxide" (1,2,3,6-dioxadiazine, $R.I.$ 127) but referred to by the author as compound $C_{14}H_{18}O_8N_2$ (LIII). The structure of LIII was assumed by Perkin to be correct on the basis of earlier work on glyoximeperoxides by Beckh[6] and others. On treating compound LIII with phenylhydrazine (eq. 27) an intensely red 1,2,3,6-oxatriazine (LIV, $R.I.$ 130) results. Hydrolysis of this oxatriazine with alkali (eq. 28) gives rise to the questionable product, reported to be 3-(3-phenyl-5-v-tetrazinyl)-2,2-dimethyl-3-oxopropionic acid (LV). The acid (LV) melts at 164° and its methyl ester at 89°.

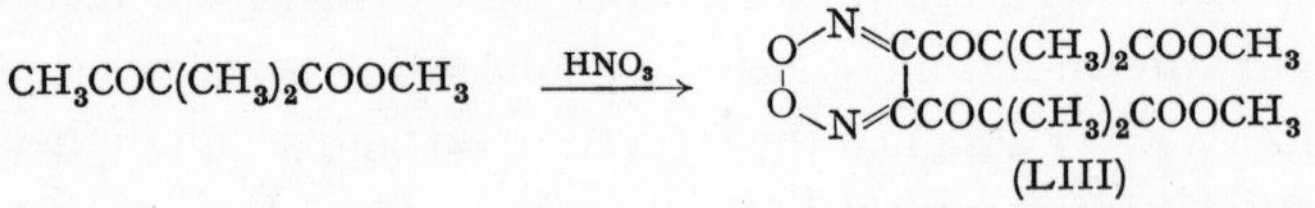

(26)

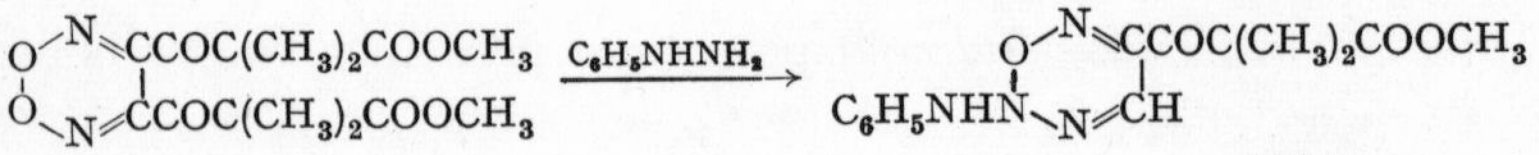

(27)

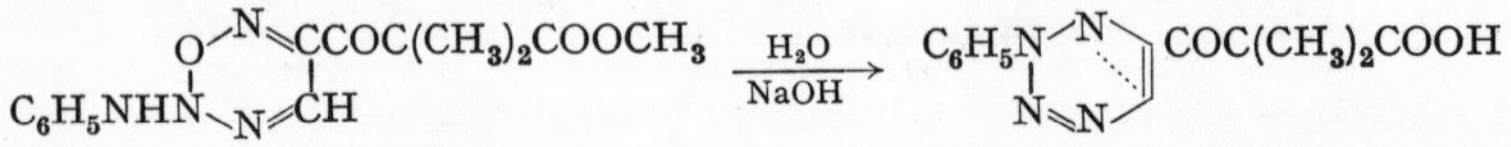

(28)

Satisfactory analyses were obtained on the barium and calcium salts and on the methyl ester, but other than that no further proof of structure is offered. Perkin himself was not entirely satisfied with the proposed structure of LV. He remarked: "It has been found very difficult to construct a satisfactory formula for this remarkable acid owing to the very small proportion of hydrogen which it contains, but it is thought that the configuration [LV] is probably correct."

2. 1,2,3,4-TETRAZINE RINGS CONDENSED WITH CARBOCYCLES

A. Condensed with a Benzene Ring

Although benzotetrazines were first prepared by Zincke and Lawson,[59] the simplest compound of this type on record has been reported by Hempel.[21] 1-Methyl-1,4-dihydrobenzotetrazine (LVI, *R.I.* 910) was obtained by treating a dilute hydrochloric acid solution of 1-methyl-1-(2-aminophenyl)hydrazine with sodium nitrite followed by neutralization with sodium carbonate (eq. 29). The product was isolated as an oil which partially solidified in a freezing mixture to a red crystalline mass. It was pressed on a gypsum plate and dried over sulfuric

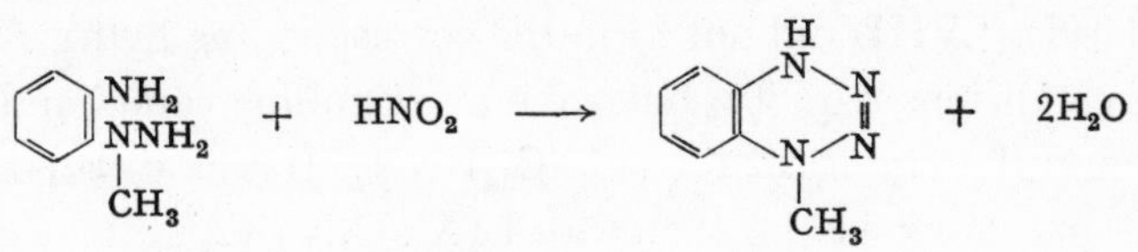

(LVI)

acid giving colorless, mother-of-pearl-like plates, m.p. 62°. Compound LVI is soluble in ether, benzene, warm alcohol, and petroleum ether. The tetrazine also dissolves in mineral acids with the formation of a beautiful red color; alkalis cause the precipitation of yellow flocs from the acid solution. Hot concentrated sodium hydroxide dissolves large amounts of the tetrazine giving the same yellow flocs on cooling. If, on the other hand, the hot alkaline solution is diluted, extremely fine, colorless needles of unknown composition precipitate.

As in the case of most *v*-tetrazines encountered in the literature, no proof is given for the formula of LVI other than an elemental analysis that agrees with the proposed structure.

Treatment of 1-methyl-1,4-dihydrobenzotetrazine (LVI) with concentrated nitric acid at 80–100° yields golden yellow prisms and needles of an unidentified material which, after many recrystallizations from absolute alcohol, melts at 127° and has the empirical formula $C_5H_4O_6N_4$. The loss of carbon and the increase in oxygen indicates a degradation of the benzene ring, perhaps accompanied by the formation of carboxyl groups. Thus, one formula consistent with the analysis and also the proposed v-tetrazine structure of LVI is 1,4-dihydro-v-tetrazine-4,5,6-tricarboxylic acid (LVII). If this possibility were correct, it would show a remarkable stability of the v-tetrazine ring towards strong acids and vigorous oxidizing conditions. At the same time it is difficult to reconcile the survival of an N-carboxyl group under such drastic conditions.

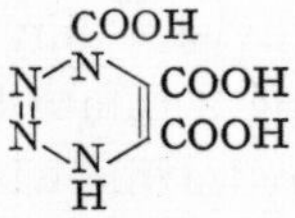

(LVII)

In 1886 Zincke and Lawson,[59] while studying the chemistry of certain azo compounds, observed that o-(p-tolylazo)-p-toluenediazonium chloride (LVIII) did not form the corresponding hydrazine under reducing conditions (eq. 30), but gave a crystalline compound of m.p. 168°, having the empirical formula $C_{14}H_{14}N_4$. It was called a "diazohydride" and assigned the structure LIX. This ring system may also be expressed by the structure LIXa, or even better by structure LIXb, which is a true 1,2-dihydrobenzotetrazine. Structure LIXa is preferred in Beilstein.[6a] Inasmuch as no rigorous arguments are presented for this

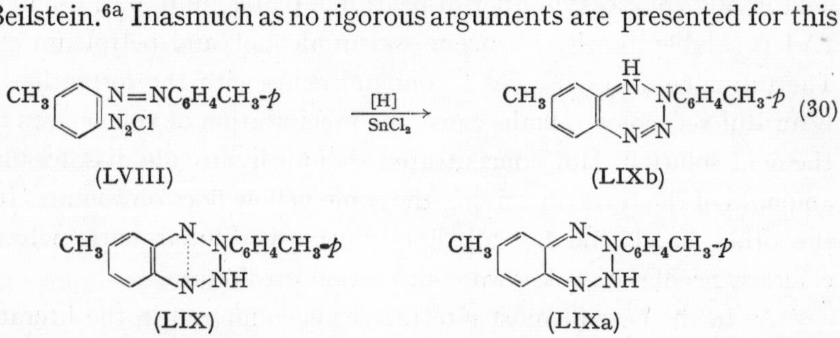

(LVIII)   (LIXb)

(LIX)   (LIXa)

valence-bridge structure, the 1,2-dihydro structure corresponding to LIXb will be used in this section to describe the compounds prepared by Zincke and his co-workers.

The general method used to synthesize this series of benzotetrazines is illustrated by reaction 30, the preparation of 7-methyl-2-(4-methylphenyl)-1,2-dihydrobenzotetrazine (LIXb) *via* LVIII. *p*-Toluidine is diazotized and coupled with a second molecule of *p*-toluidine. A second diazotization yields the diazonium chloride (LVIII), which can be isolated. The diazonium salt is then reduced to the benzotetrazine (LIXb) with sulfur dioxide, sodium bisulfite, or best with stannous chloride.

The properties of this class of compounds are exemplified by those of LIXb. It is not basic and may be recrystallized from hot concentrated hydrochloric acid without change. It is insoluble in water, soluble with difficulty in ether and chloroform, soluble in benzene and acetic acid, and very soluble in hot alcohol.

An important characteristic reaction of these heterocycles is their instantaneous and quantitative formation of perbromides on treatment with bromine in alcohol or acetic acid, for example, $C_7H_6N_4Br_3C_7H_7$. The same perbromide may also be obtained by brominating the diazonium salt (LVIII). Ammonia converts the perbromide to an "imide," $C_7H_6N_5C_7H_7$, which loses nitrogen on heating with the formation of a so-called "azimide" whose empirical formula is $C_7H_6N_3C_7H_7$.

The 2-aryl-1,2-dihydrobenzotetrazines of this series do not give definite products with amyl nitrite, benzaldehyde, ethyl chlorocarbonate, or methyl iodide. Compound LIXb forms an acetyl derivative that occurs as shiny, white leaflets, m.p. 132–134°. Reducing agents such as stannous chloride or hydrogen iodide are without effect on LIXb, but it is energetically attacked by oxidizing agents, yielding nitrogen-free products or resins. Moreover, the action of silver oxide produces a substance having the empirical formula $C_7H_7N_2C_7H_7$, which appears to be a *m,p*-azotoluene. The same material may be obtained by reducing the diazonium salt (LVIII) with zinc (and acid).

Employing the same series of reactions, Zincke and Jaenke[58] prepared 5,7-dimethyl-2-(2,4-dimethylphenyl)-1,2-dihydrobenzotetrazine (LX), m.p. 136–137°, and 5,7,8-trimethyl-2-(2,4,5-trimethyl-phenyl)-1,2-dihydrobenzotetrazine (LXI), m.p. 151–153°, from 2,4-dimethylaniline and 2,4,5-trimethylaniline, respectively. Their chemical properties are similar to those described for LIXb.

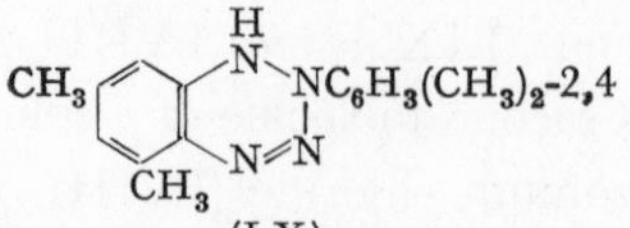

(LX) 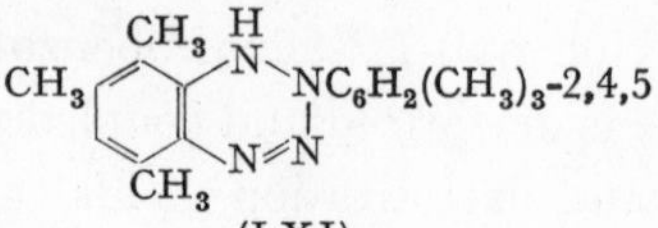   (LXI)

When o-(p-tolylazo)-p-toluenediazonium chloride (LVIII) is coupled with 1-naphthol and the intermediate coupling product is reduced with stannous chloride (eq. 31), the benzotetrazine is not formed, but rather the same "azimide," $C_7H_6N_3C_7H_7$, mentioned above, along with 2-amino-1-naphthol, toluylene-3,4-diamine and p-toluidine.[60] Substitution of 2-naphthol or 2-naphthylamine for 1-naphthol as coupling agent, or o-toluidine as the starting amine, gives similar results.

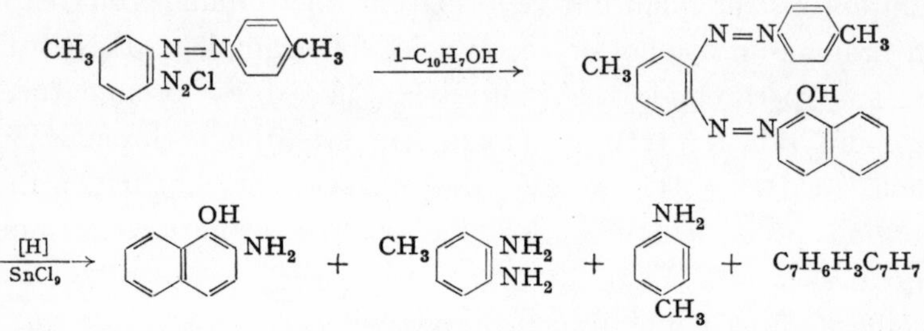

(31)

B. Condensed with a Naphthalene Ring

Coupling of 2-naphthylamine with benzenediazonium chloride, diazotization of the product, followed by reduction of the resulting diazonium salt with sulfur dioxide, sodium bisulfite or stannous chloride (eq. 32) gave 2-phenyl-1,2-dihydronaphtho[1,2]-v-tetrazine (LXII, R.I. 1801) as colorless, shiny needles, m.p. 204–205°. Zincke and Lawson[61] also referred to the product of reaction 32 as a "diazohydride" and gave it the structure LXIIa, although the formula LXII might be the more probable. The properties of LXII are similar to

those of the toluene derivative described above, and it can be acetylated to a monoacetyl derivative, m.p. 137–139°.

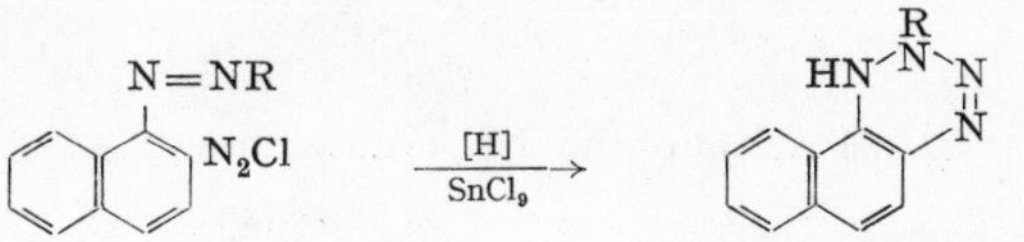

$$(32)$$

(LXII) R=C_6H_5
(LXIII) R=2-C_{10}H_7

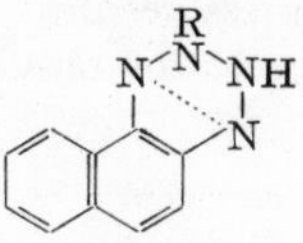

(LXIIa)

1-(2-Naphthylazo)-2-naphthylamine, diazotized and reduced with
stannous chloride likewise forms 2-(2-naphthyl)-1,2-dihydronaphtho-
[1,2]-v-tetrazine (LXIII). Unlike the corresponding phenyl derivative
(LXII), LXIII did not form an acetyl derivative with acetyl chloride
on the steam bath; increasing the temperature to 110° resulted in
resinification.

Table III-4 summarizes the properties of the benzo- and naphtho-
tetrazines that are described in the literature.

TABLE III-4.

Substituents	Color, crystal habit	M.p., °C.	Ref.
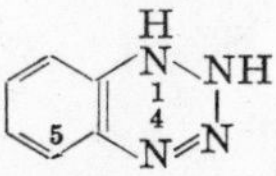 1,2-Dihydrobenzotetrazines			
5,7-Dimethyl-2-(2,4-dimethylphenyl)	Dirty yellow mono-clinic prisms	136–7	58
1-Methyl[a]	Mother-of-pearl-like plates	62	21
7-Methyl-2-(4-methylphenyl)	Colorless or weak yellow needles	168 (Acetate 132–4)	59
5,7,8-Trimethyl-2-(2,4,5-trimethyl-phenyl)	Thick monoclinic crystals or small almost colorless 6-sided tables	151–3	58

(Table continued)

TABLE III-4. *(continued)*

Substituents	Color, crystal habit	M.p., °C.	Ref.

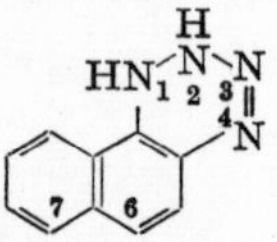

1,2-Dihydronaphtho[1,2]-v-tetrazines

Substituents	Color, crystal habit	M.p., °C.	Ref.
2-(2-Naphthyl)	White needles	202–4	61
2-Phenyl	Colorless needles	204–5	61
3-Phenyl-2-(4-sulfophenyl)[b]	Red solution only		9

[a] 1,4-Dihydro derivative.
[b] 2,3-Dihydro derivative, sodium salt.

Bucherer and Stickel[9] merely postulate that the sodium salt of 3-phenyl-2-(4-sulfophenyl)-2,3-dihydronaphtho[1,2]-v-tetrazine (LXIV) may exist as an isomeric intermediate when sodium 4-(2-phenylhydrazino-1-naphthylazo)benzenesulfonate is oxidized with nitrous acid and excess hydrochloric acid.

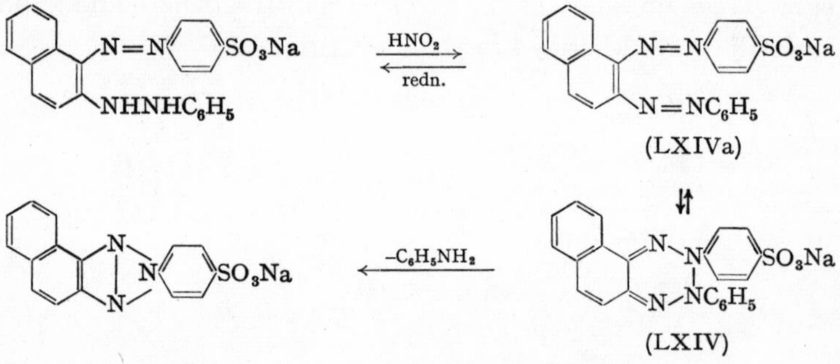

(33)

It is of historical interest that these authors were the first to recognize the possibility that the osotetrazines of von Pechmann might exist in the bis(phenylazo)ethylene forms, similar to LXIVa.

It should be of interest to investigate the oxidation (eq. 34) of the bis(semicarbazone) of spiro[4,5]decane-2,3-dione (*R.I.* 878) prepared by Kon.[28] A 2,3-dihydro-v-tetrazine substituted with carbamyl groups has never been reported. Furthermore, there is a question whether the resulting product would have the properties characteristic of the osotetrazines or the 2,3-diacyl-2,3-dihydro-v-tetrazines. One might speculate that the carbonyl function of the carbamyl group would influence the formation of products of the latter type.

$$
\begin{array}{c}
\text{CH}_2\text{--CH}_2 \quad \text{CH}_2\text{--C=NNHCONH}_2 \\
\text{CH}_2 \quad\quad\quad \text{>C<} \quad\quad | \\
\text{CH}_2\text{--CH}_2 \quad \text{CH}_2\text{--C=NNHCONH}_2
\end{array}
\xrightarrow[\text{oxidation}]{\text{mild}}
\begin{array}{c}
\text{CH}_2\text{--CH}_2 \quad \text{CH}_2\text{--C} \quad \text{N} \quad \text{NCONH}_2 \\
\text{CH}_2 \quad\quad\quad \text{>C<} \quad | \quad\quad | \\
\text{CH}_2\text{--CH}_2 \quad \text{CH}_2\text{--C} \quad \text{N} \quad \text{NCONH}_2
\end{array}
\quad (34)
$$

3. 1,2,3,4-TETRAZINE RINGS CONDENSED WITH HETEROCYCLES

A. Condensed through Two Carbon Atoms

(1) Condensed with 1,4-Pyrone

Peratoner[37] demonstrated that an unidentified compound, $C_{10}H_7NO_7$, obtained by Ost,[34] from the reaction of 3-hydroxy-1,4-pyrone and nitrogen trioxide, had the structure LXV. Upon reacting LXV with phenylhydrazine, two apparently stereoisomeric bis-(phenylhydrazono) derivatives (LXVI) occurred. Both isomers were oxidized by alcoholic ferric chloride to the same product, 2,3-diphenyl-5-oximino-2,3-dihydro-2-pyrano[3,4]-v-tetrazine (LXVII, $R.I.$ 909), m.p. 137–8°. Compound LXVII exhibits the typical deep red color of the osotetrazines in transmitted light, and appears black with a metallic luster in incident light.

$$
\underset{\substack{\text{NOH} \\ \text{(LXV)}}}{\text{O}\text{=O}}
\xrightarrow{2\,\text{C}_6\text{H}_5\text{NHNH}_2}
\underset{\substack{\text{NOH} \\ \text{(LXVI)}}}{\text{O}\underset{\text{=NNHC}_6\text{H}_5}{\text{=NNHC}_6\text{H}_5}}
\xrightarrow[\text{C}_2\text{H}_5\text{OH}]{\text{FeCl}_3}
\underset{\substack{\text{NOH} \\ \text{(LXVII)}}}{\text{O}\underset{\text{N--NC}_6\text{H}_5}{\text{N}\text{NC}_6\text{H}_5}}
\quad (35)
$$

(2) Condensed with 1,2,3-Triazole

Among the products formed in the reaction of p-bromophenylazide and acetylene bis(magnesium bromide), Kleinfeller and Bönig[25] isolated 1,6-bis(4-bromophenyl)-6,7,8,9-tetrahydro-1-triazolo[e]-v-tetrazine (LXVIII, $R.I.$ 699), or its isomer (LXVIIIa), and 1-(4-bromophenyl)-4-(4-bromophenyltriazeno)-1,2,3-triazole (LXIX). The structure assigned to LXVIII or LXVIIIa suggests that it was formed by the interaction of the 1,2,3-triazole (**LXIX**) with a second molecule of *p*-bromophenylazide *via* the intermediate **LXX**.

The reactions of **LXVIII** are similar to those already described for the mononuclear tetrazines of this series discussed earlier in this chapter. It is completely stable towards organic or mineral acids. Acetylation with acetic anhydride gives an acetyl derivative of m.p. 149° (dec.), and it forms a nitroso derivative of m.p. 103° (dec.) (nitroso nitrate, m.p. 162°, dec.). Compound **LXVIII** can be debrominated catalytically to 1,6-diphenyl-6,7,8,9-tetrahydro-1-triazolo[*e*]-*v*-tetra-zine (**LXXI** or isomer), m.p. 176° (dec.). The latter likewise is stable toward acids and forms an acetyl derivative of m.p. 148° (dec.). It is interesting that the triazolo-*v*-tetrazine (**LXXI**) was not found among the products from the reaction of acetylene bis(magnesium bromide) and phenylazide. This is an additional point of difference between the brominated and unbrominated series.

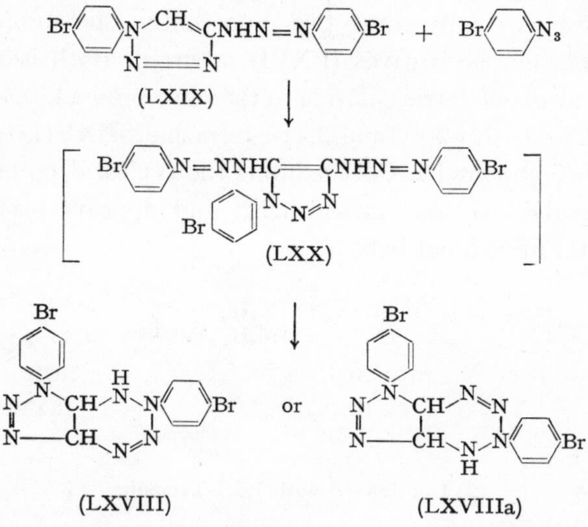

(LXIX)

(LXX)

(LXVIII)   or   (LXVIIIa)

Kleinfeller and Bönig do not present any direct proof that **LXVIII** does contain the 1,2,3,4-tetrazine ring. They contend that the formation of the nitroso derivative of **LXVIII**, which demonstrates the presence of a secondary amino group, is evidence for the tetrahydro-*v*-tetrazine structure because the possibility of **LXVIII** being an aminotriazole is excluded. However, they fail to consider the phenylaminotriazole structure (LXVIIIb or isomer), which is a logical alternative.

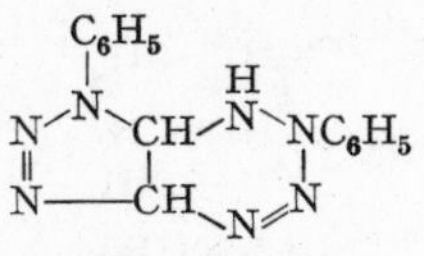

(LXXI) or isomer 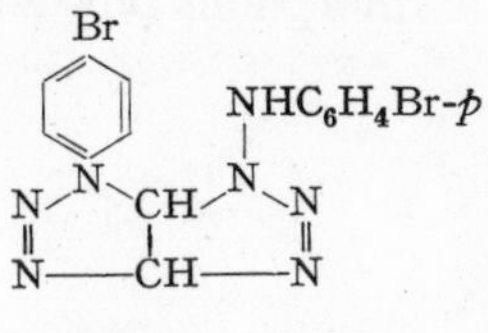   (LXVIIIb) or isomer

B. Condensed through a Carbon Atom and a Nitrogen Atom

(1) Condensed with Piperidine

Among the products formed by heating equimolar amounts of piperidine hydrochloride and sodium nitrohydroxamate in concentrated aqueous solution (eq. 36), Angeli and Castellana[1] isolated a product having the empirical formula $C_{10}H_{18}N_4$. They suggested the tetrahydro-v-tetrazine structure, LXXII. Compound LXXII crystallized from light petroleum as large colorless crystals, m.p. 154°. It can be obtained in a purer state by oxidizing the orignal reaction mixture with mercuric oxide. Compound LXXII reduces Fehling's solution, forms a benzoyl derivative, and gives a picrate, $C_{10}H_{18}N_4 \cdot 2C_6H_3O_7N_3$, m.p. 174°.

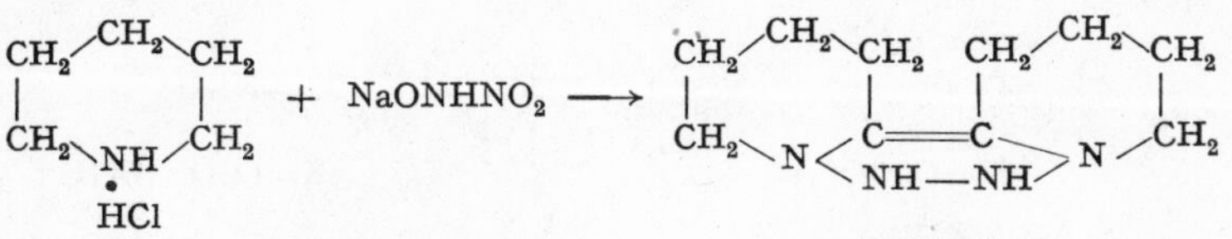

(LXXII)

Another product of this reaction is the "piperyltetrazone" of Knorr,[26, 27] originally obtained by the oxidation of N-aminopiperidine with mercuric oxide. Knorr proposed the linear structure LXXIII (his experiments were reported in 1882–4, before von Pechmann or Lawson had discovered the v-tetrazine ring), but the isomeric hexahydro-v-tetrazine formula, LXXIIIa, is also a possibility.

The "tetrazone" melts at 45° and is insoluble in water but soluble in acids. It is very unstable in hot acid solutions and decomposes with the evolution of half its nitrogen and the formation of piperidine. The hydrochloride is a heavy oil, and the chloroplatinate, $(C_{10}H_{20}N_4)_2 \cdot H_2PtCl_6$ is an amorphous powder which detonates at 70°.

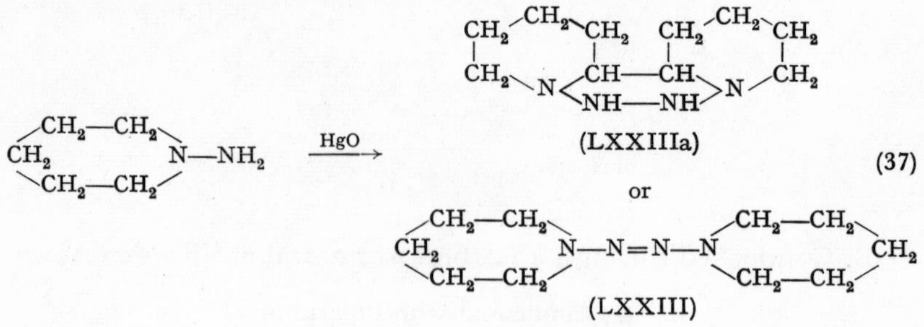

(LXXIIIa)

or

(LXXIII)

(37)

(2) Condensed with 1,2,4-Triazole

Bülow and Seidel[11] reacted ethyl 4-(2,4-dichlorophenyl)-5-thioxo-2-thiadiazolecarboxylate (LXXIV) with excess hydrazine hydrate and obtained a product which they thought was 6-(2,4-dichlorophenyl)-4-oxo-7-thioxo-1,2,3,4-tetrahydro-5-triazolo[4,3-*d*]-*v*-tetrazine (LXXV, *R.I.*700). Their basis for this conclusion was a satisfactory analysis for LXXV and the elimination of ammonia, which, however, was only demonstrated qualitatively. To accomplish this cyclization the hydrazine must be, in effect, an oxidizing agent.

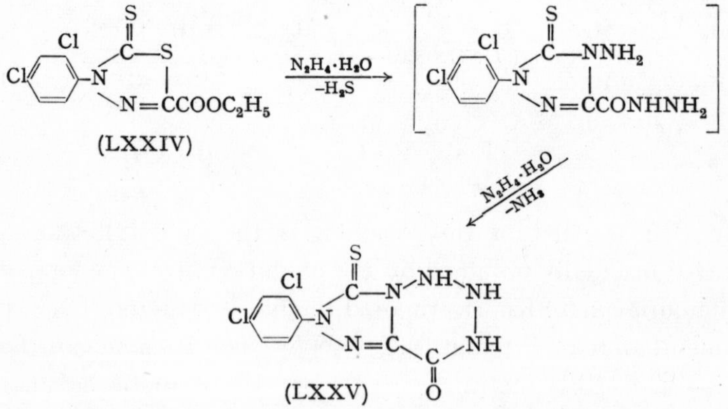

(LXXIV)

(LXXV)

(38)

The final product (LXXV) is obtained as white needles that decompose with gas evolution at 196–197°, after sintering at 191–192°.

The color of LXXV changes to red-violet after 2 days' exposure to light in a nonevacuated desiccator, possibly because of oxidation to a dehydro form. Compound LXXV is soluble in alcohol, acetic acid, and 10% sodium hydroxide, slightly soluble in acetone and sodium carbonate solution, and insoluble in ether, ligroin, benzene, and concentrated hydrochloric acid.

Bibliography

1. Angeli and Castellana, *Chem. Zentr.*, **1905**, 1260; *Atti Reale Accad. Lincei*, 1905, [V], 14, (1), p. 272.
2. Anschütz and Pauly, *Ber.*, **28**, 64 (1895).
3. Auden, Dissertation, Tübingen, 1897.
4. Auwers and Meyer, *Ber.*, **21**, 2806 (1888).
5. Bauer, *Chem. Ztg.*, **1901**, *I*, 267.
6. Beckh, *Ber.*, **30**, 152 (1897).
6a. Beilstein's *Handbuch der organischen Chemie*, Springer, Berlin, Vol. 26, p. 359.
7. Bodforss, *Chem. Abstr.*, **36**, 1544 (1942); *Svensk. Kem. Tid.*, **53**, 183 (1941).
8. Braun, Dissertation, Giessen, 1937.
9. Bucherer and Stickel, *J. prakt. Chem.*, **110**, 309 (1925).
10. Bülow and Huss, *Ber.*, **51**, 399 (1918).
11. Bülow and Seidel, *Ber.*, **57**, 357 (1924).
12. Busch and Stöve, *Ber.*, **49**, 1063 (1916).
13. Dieckmann and Platz, *Ber.*, **38**, 2986 (1905).
14. Diels, Cluss, Stephan, and König, *Ber.*, **B71**, 1189 (1938).
15. Diels, Meyer, and Onnen, *Ann.*, **525**, 94 (1936).
16. Grammaticakis, *Compt. rend.*, **224**, 1509 (1947).
17. Guha and De, *Chem. Abstr.*, **21**, 2132 (1927); *Quart. J. Ind. Chem. Soc.*, **3**, 41 (1926).
18. Hann and Hudson, *J. Am. Chem. Soc.*, **66**, 735 (1944).
19. Hardegger and El Khadem, *Helv. Chim. Acta*, **30**, 900, 1478 (1947).
20. Haskins, Hann, and Hudson, *J. Am. Chem. Soc.*, **67**, 939 (1945); **68**, 1766 (1946); **69**, 1050, 1461 (1947).
21. Hempel, *J. prakt. Chem.*, [2], **41**, 161 (1890).
22. Ingold and Weaver, *J. Chem. Soc.*, **127**, 378 (1925).
23. Jonas and von Pechmann, *Ann.*, **262**, 277 (1891).
24. Kleinfeller, *J. prakt. Chem.*, [2], **119**, 61 (1928).
25. Kleinfeller and Bönig, *J. prakt. Chem.*, [2], **132**, 175 (1931).
26. Knorr, *Ann.*, **221**, 297 (1883).
27. Knorr, *Ber.*, **15**, 859 (1882).
28. Kon, *J. Chem. Soc.*, **121**, 522 (1922).
29. Krollpfeiffer and Hartmann, *Ber.*, **83**, 90 (1950).
30. Maccoll, *J. Chem. Soc.*, **1946**, 670.
31. Müller and Disselhoff, *Ann.*, **512**, 250 (1934).
32. Münch, Dissertation, Heidelberg, 1903.
33. Northey, *Sulfonamides and Allied Compounds*, Reinhold, New York, 1948, pp. 32, 83.
34. Ost, *J. prakt. Chem.*, [2], **19**, 177 (1879).

35. U.S. Patent 2,160,293 (May 30, 1939), to Shoemaker and Loane, assignors to Standard Oil Co. of Indiana.
36. Patterson and Capell, *The Ring Index*, Reinhold, New York, 1940.
37. Peratoner, *Gazz. chim. ital.*, **41**, *II*, 619 (1911).
38. Perkin, *J. Chem. Soc.*, **83**, 1217 (1903).
39. Regna, *J. Am. Chem. Soc.*, **69**, 246 (1947).
40. Sanna, *Gazz. chim. ital.*, **52**, *II*, 165 (1922).
41. Sidgwick, *Organic Chemistry of Nitrogen*, New Edition, Oxford, London, 1942, p. 362.
42. Stollé, *Ber.*, **42**, 1047 (1909).
43. Stollé, *Ber.*, **59**, 1742 (1926).
44. Stollé, *J. prakt. Chem.*, [2], **68**, 469 (1903).
45. Stollé, *J. prakt. Chem.*, [2], **78**, 544 (1908).
46. Stollé, Münch, and Kind, *J. prakt., Chem.*, [2], **70.** 433 (1904).
47. von Pechmann, *Ann.*, **262**, 265 (1891).
48. von Pechmann, *Ber.*, **21**, 2751 (1888).
49. von Pechmann, *Ber.*, **30**, 2459 (1897).
50. von Pechmann and Bauer, *Ber.*, **33**, 644 (1900).
51. von Pechmann and Bauer, *Ber.*, **42**, 659 (1909).
52. von Pechmann and Wehsarg, *Ber.*, **19**, 2465 (1886).
53. von Pechmann and Wehsarg, *Ber.*, **21**, 2994 (1888).
54. Vorländer, Zeh, and Enderlein, *Ber.*, **B60**, 849 (1927).
55. Weygand, Grisebach, and Schmeiser, *Angew. Chem.*, **63**, 27 (1951).
56. Weygand and Siebenmark, *Ber.*, **73**, 765 (1940).
57. Wolff and Hall, *Ber.*, **36**, 3612 (1903).
58. Zincke and Jaenke, *Ber.*, **21**, 540 (1888).
59. Zincke and Lawson, *Ber.*, **19**, 1452 (1886).
60. Zincke and Lawson, *Ber.*, **20**, 1176 (1887).
61. Zincke and Lawson, *Ber.*, **20**, 2896 (1887).

CHAPTER IV

The 1,2,3,5-Tetrazines

No one has yet described a compound containing the *1,2,3,5-* or
as-tetrazine ring. There are doubtless several types of reactions that
might give rise to such compounds. One of these is the reaction of
nitrous acid with biurets, guanylureas, or biguanides. Thus, with
biguanide, one would expect 4,6-diamino-*as*-tetrazine (eq. 1). Several

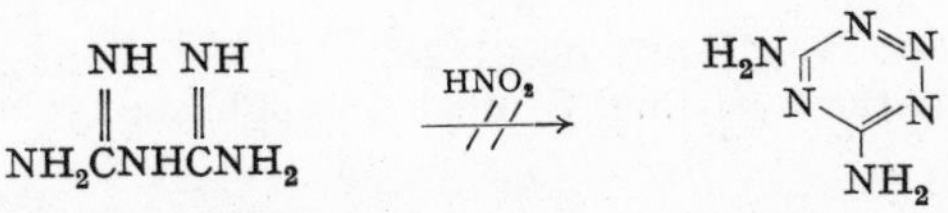

$$\underset{\underset{NH_2CNHCNH_2}{\parallel\ \ \parallel}}{NH\ NH} \quad \xrightarrow[]{HNO_2} \quad \begin{array}{c} H_2N \\ \end{array} \underset{NH_2}{\overset{N\!\!\!\diagup N}{\underset{N\diagdown N}{\bigcirc}}} \qquad (1)$$

studies of this sort have been made. Pellizzari[2] reported that the reaction
of nitrous acid with biguanide yields dicyandiamide and, presumably,
nitrogen and water (eq. 2). Rosenthaler[4] has also studied this reaction.

$$\underset{\underset{NH_2CNHCNH_2}{\parallel\ \ \parallel}}{NH\ NH} \quad \xrightarrow{HNO_2} \quad \underset{\underset{NH_2CNHCN}{\parallel}}{NH} \quad +\ N_2\ +\ 2H_2O \qquad (2)$$

His results indicate that the Van Slyke reaction gives less than half a
mole of nitrogen per mole of biguanide sulfate. He made no attempt to
isolate any reaction products other than nitrogen. It is possible that an
as-tetrazine is formed in this reaction; this would account for the low
yield of nitrogen.

Wystrach[5] attempted to prepare 4,6-dianilino-*as*-tetrazine by the
reaction of nitrous acid with 1,5-diphenylbiguanide hydrochloride

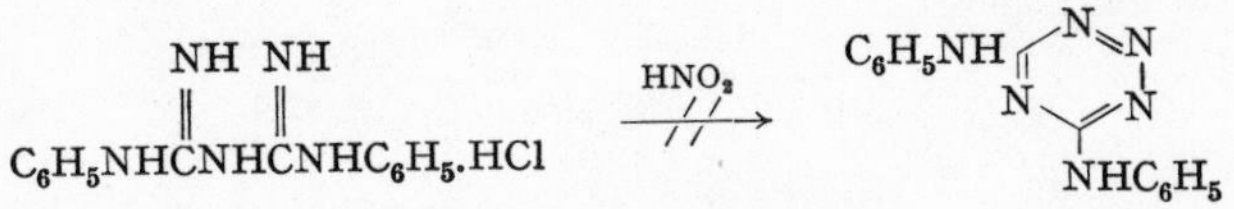

$$\underset{\underset{C_6H_5NHCNHCNHC_6H_5.HCl}{\parallel\ \ \parallel}}{NH\ NH} \quad \xrightarrow[]{HNO_2} \quad \begin{array}{c} C_6H_5NH \\ \end{array} \underset{NHC_6H_5}{\overset{N\!\!\!\diagup N}{\underset{N\diagdown N}{\bigcirc}}} \qquad (3)$$

(eq. 3). He used two moles of nitrous acid at 25°; one mole of nitrogen
was evolved per mole of diphenylbiguanide. The solid product from

this reaction was identified as 1,5-diphenylguanylurea. Similarly, Pellizzari[3] obtained phenylguanylurea from 1-phenylbiguanide and nitrous acid.

Maccoll[1] has calculated the resonance energy (20 kilocalories per mole) and long wave length electronic absorption band 5200 A.) of *as*-tetrazine.

Bibliography

1. Maccoll, *J. Chem. Soc.*, **1946**, 670.
2. Pellizzari, *Atti accad. Lincei*, **30**, *I*, 171 (1921); through *Chem. Abstracts*, **15**, 3982 (1921).
3. Pellizzari, *Gazz. chim. ital.*, **53**, 382 (1923); through *Chem. Abstracts*, **18**, 229 (1924).
4. Rosenthaler, *Biochem. Z.*, **207**, 298 (1929).
5. Wystrach, American Cyanamid Company, unpublished research.

CHAPTER V

The 1,2,4,5-Tetrazines

Introduction

The fundamental compound in this series is 1,2,4,5-tetrazine (I), which is No. 134 in *The Ring Index*. The preferred *Ring Index* and *Chemical Abstracts* name is s-tetrazine. This compound is usually

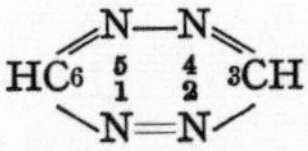

$$HC_6 \overset{\displaystyle N\!-\!N}{\underset{\displaystyle N\!=\!N}{\overset{5\quad 4}{\underset{1\quad 2}{}}}} {}_3CH$$

(I)

referred to in the literature as simply tetrazine. The dihydro-, tetra-hydro-, and most of the hexahydro-s-tetrazines are named as substituted tetrazines, s-tetrazines, or 1,2,4,5-tetrazines. In the older literature trivial names are frequently encountered, but they will be used in-frequently in this chapter. The tetrahydro-3,6-s-tetrazinediones are usually referred to in the literature as urazines or p-urazines with tetrahydro-3,6-s-tetrazinedione being called p-urazine. This compound and its derivatives are listed under p-urazine in *Chemical Abstracts*, but they are also called tetrahydro-3,6-s-tetrazinediones. The urazine and p-urazine nomenclature will not be used in this chapter because of the confusion as to whether or not they are actually s-tetrazines. In this discussion, where the position of the nitrogen atoms in tetrazines is not specified, 1,2,4,5-tetrazines are the compounds intended.

In addition to s-tetrazines, dihydro-, tetrahydro-, and hexahydro-s-tetrazines are known. Of these the dihydro series is much more exten-sive than is any of the others including the completely unsaturated s-tetrazines. Very few tetrahydro derivatives and only a small number of hexahydro derivatives are known. There are four possible isomeric dihydro-s-tetrazines. These are 1,2-, 1,4-, 1,6- and 3,6-, of which the

1,2-dihydro-s-tetrazines are best known. Only two isomeric tetrahydro-s-tetrazines (1,2,3,4- and 1,2,3,6-tetrahydro-) are possible and both are known.

The principal preparative method for s-tetrazines is oxidation of dihydro-s-tetrazines by mild oxidizing agents such as amyl nitrite, bromine, air, ferric chloride, hydrogen peroxide, chromic oxide, etc. (eq. 1).

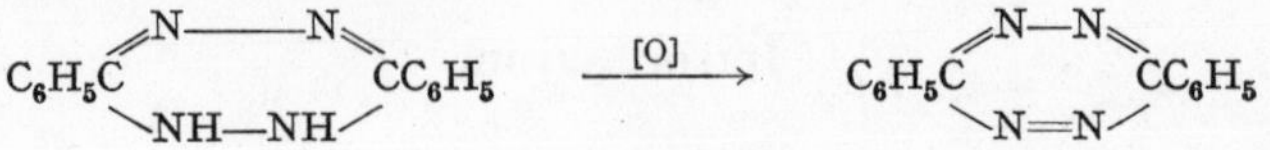

$$C_6H_5C \underset{NH-NH}{\overset{N----N}{\diagup}} CC_6H_5 \quad \xrightarrow{[O]} \quad C_6H_5C \underset{N=N}{\overset{N-N}{\diagup}} CC_6H_5 \tag{1}$$

$$\text{(II)} \qquad\qquad\qquad\qquad \text{(III)}$$

There are several methods for preparing dihydro-s-tetrazines. Reactions illustrative of the chief methods of preparation are shown in

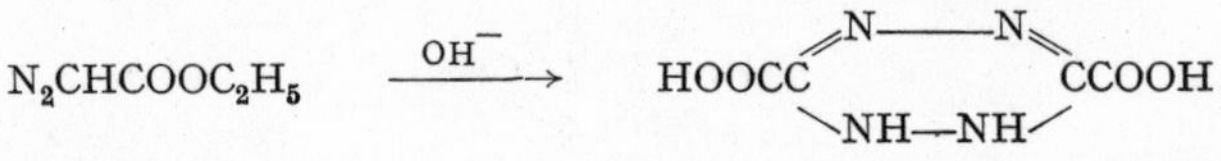

$$N_2CHCOOC_2H_5 \quad \xrightarrow{OH^-} \quad HOOCC \underset{NH-NH}{\overset{N----N}{\diagup}} CCOOH \tag{2}$$

$$\text{(IV)}$$

$$C_6H_5CN + NH_2NH_2 \quad \xrightarrow{\Delta} \quad C_6H_5C \underset{NH-NH}{\overset{N----N}{\diagup}} CC_6H_5 \tag{3}$$

$$\text{(II)}$$

$$C_6H_5\overset{\overset{\displaystyle S}{\|}}{C}NH_2 + NH_2NH_2 \quad \xrightarrow{\Delta} \quad C_6H_5C \underset{NH-NH}{\overset{N----N}{\diagup}} CC_6H_5 \tag{4}$$

$$\text{(II)}$$

$$C_6H_5\overset{\overset{\displaystyle NH \cdot HCl}{\|}}{C}OC_2H_5 + NH_2NH_2 \quad \longrightarrow \quad C_6H_5C \underset{NH-NH}{\overset{N----N}{\diagup}} CC_6H_5 \tag{5}$$

$$\text{(II)}$$

$$\underset{\begin{matrix} | & & | \\ Cl & & Cl \end{matrix}}{C_6H_5C=N-N=CC_6H_5} + NH_2NH_2 \quad \longrightarrow \quad C_6H_5C \underset{NH-NH}{\overset{N---N}{\diagup}} CC_6H_5 \tag{6}$$

$$\text{(V)} \qquad\qquad\qquad\qquad \text{(II)}$$

$$C_6H_5NHNHCH \quad \xrightarrow{CH_3ONa} \quad \underset{\underset{C_6H_5}{|}}{HC} \overset{\overset{C_6H_5}{|}}{\underset{N-N}{\overset{N-N}{\diagup}}} CH \tag{7}$$

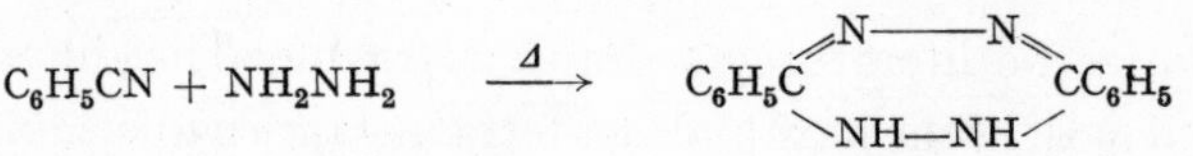

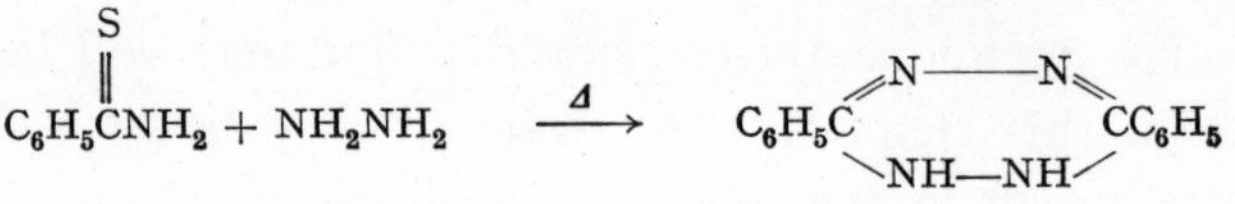

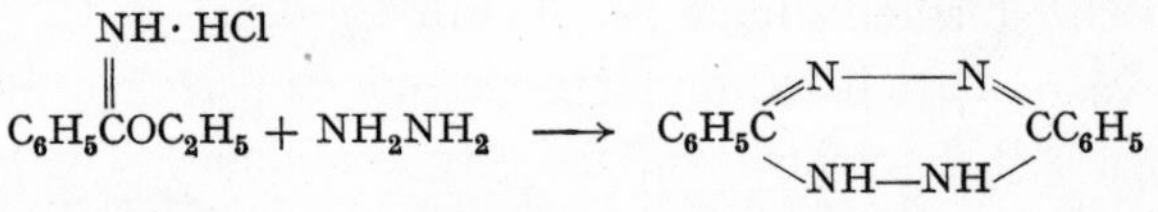

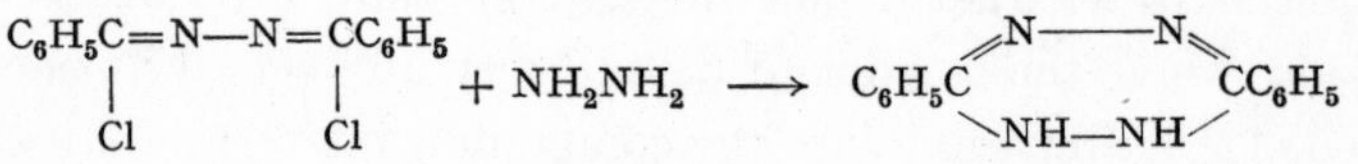

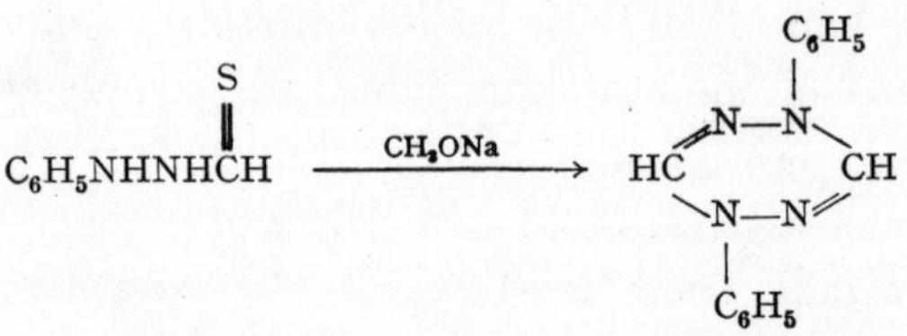

$$\text{(VI)}$$

equations 2 to 7. A number of modifications of the above procedures have been used as well as a number of special procedures. Although most of the above series of reactions have been shown as applying only to aromatic compounds, the methods of equations 3 and 5 can be used to prepare 3,6-dialkyl-1,2-dihydro-s-tetrazines. The only examples of N-alkyldihydro-s-tetrazines have not been prepared by direct cyclization but by action of diazoalkanes on 1,6-dihydro-s-tetrazines (eq. 41, p. 204). In general, the reactions used to prepare dihydro-s-tetrazines give low yields and other compounds are frequently the principal products.

So few tetrahydro-s-tetrazines have been prepared that methods of preparation will be discussed in the sections dealing only with them.

The hexahydro-s-tetrazines are prepared by the reaction of aliphatic aldehydes, usually formaldehyde, with hydrazines (eq. 8).

$$
RCHO + R'NHNHR'' \longrightarrow
\begin{array}{c}
R' \quad R'' \\
| \quad | \\
N—N \\
RCH \qquad CHR \\
N—N \\
| \quad | \\
R' \quad R'' \\
\text{(VII)}
\end{array}
\quad \text{or} \quad
\begin{array}{c}
R'' \quad R' \\
| \quad | \\
N—N \\
RCH \qquad CHR \\
N—N \\
| \quad | \\
R' \quad R'' \\
\text{(VIII)}
\end{array}
\qquad (8)
$$

Only aliphatic aldehydes have been used in this method, but the hydrazines have been substituted with either aliphatic or aromatic groups or with both. If R' and R'' in eq. 8 are the same, VII and VIII are identical and the structure of the product is known, but there are two isomeric possibilities if R' and R'' are different. In these cases only one product is obtained but which isomeric form it may be has not been determined in any reported case.

Tetrahydro-3,6-s-tetrazinedione and similar compounds such as tetrahydro-3,6-s-tetrazinedithione and tetrahydro-3,6-s-tetrazinediimine have been prepared in a variety of ways and there is no good general method of preparation. The methods that are used will be discussed as the classes of compounds are considered.

s-Tetrazines are very weakly basic compounds. They are deeply colored, being deep red, bluish-red, or violet-red. The dihydro derivatives are usually white or yellow solids and are not basic; in some cases they are actually acidic. The tetrahydro and hexahydro-s-tetrazines are white solids, and are usually basic. s-Tetrazines and dihydro-s-tetrazines can be decomposed easily with heat, the latter class usually giving 1,2,4,4H-triazoles. Hydrolysis of s-tetrazines and dihydro-s-tetrazines in basic or acidic solutions to give hydrazine, nitrogen, and acids is very easy.

1,2-Dihydro-s-tetrazines can be converted to 1,2,4,4H-triazoles by heating at temperatures of about 100° or higher. Many reported preparations of dihydro-s-tetrazines have involved use of temperatures in this range. In these cases the products claimed to be dihydro-s-tetrazines are very likely 1,2,4,4H-triazoles. This has led to considerable confusion and it is well to keep in mind that many compounds claimed to be hydro-s-tetrazines are triazoles. This last statement also applies to p-urazines.

No s-tetrazines or hydro-s-tetrazines have been found in nature. Several patents[65-67,142] have been issued covering s-tetrazines or hydro-s-tetrazines and mentioning such uses as ingredients in the preparation of resins, as desensitizing agents in photographic emulsions, and as drugs. However, it is doubtful that any are being used commercially.

1. UNCONDENSED s-TETRAZINES

A. Mononuclear s-Tetrazines

(1) s-Tetrazine and Hydro Derivatives

s-Tetrazine (I) was first prepared by Hantzsch and Lehmann[73] in 1900 by thermal decarboxylation of 3,6-s-tetrazinedicarboxylic acid. These authors erroneously reported the product to be X obtained by decarboxylation of IX. These were called *bisazoxymethane* and *bisazoxy-*

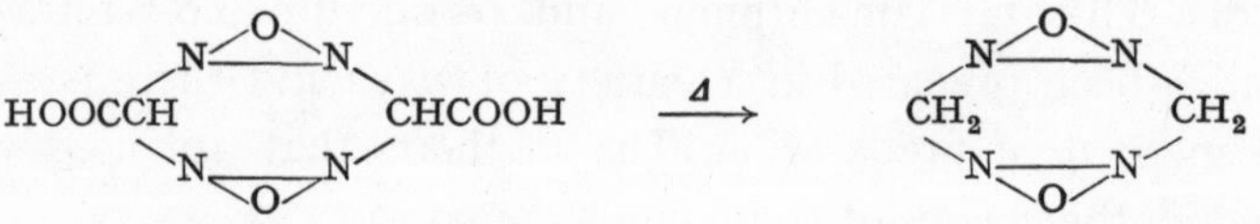

$$\text{(IX)} \xrightarrow{\Delta} \text{(X)} \tag{9}$$

acetic acid, respectively. The yield was only 1–2% and the melting point of 75° was much lower than that of 99° which was later found to be correct for s-tetrazine. Their incorrectly formulated structure was probably a result of analytical work on very impure material. A few years later Curtius, Darapsky, and Müller[45] prepared s-tetrazine in the same way and obtained a product melting at 99° and crystallizing in purplish-red rods. The yield was 14%. In a later paper[50] it was stated that purification by sublimation with barium oxide caused a severe explosion. Wood and Bergstrom[167] also prepared s-tetrazine by decarboxylation of 3,6-s-tetrazinedicarboxylic acid in 17% yield. These authors as well as Müller and Herrdegen[95] have prepared s-tetrazine by oxidation of 1,2-dihydro-s-tetrazine with air or nitrous acid.

s-Tetrazine is readily decomposed by air and can be stored only in a sealed tube under its own vapor. Mild alkaline treatment does not change s-tetrazine but in stronger alkaline solution it turns brown. Mester[91] has proposed to determine s-tetrazine quantitatively by hydrolysis with 33% sodium hydroxide solution in the presence of Devarda alloy. The ammonia so formed would then be distilled and titrated. Extremely mild acid treatment such as dilute hydrochloric acid gives hydrazine hydrochloride, nitrogen, and formic acid.[47] It has been stated by Müller[94] that s-tetrazine reacts with diazomethane to give a saturated s-tetrazine (XI). Mild reducing agents such as hydrogen

$$
\underset{(\text{I})}{\overset{\displaystyle \begin{array}{c} N\!-\!N \\ CH \qquad CH \\ N\!=\!N \end{array}}{}} + 3CH_2N_2 \longrightarrow \underset{(\text{XI})}{\overset{\displaystyle \begin{array}{c} CH_2 \\ N \qquad N \\ CH \qquad CH \\ CH_2\!-\!N \qquad N\!-\!CH_2 \end{array}}{}} \qquad (10)
$$

sulfide or zinc dust in acid reduce s-tetrazine to 1,2-dihydro-s-tetrazine. s-Tetrazine is soluble in water and most organic solvents.

The absorption spectrum of s-tetrazine in the visible region has been studied by Müller and Herrdegen,[95] Koenigsberger and Vogt,[83] and Maccoll.[89] The principal absorption is at 520 mμ with bands at 543 and 553–568 mμ. Maccoll has calculated that s-tetrazine has a resonance energy of 20 kilocalories per mole.

Although s-tetrazine is neutral to litmus, potassium amide in liquid ammonia forms a salt of approximate composition $K_2C_2N_4$.[167] This salt decomposes rapidly when it is warmed. Wood and Bergstrom[167] state that s-tetrazine reacts with aqueous solutions of silver nitrate, mercuric chloride, auric chloride, and chloroplatinic acid, but compounds of definite composition are not formed although Curtius, Darapsky, and Müller[45] have reported that reaction of s-tetrazine with silver nitrate forms a green crystalline salt. An addition complex is formed with methyl magnesium bromide.

Of the four possible dihydro-s-tetrazines all but 1,6-dihydro-s-tetrazine have been reported and derivatives of 1,6-dihydro-s-tetrazine have been claimed. However, 1,2-dihydro-s-tetrazine is the only well authenticated isomer. This has been prepared by the action of hydrazine on hydrogen cyanide (eq. 3, C_6H_5 is H)[95], from ethyl formimidate (eq. 5, C_6H_5 is H),[167] and by reduction of s-tetrazine with hydrogen sulfide.[46] The yields were either not stated or were given as being very poor.

1,2-Dihydro-s-tetrazine crystallizes in yellow prisms. Two melting points, 117–119° and 125–126°, have been recorded. The compound is easily oxidized with nitric acid to s-tetrazine. Acid hydrolysis gives hydrazine and formic acid.[46]

A compound once believed to be 1,4-dihydro-s-tetrazine (XII) was first reported by Curtius and Lang[58] under the name *trimethinetriazimide*. Hantzsch and Silberrad[75] obtained the same compound and first called it *isobisdiazomethane* and later *N-dihydrotetrazine*. In both cases the product was obtained by the action of hot potassium hydroxide on 1,2-dihydro-3,6-s-tetrazinedicarboxylic acid (eq. 11). The same product

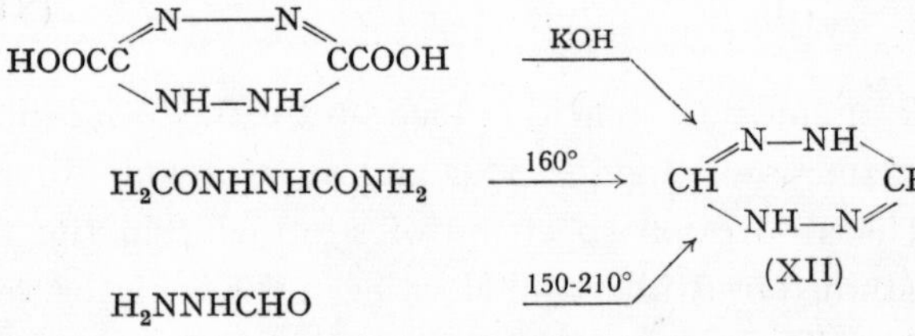

was reported by Pellizzari[99] from the thermal condensation of biurea (eq. 12) and by Ruhemann and Stapleton[138] from heating formhydrazide (eq. 13). The reaction of ethyl orthoformate with hydrazine[148] also gave this compound. In most cases the hydrochloride, m.p. 151°, was isolated. The free base melted at 70° according to one report[58] and 82–83° according to another.[138]

It was shown by Bülow[18,19] that the supposed 1,4-dihydro-*s*-tetrazine reacted with 1,4-diketones to give bicyclic compounds (eq. 14). It had previously been shown that this was characteristic of a primary

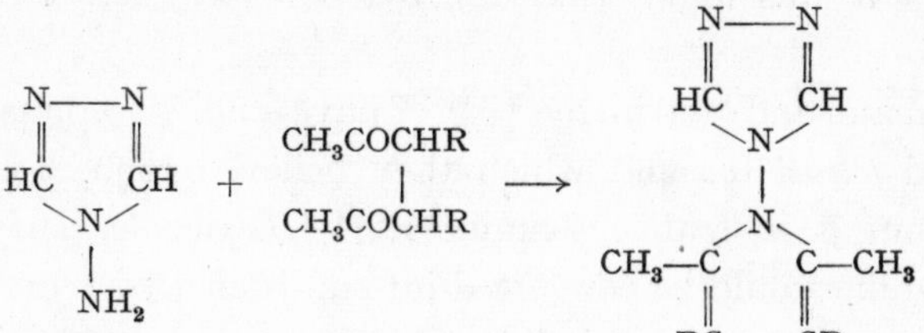

(14)

amino group so the structure 4-amino-1,2,4,4H-triazole (XIII) was proposed. In later papers Curtius and co-workers[46,48,50] agreed with Bülow and showed that 1,2-dihydro-3,6-*s*-tetrazinedicarboxylic acid was isomerized by heat or hot potassium hydroxide solution to 4-amino-1,2,4,4*H*-triazole-3,5-dicarboxylic acid which readily decarboxylates to 4-amino-1,2,4,4*H*-triazole.

Curtius and Lang[58] isolated an acid from the prolonged action of hot potassium hydroxide solution on 1,2-dihydro-3,6-*s*-tetrazinedicarboxylic acid (IV). Vigorous heating of the acid product gave a compound melting at 145° that was reported to have the formula $C_3H_6N_6$. Hantzsch and Silberrad[75] obtained the 145° compound by heating 1,2-dihydro-3,6-*s*-tetrazinedicarboxylic acid in acid. These workers found that the formula was $C_2H_4N_4$ and reported a melting point of 155°. They proposed the name *bisdiazomethane* and the structure XIV (3,6-dihydro-*s*-tetrazine). This same compound was also

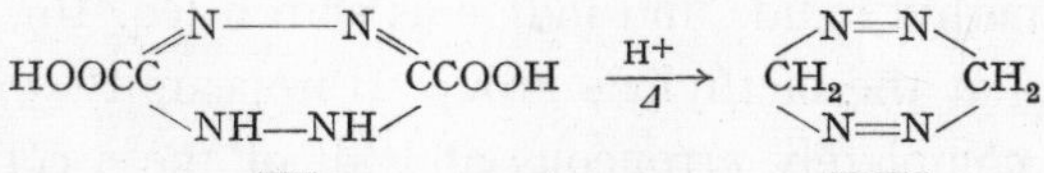

(15)

prepared by Ruhemann.[133] After Bülow's criticism of the structures of various tetrazines Curtius, Darapsky, and Müller[46] reinvestigated the series of reactions leading to *bisdiazomethane*. They found that the acid isolated from prolonged action of potassium hydroxide on IV was the already known 3-amino-1,2,4-triazole-5-carboxylic acid, which then decarboxylated to form 3-amino-1,2,4-triazole. This triazole was identical with the so-called bisdiazomethane. In attempting to repeat the dimerization of diazomethane under the influence of sunlight to 3,6-dihydro-s-tetrazine, which was reported by Hantzsch and Lehmann,[74] it was found that the reaction gave only ethylene and nitrogen.

Ruhemann and Merriman[133,136,137] have studied a compound which they called *tetrazoline* and which they believed to be 1,4-dihydro-s-tetrazine but is in reality 4-amino-1,2,4,4H-triazole. They proposed that tetrazoline could be converted into an isomer by recrystallization or by reaction with methyl iodide. This was based on the finding that before recrystallization of tetrazoline hydrochloride it formed with platinum chloride a salt of the composition $(C_2H_4N_4)_2PtCl_4$ but after recrystallization the salt formed was $(C_2H_4N_4)_2H_2PtCl_6$. Also reaction with methyl iodide gave a salt with the formula $C_3H_7N_4I$ which added iodine. Furthermore it was found that tetrazoline gave aldehyde derivatives. These reactions were accounted for by isomerization of tetrazoline (believed to have structure XII) to 1,6-dihydro-s-tetrazine (XV), which then formed a different salt with platinum chloride,

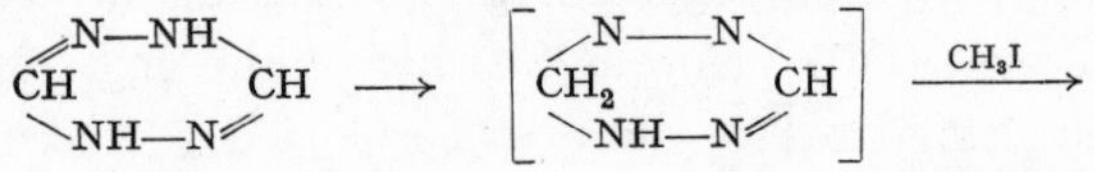

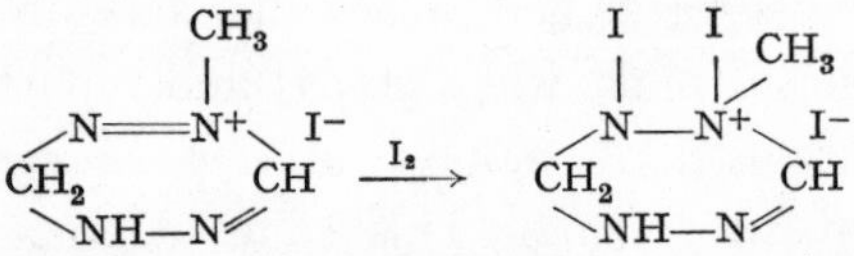

$$\text{(16)}$$

reacted with methyl iodide and iodine as shown (eq. 16), and reacted with aldehydes at the methylene group. It appears that Ruhemann's proposals are completely erroneous and all of these compounds are derivatives of 4-amino-1,2,4,4H-triazole.

Neither of the theoretically possible tetrahydro-s-tetrazines is known nor is hexahydro-s-tetrazine.

(2) Substituted s-Tetrazines and Hydro Derivatives

Alkyl Derivatives.   Only two simple alkyl-s-tetrazines are known. These are 3,6-dimethyl-s-tetrazine crystallizing in red needles, m.p. 74° [52] and

3,6-diethyl-s-tetrazine which has been obtained only in solution.[95] These were prepared by oxidation of the corresponding dihydro-

$$RCN + NH_2NH_2 \xrightarrow{80°} \underset{\text{(XVI)}}{RC\overset{N—N}{\underset{NH—NH}{\diagdown}}CR} \xrightarrow{HNO} RC\overset{N—N}{\underset{N=N}{\diagdown}}CR \quad (17)$$

$$R = CH_3 \text{ or } C_2H_5$$

tetrazines with nitrous acid (eq. 17). Acid hydrolysis of 3,6-dimethyl-s-tetrazine gives acetaldehyde, acetic acid, hydrazine, and nitrogen.

3,6-Dimethyl-1,2-dihydro-s-tetrazine, m.p. 180°, has been prepared (eq. 17) using acetonitrile and anhydrous hydrazine.[52] The reaction required several days heating in boiling alcohol and gave only 5% yield of the dihydro compound. Müller and Herrdegen[95] have prepared the diethyl derivative (XVI, $R = C_2H_5$) in the same manner. The principal product was 3,5-diethyl-4-amino-1,2,4,4H-triazole. The reaction failed to yield a dihydro-s-tetrazine when propionitrile was used. 3,6-Dimethyl-1,2-dihydro-s-tetrazine isomerizes at its melting point to 3,5-dimethyl-4-amino-1,2,4,4H-triazole. Mild acid hydrolysis of 3,6-diethyl-1,2-dihydro-s-tetrazine gives sym-diproprionylhydrazine but more vigorous hydrolysis forms propionic acid, hydrazine, and nitrogen.

Pellizzari[99] reported the preparation of 3,6-dimethyl-1,4-dihydro-s-tetrazine by heating acethydrazide at 180–190°. In a later paper[100] he agrees with Bülow that the supposed 1,4-dihydro-s-tetrazines are triazoles and reports the structure of his compound as 3,5-dimethyl-4-amino-1,2,4,4H-triazole. In view of the easy thermal isomerization of dihydrotetrazines to triazoles it is likely that Pellizzari is correct in his revised view. Ruhemann and Merrimann[136] have also prepared the triazole in the same way and erroneously called it a 1,4-dihydro-s-tetrazine. Heating diacetylaniline with hydrazine hydrate at 260° was reported by Silberrad[143] to give 3,6-dimethyl-1,4-dihydro-s-tetrazine but this too is the same 3,5-dimethyl-4-amino-1,2,4,4H-triazole. Stollé[148] has claimed the preparation of 3,6-dipropyl- and 3,6-diundecyl-1,4-dihydro-s-tetrazine by heating n-butyrylhydrazide and undecyl-hydrazide, respectively, at 180°. Since it has been shown that condensations of this type produce triazoles it is likely that these compounds are also triazoles.

Amino Derivatives.   3,6-Diamino-s-tetrazine (XVII) was prepared by Lin, Lieber, and Horowitz[170] from 1,2-dihydro-3,6-s-tetrazinedicarboxylic acid by way of the dimethyl ester, the dihydrazide, and 3,6-s-tetrazinedicarboxylic acid diazide. The same product was obtained by oxidation of diaminoguanidine nitrate (eq. 18a), and by the self-

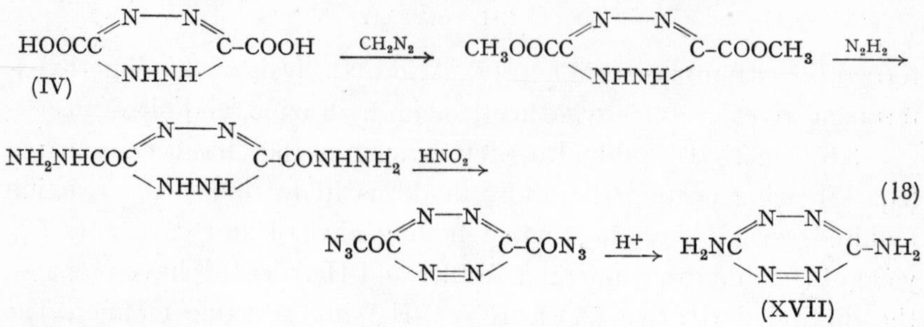

condensation of *S*-methylthiosemicarbazide hydroiodide presumably through 3,6-diamino-1,2-dihydro-s-tetrazine (XVIII).

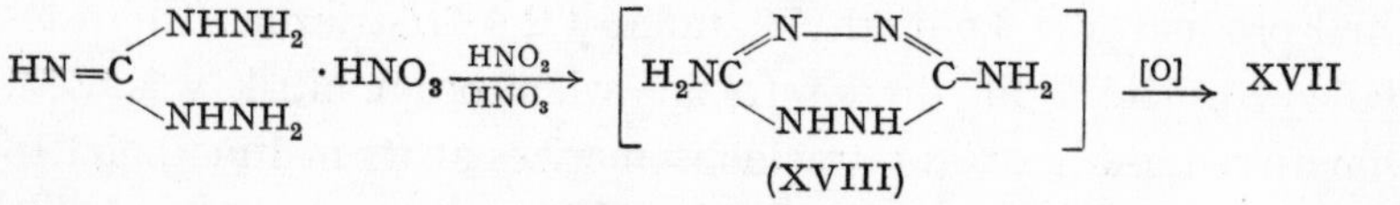

Crystallization of 3,6-diamino-s-tetrazine from water gave a microcrystalline orange-red powder melting above 300°. This compound gives the characteristic s-tetrazine absorption[95] at 528 mμ, log ε_{max} 2.77. The synthesis of XVII has been reported by Ponzio and Gastaldi.[116, 119] However, their compound, m.p. (dec.) 204–205°, was obviously different from that reported by Lin and co-workers[170] and so was not 3,6-diamino-s-tetrazine.

A French patent[65] has suggested the use of 3,6-diamino-s-tetrazine and its N^3,N^6-tetraalkyl derivatives as photographic emulsion desensitizers.

The synthesis of 3,6-diamino-1,2-dihydro-s-tetrazine (XVIII) has been reported by Lin, Lieber, and Horowitz[170] as an intermediate in the corresponding tetrazine synthesis and also from reduction of the tetrazine. However, the dihydrotetrazine was not isolated. Ponzio and Gastaldi[116, 117, 119] have also reported XVIII as an intermediate in synthesizing XVII, so this report also must be erroneous.

3,6-Diamino-3,6-dihydro-s-tetrazine (XIX) has been reported by Seiberlich[142] in a patent. Neither the method of preparation nor the physical properties were mentioned, and there was no discussion of any proof of structure. It would be of considerable interest to find a 3,6-

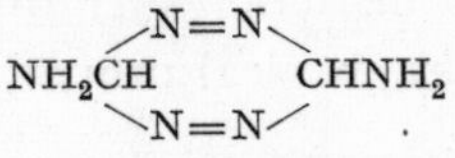

$$NH_2CH \overset{N=N}{\underset{N=N}{\diagup\diagdown}} CHNH_2$$

(XIX)

dihydro-s-tetrazine that had a hydrogen atom in both the 3- and 6-positions, as no well authenticated cases are known. However, until further proof appears this structure must be questioned. The compound was said to react with formaldehyde giving useful resinous materials.

Walter[163] has recently reported the preparation of 3,6-diamino-1,4-dihydro-s-tetrazine by the reaction of urethans with hydrazine hydrate under pressure at temperatures of 120–175° (eq. 19). It was

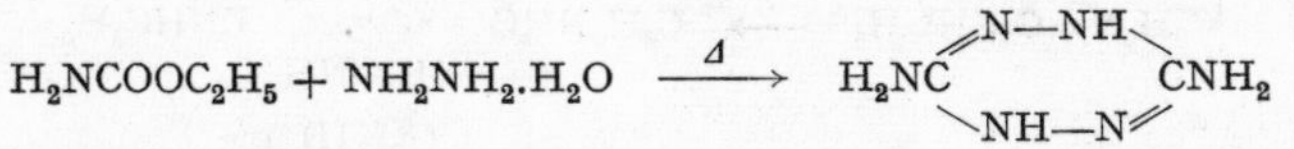

$$H_2NCOOC_2H_5 + NH_2NH_2\cdot H_2O \xrightarrow{\Delta} H_2NC \overset{N-NH}{\underset{NH-N}{\diagup\diagdown}} CNH_2 \qquad (19)$$

necessary to use excess urethan in order to prevent replacement of amino groups by hydrazino groups. The product was a white solid which was recrystallized from water. No other physical properties and no proof of structure were given. Here again acceptance of such an unusual structure as this, a 1,4-dihydro-s-tetrazine in which the 1,4-positions are unsubstituted, must await more proof.

Stollé and Gaertner[154] have isolated two products from the action of lead monoxide and sodium azide on 4-allylthiosemicarbazide. The principal product was shown to be 1-amino-5-allylaminotetrazole (XX). A second product formed in small yields was 3,6-bis(allylamino)-s-

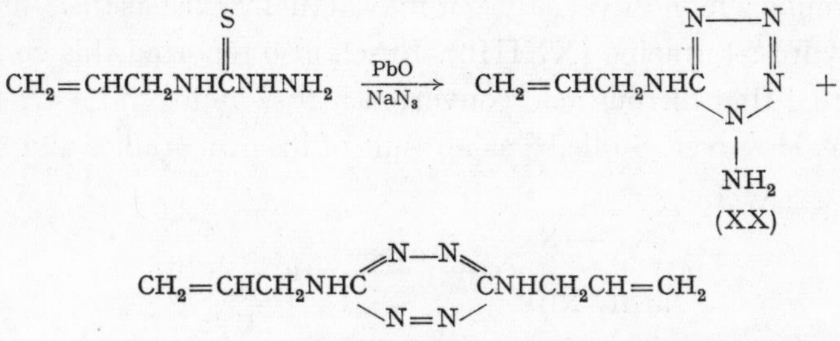

$$CH_2=CHCH_2NHCNHNH_2 \overset{S}{\overset{\|}{}} \xrightarrow[NaN_3]{PbO} CH_2=CHCH_2NHC \overset{N-N}{\underset{N}{\diagup\diagdown}} N +$$

NH_2

(XX)

$$CH_2=CHCH_2NHC \overset{N-N}{\underset{N=N}{\diagup\diagdown}} CNHCH_2CH=CH_2 \qquad (20)$$

(XXI)

tetrazine (XXI) (red flakes from water, m.p. 118°). A solution of this compound is readily decolorized by sodium hydrosulfite.

The synthesis of 3,6-bis(hydroxymethylamino)-3,6-dihydro-s-tetrazine has been claimed by Seiberlich.[142] This compound was purportedly prepared by the action of formaldehyde on 3,6-diamino-3,6-dihydro-s-tetrazine. No physical properties and no proof of structure were given.

3,6-Dianilino-1,2-dihydro-s-tetrazine[154] was prepared by reaction of 4-phenylthiosemicarbazide with lead monoxide and sodium azide or with lead monoxide at 80°. The reaction was pictured as proceeding as shown in equations 21 and 22. The principal product in this reaction

$$
\underset{\text{S}}{\overset{\text{S}}{\text{C}_6\text{H}_5\text{NHCNHNH}_2}} + \text{PbO} \longrightarrow \text{C}_6\text{H}_5\text{N}=\text{C}=\text{NNH}_2 + \text{PbS} + \text{H}_2\text{O} \qquad (21)
$$

$$
\text{C}_6\text{H}_5\text{N}=\text{C}=\text{NNH}_2 \longrightarrow \text{C}_6\text{H}_5\text{NHC} \overset{\text{N}-\!\!-\!\!-\text{N}}{\underset{\text{NH}-\text{NH}}{}} \text{CNHC}_6\text{H}_5 \qquad (22)
$$
$$
\text{(XXII)}
$$

was the anilino tetrazole corresponding to XX while the dihydro-s-tetrazine (XXII) was formed in very small yields. The compound XXII crystallizes in white needles melting with decomposition at 275°.

Oxo and Polyoxo Derivatives.   Curtius and Heidenreich[54,55] have reported that the reaction of carbohydrazide with ethyl orthoformate at 100° gives 1,2,3,4-tetrahydro-3-s-tetrazinone (XXIIIa). It is a monobasic

$$
\text{NH}_2\text{NHCONHNH}_2 + (\text{C}_2\text{H}_5\text{O})_3\text{CH} \xrightarrow{100°} \text{HC} \overset{\text{N}-\!\!-\!\!\text{NH}}{\underset{\text{NH}-\text{NH}}{}} \text{C}=\text{O} \qquad (23)
$$
$$
\text{(XXIIIa)}
$$

acid forming a monosilver salt so it may actually exist as the 3-hydroxy-1,2-dihydro-s-tetrazine (XXIIIb). Busch also reported this compound and stated that nitrous acid converted it to 3-hydroxy-1,4,4H-triazole (XXIV). However, Stollé,[152] as a result of his own studies and those of

$$
\text{CH} \overset{\text{N}-\!\!-\!\!-\text{N}}{\underset{\text{NH}-\text{NH}}{}} \text{COH} \xrightarrow{\text{HNO}_2} \text{HC} \overset{\text{N}-\!\!-\!\!\text{N}}{\underset{\underset{\text{H}}{\text{N}}}{}} \text{COH} \qquad (24)
$$
$$
\text{(XXIIIb)} \qquad\qquad\qquad \text{(XXIV)}
$$

Busch and Bülow on the relationship of *s*-tetrazine to triazoles (this will be discussed in later sections), concluded that the probable structure for the product of the reaction shown in equation 23 was that of the triazole XXV. Evidence cited for this was the formation of a

$$
\begin{array}{c}
N{\longrightarrow}N \\
\| \quad \| \\
HC \quad \ COH \\
\diagdown N \diagup \\
| \\
NH_2 \\
\end{array}
$$

(XXV)

benzylidene derivative by reaction with benzaldehyde and analogy to *p*-urazine which was also believed to be a triazole.

1,2-Dihydro-3,6-*s*-tetrazinedione (XXVII) has been claimed by Linch[87] to be a product of the action of potassium dichromate in

$$
NH_2CONHNH_2 \xrightarrow{\text{NaOBr}} O{=}C \overset{\diagup NH{-}NH \diagdown}{\underset{\diagdown NH{-}NH \diagup}{}} C{=}O \xrightarrow{K_2Cr_2O_7} O{=}C \overset{\diagup N{=\!=}N \diagdown}{\underset{\diagdown NH{-}NH \diagup}{}} C{=}O \quad (25)
$$

(XXVI)   (XXVII)

sulfuric acid on *p*-urazine (25). The *p*-urazine was obtained by the action of sodium hypobromite on semicarbazide hydrochloride. The product (XXVII) crystallizes in small orange needles which have no definite melting point. Stannous chloride reversed the dichromate oxidation to give *p*-urazine which was believed to have the structure XXVI. Once more Stollé[153] entered the controversy and declared that Linch's interpretation of these reactions was incorrect. He reported that the product of the reaction of the hypobromite with semicarbazide was biurea, which Linch had mistaken for *p*-urazine. The biurea was then oxidized to azodicarbonamide (XXVIII). In support of these statements

$$
H_2NCONHNH_2 \xrightarrow{\text{NaOBr}} H_2NCONHNHCONH_2 \xrightarrow{CrO_3} H_2NCON{=}NCONH_2 \quad (26)
$$

(XXVIII)

Stollé claimed that *p*-urazine is unstable to chromic acid and heat and that the azo compound actually obtained by oxidizing *p*-urazine is 4-amino-1,2,4,4*H*-triazole-3,5-dione, which explodes at 72° and is decomposed by cold water. Linch's compound was quite stable to water. Stollé gave no experimental results to support his contentions. However, further investigation[156] of the reaction of sodium hypobromite with semicarbazide hydrochloride has shown that biurea is obtained using the conditions that Linch used. Linch reports that his compound (supposedly XXVII) does not react with aldehydes while *p*-urazine does. This result casts doubt on his conclusions as it seems likely that a product obtained by removal of only two ring hydrogen atoms should still react with aldehydes. Also, the fact that semicarbazide does not give *p*-urazine by reaction with sodium hypobromite is additional evidence that Linch did not have XXVII.

    p-Urazine (believed to be tetrahydro-3,6-s-tetrazinedione) was first reported by Curtius and Heidenreich[54, 55] as a product of the reaction of diethyl bicarbamate with hydrazine (eq. 27.) The product was

$$C_2H_5OOCNHNHCOOC_2H_5 + NH_2NH_2 \longrightarrow O=C \begin{matrix} NH-NH \\ \\ NH-NH \end{matrix} C=O \quad (27)$$

$$\text{(XXVI)}$$

obtained as its hydrazine salt which, when treated with acid, gave *p*-urazine crystallizing from water in white prisms melting at 270°. This product was a monoacidic base forming silver, ammonium and barium salts. It reacted readily with aldehydes in a mole to mole ratio to give products formulated as shown in eq. 28. *p*-Urazine was later prepared by

$$O=C \begin{matrix} NH-NH \\ \\ NH-NH \end{matrix} C=O + C_6H_5CHO \longrightarrow O=C \begin{matrix} NH-NH \\ \\ N \quad N \\ CH \\ | \\ C_6H_5 \end{matrix} C=O \quad (28)$$

Purgotti[122-124] by heating biurea with hydrazine sulfate at 210°. Shortly thereafter Purgotti and Vigano[125] reported that *p*-urazine formed a dimethiodide, m.p. 200°. These workers prepared both the diacetyl

$$\begin{matrix} & & & O \\ & & & \| \\ & & & C \\ C_6H_5 & & N & \nearrow \searrow & N & & C_6H_5 \\ \quad \diagdown C & & & & & C \diagup \\ C_6H_5 & \diagup & N & \searrow \nearrow & N & & \diagdown C_6H_5 \\ & & & C \\ & & & \| \\ & & & O \quad \text{(XXIX)} \end{matrix}$$

derivative, which was a syrup, and a crystalline monoacetate, m.p. 235°, by the action of boiling acetic anhydride on p-urazine. They prepared a series of ketone derivatives thought to be of the type of XXIX. Chattaway[34] obtained p-urazine in 20% yield by the reaction of N,N'-dichlorourea with ammonia. The claimed preparation of p-urazine by the action of sodium hypobromite on semicarbazide or biurea has already been mentioned. p-Urazine has also been prepared by Guha and De[70] by the reaction of urea with carbohydrazide at 120°. Recently the reaction of carbon dioxide and hydrazine at 100–300 atmospheres pressure has been used to prepare p-urazine.[17]

The chief reasons for proposing tetrahydro-3,6-s-tetrazinedione as the structure for p-urazine were analyses and methods of synthesis. Busch and Grohmann,[24] Stollé,[152] and Diels[62] have contended that the true structure of the compound usually called p-urazine is 4-amino-1,2,4,1H-triazole-3,5(2H,4H)-dione (XXXa) or its tautomer XXXb.

$$\begin{array}{cc}
\begin{array}{c} HN\!\!-\!\!\!-NH \\ |\qquad\ | \\ O\!=\!C\quad C\!=\!O \\ \diagdown N \diagup \\ | \\ NH_2 \\ (XXXa) \end{array}
&
\begin{array}{c} HN\!\!-\!\!\!-N \\ |\qquad\ \| \\ O\!=\!C\quad COH \\ \diagdown N \diagup \\ | \\ NH_2 \\ (XXXb) \end{array}
\end{array}$$

Busch and Grohmann[25, 27] have shown that a number of aryl substituted p-urazines are actually triazoles. This will be discussed in detail in a later section. Stollé has carried this work further and concluded that in analogy p-urazine must have either structure XXXa or XXXb, preferably the latter, as p-urazine is a monobasic acid. In addition, since p-urazine gives a benzal and other aldehyde and ketone derivatives it must have a primary amino group and react in a straightforward fashion to give normal Schiff bases. Stollé found that the compounds reported by Purgotti and Vigano as arising from the combination of two molecules of ketone with one of p-urazine were identical with the azines prepared from the same ketone and hydrazine. This must occur by decomposition of the triazolidine to hydrazine followed by reaction with the ketone.

Guha and De[70] have synthesized tetrahydro-3,6-s-tetrazinedithione and find that it does not react with aldehydes, using this as evidence for the proposed *s*-tetrazine structure. Rather surprisingly they report the synthesis of *p*-urazine with no comment on the fact that in analogy to their thiono compound, the accepted tetrahydro-3,6-*s*-tetrazinedione structure for *p*-urazine would not permit aldehyde condensation. The evidence indicates that the compound usually called *p*-urazine in the literature has structure XXXa or XXXb rather than XXVI.

In summary it would appear that the structure of all reported unsubstituted and alkyl substituted tetrahydro-3,6-*s*-tetrazinediones should be considered as not fully established and that triazole structures are the most probable ones.

Thiol and Thiono Derivatives. 6-Thionotetrahydro-3-*s*-tetrazinone (XXXI) has been prepared by Guha and De[70] by two methods: (1) the reaction of carbohydrazide with potassium ethyl xanthate, and (2) the reaction of thiocarbohydrazide with urea at 130°. It is a white compound melting at 238°. Purgotti and Vigano[125] reported the preparation

$$\underset{S}{\overset{S}{\parallel}} \quad NH_2NHCONHNH_2 + C_2H_5OCSK \longrightarrow S=C\overset{\diagup NH-NH\diagdown}{\underset{\diagdown NH-NH\diagup}{}}C=O \qquad (29)$$

$$(XXXI)$$

$$NH_2NH\overset{S}{\overset{\parallel}{C}}NHNH_2 + NH_2CONH_2 \quad \underline{\hspace{2cm}} \qquad (30)$$

of tetrahydro-3,6-*s*-tetrazinedithione (XXXII), m.p. 198–199°, by the reaction of dithiobiurea with hydrazine hydrate. Later Guha and De[71] prepared this compound in nearly quantitative yield by heating carbon disulfide and hydrazine hydrate at 130–140° for several hours. Other preparations by the same authors were from thiocarbohydrazide and potassium ethyl xanthate (eq. 31) and from carbon disulfide and hydrazine in alkali.[71] Beckett and Dyson[13] prepared XXXII by the

$$H_2NNH\overset{S}{\overset{\parallel}{C}}NHNH_2 + C_2H_5O\overset{S}{\overset{\parallel}{C}}SK \xrightarrow{100°} S=C\overset{\diagup NH-NH\diagdown}{\underset{\diagdown NH-NH\diagup}{}}C=S \qquad (31)$$

$$(XXXII)$$

reaction of *s*-dithiocarbimidothiourea (XXXIII) with aniline or *p*-toluidine in alcohol (33). In addition the corresponding diarylthiourea

was obtained. The product obtained by Guha and De melted at 203–204°
in good agreement with the melting point of Beckett and Dyson and in

$$Cl_2C=S + NH_2NH_2.H_2SO_4 \longrightarrow S=C(NHN=C=S)_2 \qquad (32)$$
$$\text{(XXXIII)}$$

$$S=C(NHN=C=S)_2 + ArNH_2 \longrightarrow S=C \overset{\displaystyle NH-NH}{\underset{\displaystyle NH-NH}{\diagup\diagdown}} C=S + ArN\overset{S}{\overset{\|}{H C}}NHAr \quad (33)$$
$$\text{(XXXII)}$$

fair agreement with the melting point reported by Purgotti. However,
Guha and De state that their product did not react with aldehydes,
whereas Purgotti and Vigano reported that their product gave benzaldehyde and salicylaldehyde derivatives believed to have structures
XXXIV and XXXV. The products prepared by both groups crystallized

$$S=C \overset{\displaystyle NH-NH}{\underset{\displaystyle N \diagdown \diagup N}{\diagup\diagdown}} C=S \qquad S=C \overset{\displaystyle NH-NH}{\underset{\displaystyle N \diagdown \diagup N}{\diagup\diagdown}} C=S$$
$$\underset{C_6H_5}{\overset{\displaystyle CH}{|}} \qquad \underset{o\text{-}HOC_6H_4}{\overset{\displaystyle CH}{|}}$$
$$\text{(XXXIV)} \qquad \text{(XXXV)}$$

in white platelets. Guha and De oxidized tetrahydro-3,6-s-tetrazine-
dithione to a disulfide, m.p. 218° (dec.) and converted it to a dibenzyl
derivative, m.p. 142°. They reported a disilver salt while Purgotti and
Vigano reported a monosilver salt. Both compounds were soluble in
water but insoluble in organic solvents.

In view of the methods and conditions used by Guha and De and
Beckett and Dyson, it appears certain that their product actually is
tetrahydro-3,6-s-tetrazinedithione or more likely 1,2-dihydro-3,6-s-
tetrazinedithiol. In accordance with their findings such a compound
would not be expected to react with aldehydes. The compound prepared
by Purgotti and Vigano, in spite of its similarity in melting point, is
probably different. Arndt and Bielich[2] attempted to repeat the Purgotti experiments exactly. Three products (XXXVI, XXXVII and
XXXVIII) were obtained, and none was identical with that of Purgotti
and Vigano. This refuted Stollé's[152] suggestion that the compound of
Purgotti and Vigano was the triazolidine XXXVII a or its isomer

XXXVIIb. About the same time Fromm and co-workers[68] also repeated this reaction. They isolated a compound they thought was

$$
\begin{array}{ccc}
\text{NH—NH} & \text{HN——NH} & \text{N——N} \\
|\quad\ | & |\quad\ |\ \ \text{or} & \|\quad\ \| \\
\text{HN=C}\quad\text{C=S} & \text{S=C}\quad\text{C=S} & \text{HS—C}\quad\text{CSH} \\
\diagdown\text{N}\diagup & \diagdown\text{N}\diagup & \diagdown\text{N}\diagup \\
| & | & | \\
\text{NH}_2 & \text{NH}_2 & \text{NH}_2 \\
\text{(XXXVI)} & \text{(XXXVIIa)} & \text{(XXXVIIb)}
\end{array}
$$

$$
\left[
\begin{array}{c}
\text{HN——NH} \\
|\quad\ | \\
\text{S=C}\quad\ \text{C=N—} \\
\diagdown\text{N}\diagup \\
| \\
\text{NH}_2
\end{array}
\right]_2
$$
(XXXVIII)

3,4-diamino-1,2,4,4H-triazole-5-thiol (a tautomer of XXXVI) but also considered it might be 3-amino-1,4-dihydro-6-s-tetrazinethiol (XXXIXa). It crystallizes from water in yellow needles, m.p. 217°. It

$$
\begin{array}{cc}
\text{HSC}\diagup\overset{\text{N—NH}}{\diagdown\text{NH—N}}\diagdown\text{CNH}_2 & \text{HSC}\diagup\overset{\text{N——N}}{\diagdown\text{NH—NH}}\diagdown\text{CNH}_2 \\
\text{(XXXIXa)} & \text{(XXXIXb)}
\end{array}
$$

gives a benzylidene derivative, m.p. 270°, and a monoacetyl derivative, m.p. 265°. The benzylidene derivative can be oxidized to a disulfide which is a yellow powder, m.p. 265°. It forms a S-benzyl derivative, m.p. 220°, which then gives a crystalline benzoyl derivative, m.p. 198°, and an amorphous acetyl derivative melting at the same place. If this compound is indeed an s-tetrazine the structure XXXIXb would be much more likely than XXXIXa.

Holmberg[79] has prepared 1,4-bis(thiobenzoyl)-1,4-dihydro-3,6-s-tetrazinedithiol (XL) in very small yields by the reaction shown in equation 34. This is a colorless solid melting at 211–213°.

$$
\underset{\text{S}}{\overset{\text{S}}{\text{C}_6\text{H}_5\overset{\|}{\text{C}}\text{NHNH}_2}} + \underset{\text{O}}{\text{C}_2\text{H}_5\text{O}\overset{\|}{\text{C}}\text{SCH}_2\text{COOH}} \xrightarrow{\text{NaOH}}
\begin{array}{c}
\text{S=CC}_6\text{H}_5 \\
| \\
\text{HSC}\diagup\overset{\text{N—N}}{\diagdown\text{N—N}}\diagdown\text{CSH} \\
| \\
\text{C}_6\text{H}_5\text{C=S}\quad\text{(XL)}
\end{array}
\qquad (34)
$$

Amino-Oximino Derivatives. Dihydroxyguanidine in ammonia solution reacts to give the monoammonium salt of 1,2-dihydro-3,6-s-tetrazinedione dioxime (XLI)[164] crystallizing in feathery red crystals

$$\underset{(XLI)}{\text{HONHCNHOH}\ \overset{NH_3}{\longrightarrow}\ \underset{\begin{array}{c}\\ \diagdown \text{NH—NH} \diagup \end{array}}{\overset{\begin{array}{c}\text{N}=\!=\!=\text{N}\\ \diagup \qquad \diagdown\end{array}}{\text{HON}=\text{C} \qquad \text{C}=\text{NOH.NH}_3}}} \qquad (35)$$

with NH above HONHCNHOH (double bond).

that explode at 158°. Treatment of dihydroxyguanidine hydrobromide with sodium hydroxide[165] was reported to give 3-amino-1,6-dihydro-6-s-tetrazinone oxime, an orange powder melting above 350°.

s-Tetrazinecarboxylic Acids and Derivatives. 3,6-s-Tetrazinedicarboxylic acid was first reported in 1900 as bisazoxyacetic acid (IX) by Hantzsch and Lehmann.[73] The correct structure (XLII) was assigned to this compound by Curtius, Darapsky, and Müller.[43] The usual method of preparation has been oxidation of 1,2-dihydro-3,6-s-tetrazinedicarboxylic acid using nitrous acid or nitrogen trioxide although several other mild oxidizing agents such as chlorine, bromine, and ferric chloride have been used. This oxidation usually occurs in yields of 90% or better. The oxidation is easily reversible. For example hydrogen sulfide reduces the s-tetrazine to 1,2-dihydro-s-tetrazinedicarboxylic acid. Reduction of 3,6-s-tetrazinedicarboxylic acid in ammonia using sodium amalgam has been reported to give hydrazinoacetic acid. Very mild aqueous hydrolysis forms the monohydrazide of oxalic acid. Using more vigorous hydrolysing conditions such as dilute sulfuric acid, glyoxylic acid, hydrazine, and the glyoxylic acid derivative (XLIII) of the monohydrazide of oxalic acid (36) are obtained. 3,6-s-Tetrazinedicarboxylic acid decarboxylates readily on heating to give s-tetrazine.

$$\underset{(XLII)}{\overset{\begin{array}{c}\text{N—N}\\ \diagup \qquad \diagdown\end{array}}{\underset{\begin{array}{c}\diagdown \text{N}=\text{N}\diagup\end{array}}{\text{HOOC} \qquad \text{CCOOH}}}}\ \overset{H_2O}{\longrightarrow}\ \underset{(XLIII)}{\underset{\text{N}=\text{CHCOOH}}{\overset{\text{NHCOCOONH}_3\text{NH}_2}{|}}}\ +\ \text{NH}_2\text{NH}_2\ +\ \underset{\text{COOH}}{\overset{\text{CHO}}{\underset{|}{}}}\ (36)$$

The acid is somewhat soluble in water and alcohol but insoluble in most organic solvents. This acid and its carboxyl derivatives are listed in Table V-1.

TABLE V-1. 3,6-s-Tetrazinedicarboxylic Acid Derivatives ROCC⟨N—N⟩CCOR

R	M.p.,°C.	Color and crystal form	Ref.
HO[a]	148 (dec.)	Carmine red, purple-red or blue-violet needles	43, 50, 73, 92, 167
C_2H_5O	135–136	Purplish	92
NH_2	210–280 (dec.)	Bluish-red	43
CH_3NH	237	Carmine red platelets	93
C_2H_5NH	195	Carmine red platelets	93
⬡H	196 (dec.)	Red platelets	93

[a] Forms monohydrazino salt crystallizing in yellow needles, m.p. 185° (dec.).

Derivatives of 3,6-s-tetrazinedicarboxylic acid have been obtained by oxidation of dihydro-s-tetrazines with nitrous acid. In the case of the diethyl ester the 1,2-dihydro ester was used. The diamides listed in Table V-1 were prepared by oxidation of 1,2-dihydro-3,6-s-tetrazine-

$$\text{RNHCOC}\underset{\text{NH—NH}}{\overset{\text{N——N}}{\diagup\diagdown}}\text{CCONHR} \xrightarrow{\text{HNO}_2} \text{RNHCOC}\underset{\text{N=N}}{\overset{\text{N—N}}{\diagup\diagdown}}\text{CCONHR} \quad (37)$$

dicarboxamides (eq. 37).[93] These compounds are insoluble in ether, somewhat more soluble in water, and moderately soluble in alcohol.

Although 1,6-dihydro-3,6-s-tetrazinecarboxylic acid (XLV) has been obtained only in solution, its potassium salt can be obtained by the action of potassium hydroxide on ethyl diazoacetate. If the ester is treated for a short time at room temperature or lower with concentrated aqueous or alcoholic potassium hydroxide solutions the potassium salt of the 1,6-dihydroacid is obtained. 1,2-Dihydro-3,6-s-tetrazine-dicarboxylic acid (IV) can also be prepared by the action of base, either sodium or potassium hydroxide, on ethyl diazoacetate (eq. 2). The potassium salt of the 1,6-dihydro acid is converted to the salt of the 1,2-dihydro acid by warming for a short time with potassium or sodium hydroxide solution. If the heating is continued too long, rearrangement occurs and a triazole is formed. The salt of 1,2-dihydro-3,6-s-tetrazine-dicarboxylic acid can be obtained directly by adding ethyl diazoacetate to a solution of sodium hydroxide at 100°. The reaction is extremely vigorous. The two other theoretically possible dihydro-3,6-s-tetrazine-dicarboxylic acids are unknown.

Curtius[39] was the first to report that the action of either potassium hydroxide or sodium hydroxide on ethyl diazoacetate gives an acid. It was his belief[58] that the acid was a trimer of diazoacetic acid and he called it *triazoacetic acid*. This acid was obtained at steam bath temperature and was the 1,2-dihydro acid. The yield of sodium salt was nearly quantitative. The free acid crystallized as a dihydrate, m.p. 152° (dec.). The formula XLIV was proposed.[40] Hantzsch and Silberrad[75]

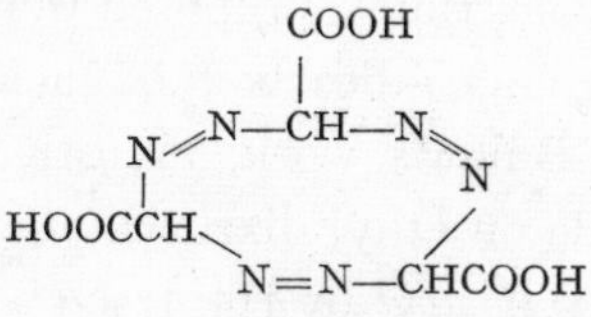

$$
\begin{array}{c}
COOH \\
| \\
N{=}N{-}CH{-}N \\
HOOCCH \quad\quad N \\
N{=}N{-}CHCOOH
\end{array}
$$
(XLIV)

found that the compound called *triazoacetic* acid was a dimer of diazo-acetic acid so they proposed the structure 3,6-dihydro-3,6-s-tetrazine-dicarboxylic acid (XLVI) and called it *bisdiazoacetic acid*. They reported

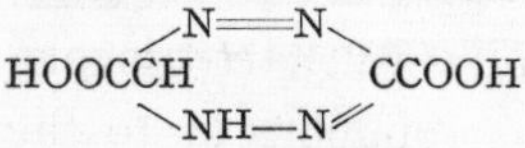

$$
\begin{array}{ccc}
\text{N=N} & \text{N=N} & \text{N—NH} \\
\text{HOOCCH \quad CCOOH} & \text{HOOCCH \quad HCCOOH} & \text{HOOCC \quad CCOOH} \\
\text{NH—N} & \text{N=N} & \text{NH—N} \\
\text{(XLV)} & \text{(XLVI)} & \text{(XLVII)}
\end{array}
$$

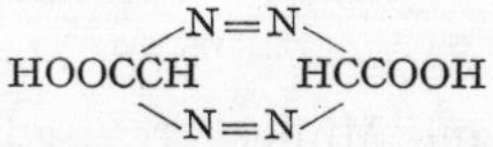

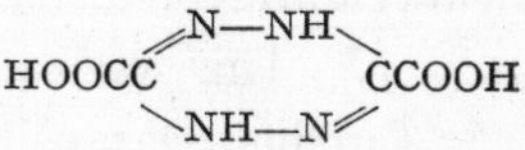

a melting point of 180° for the anhydrous compound. These authors reported that a second acid could be obtained by long action of hot potassium hydroxide on "bisdiazoacetic acid." The second acid forms colorless needles, m.p. 287°. The structure proposed was 1,4-dihydro-3,6-s-tetrazinedicarboxylic acid (XLVII). Still a third acid is obtained

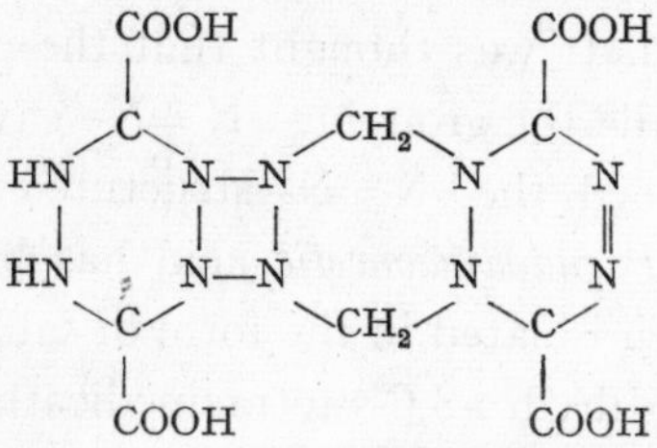

$$
\text{(XLVIII)}
$$

from the reaction mixture that yields the second acid. The structure proposed for this was XLVIII and it was called *trisbisdiazomethane-tetracarboxylic acid*. A fourth acid was obtained by Müller[92] as its potassium salt and was called *pseudodiazoacetic acid*. Derivatives of this acid had been prepared earlier[38,43] and the structure proposed was 1,2-dihydro-3,6-s-tetrazinedicarboxylic acid (IV).

It was discovered that the acid, m.p. 287°, obtained by Hantzsch and which he believed was the 1,4-dihydro acid could be decarboxylated to a compound believed to be 1,4-dihydro-s-tetrazine. As mentioned previously, Bülow found that this supposed 1,4-dihydro-s-tetrazine was 4-amino-1,2,4,4H-triazole. Bülow proposed that the acid precursor was 4-amino-1,2,4,4H-triazole-3,5-dicarboxylic acid. Curtius and coworkers,[50] as a result of Bülow's work, investigated further the action of potassium hydroxide on ethyl diazoacetate. The acid called *trisbis-diazomethanetetracarboxylic acid* by Hantzsch was shown to be identical with the already known 3-amino-1,2,4-triazole-5-carboxylic acid hemihydrate melting at 182°. The acid that Hantzsch had described as 1,4-dihydro-3,6-s-tetrazinedicarboxylic acid, m.p. 287°, was found to be the monopotassium salt of 4-amino-1,2,4,4H-triazole-3,5-dicarboxylic acid readily converted by treatment with mineral acid to the free acid, m.p. 77°. This was easily decarboxylated to 4-amino-1,2,4,4H-triazole.

Curtius, Darapsky, and Müller[44] revised their opinions as to the structure of *bisdiazoacetic acid* and *pseudodiazoacetic* on the basis of hydrolysis studies. Hydrolysis of *bisdiazoacetic* acid gave oxalic acid and hydrazine and this was believed to indicate the 1,2-dihydro struc-

$$
\underset{\text{(IV)}}{\overset{\displaystyle \text{N}\!\!-\!\!-\!\!-\!\!\text{N}}{\underset{\displaystyle \text{NH}\!\!-\!\!\text{NH}}{\text{HOOCC} \qquad\qquad \text{CCOOH}}}} \xrightarrow{\text{H}_2\text{O}} \quad \begin{array}{c} \text{COOH} \\ | \\ \text{COOH} \end{array} \; + \; \text{NH}_2\text{NH}_2 \qquad (38)
$$

ture IV for this acid. It was thought that the grouping –N–N– gave rise to hydrazine while the grouping –N=N– gave rise to nitrogen. As no nitrogen was formed, the –N=N– structure could not be present in *bisdiazoacetic acid*. *Pseudodiazoacetic* acid has been obtained only in solution and has been isolated in the form of salts. It forms a tripotassium salt[92] while 1,2-dihydro-3,6-s-tetrazinedicarboxylic acid forms only a dipotassium salt. For purposes of structure determination the amide of the "pseudo" acid has been used. Hydrolysis of this amide gave glyoxylic acid amide, nitrogen, and hydrazine. From this fact the 3,6-dihydro structure (XLVI) was inferred for the acid. However, since both *bisdiazoacetic acid* and *pseudodiazoacetic* can be oxidized to 3,6-*s*-tetrazinedicarboxylic acid, the conclusion was reached that the hydrogen atoms must be adjacent in both. This indicates that *pseudodiazoacetic acid* must be 1,6-dihydro-3,6-*s*-tetrazinedicarboxylic acid (XLV). This would also be in better agreement with the fact that both hydrazine and nitrogen were obtained from hydrolysis of *pseudodiazoacetamide*. Although the arguments presented by workers in this field are not conclusive, their final structural assignments are undoubtedly correct. The "pseudo" acid and its derivatives have a ring hydrogen which is acidic. Only in the 1,6-dihydro series is there nonequivalence of the hydrogen atoms. Consequently, the "pseudo" series is the 1,6-dihydro one (XLV). The "bis" acid must be the 1,2-dihydro acid (IV) since the bonds in the ring would certainly be conjugated rather than isolated.

The reaction of the dipotassium salt of 1,6-dihydro-3,6-*s*-tetrazinedicarboxylic acid with nitrous acid has given the potassium salt of 6-nitroso-1,2-dihydro-3-*s*-tetrazinecarboxylic acid (XLIX), a yellow solid melting at 170°.[92] Treatment of an aqueous solution of the

$$\underset{\text{(XLIX)}}{\text{HOOCCH}\overset{\displaystyle N = N}{\underset{\displaystyle NH-N}{\diagup \diagdown}}\text{C-COOH} \xrightarrow{\text{HNO}_2} \text{HOOCC}\overset{\displaystyle N-N}{\underset{\displaystyle NH-NH}{\diagup \diagdown}}\text{C-NO}}$$

$$\xrightarrow{\text{H}_2\text{S}} \xrightarrow{\text{H}_2\text{SO}_4} \text{HOOCC}\overset{\displaystyle N-N}{\underset{\displaystyle NH-NH}{\diagup \diagdown}}\text{CH} \qquad (39)$$

potassium salt of the nitroso compound with hydrogen sulfide followed by sulfuric acid (eq. 39) gives 1,2-dihydro-3-*s*-tetrazinecarboxylic acid. This compound was obtained as the monohydrate melting at 93–105° (dec.).

Potassium salts of either 1,6-dihydro-3,6-*s*-tetrazinedicarboxylic

$$\text{HOOCC}\overset{\displaystyle N-N}{\underset{\displaystyle NH-N}{\diagup \diagdown}}\text{CCOOH}\cdot\tfrac{1}{2}\text{Br}$$
$$\underset{\text{Br} \qquad \text{(L)}}{\mid}$$

acid or 1,2-dihydro-3,6-s-tetrazinedicarboxylic acid have been reported[92] to react with bromine to yield a bromo-1,2-dihydrotetrazine (L).
Treatment of this compound with potassium acetate gives the dipotassium salt of 3,6-s-tetrazinedicarboxylic acid.

Only three esters of 1,2-dihydro-3,6-s-tetrazinedicarboxylic acid
are known. These are the dimethyl, diethyl and diisopropyl (Table V-2).
These esters have been prepared from the silver or potassium salts of

TABLE V-2. Carboxyl Derivative of 1,2-Dihydro-3,6-s-tetrazinedicarboxylic Acids

$$\begin{array}{c} N\!-\!N \\ ROCCCCOR' \\ NH\!-\!NH \end{array}$$

R	R'	M.p., °C.	Color and crystal form	Ref.
HO[a]	HO	185	Yellow rods	47, 58
HO	NH_4O	192	Orange-red crystals	59
NH_4O	NH_4O	217, 222		58, 59
NH_2NH_3O	NH_2NH_3O	183–188	Yellow needles	59
$C_2H_5NH_2O$	$C_2H_5NH_3O$	179–180	Orange-yellow	93
CH_3O	CH_3O	167–168	Red biaxial platelets	58
C_2H_5O	C_2H_5O	113	Yellow-red prisms	58, 59
$(CH_3)_2CHO$	$(CH_3)_2CHO$			58
CH_3O	NH_2NH	211		59
C_2H_5O	NH_2NH	228–231	Yellow needles	59
C_2H_5O	$NH_2NH.HCl$	212	Yellow needles	59
C_2H_5O	$C_6H_5CH\!=\!NNH$	233	Yellow powder	59
C_2H_5O	$p\text{-}CH_3C_6H_4CH\!=\!NNH$	237	Yellow needles	59
C_2H_5O	$(CH_3)_2C\!=\!NNH$	115	Yellow needles	59

C_2H_5O	$C_6H_5C\!=\!NNH$
	    $\mid$
	    CH_3
		182–185	Yellow needles	59

C_2H_5O	$CH_3CONHNH$	166	Yellow powder	59
C_2H_5O	N_3	decomposes	Violet-red needles	59
NH_2	NH_2	>300	Golden leaflets	58
CH_3NH	NH_2	234 (dec.)	Rectangular leaflets	51
CH_3NH	CH_3NH	295 (dec.)	Prisms	93
C_2H_5NH	C_2H_5NH	287 (dec.)	Yellow needles	93
$n\text{-}C_7H_{15}NH$	$n\text{-}C_7H_{15}NH$	240	Yellow leaflets	93
$(CH_3)_2N$	$(CH_3)_2N$	225	Yellow prisms	93
$C_5H_{10}N$	$C_5H_{10}N$	266	Yellow needles	93
NH_2NH	NH_2NH	265–275		59
$C_6H_5CH\!=\!$ NNH	$C_6H_5CH\!=\!NNH$	290	Yellow powder	59

[a] Forms dihydrate crystallizing in yellow needles, m.p. 152° (dec.)

the acid and the appropriate alkyl halide.[58,75] In addition the methyl and ethyl esters have been synthesized from the acid and diazomethane and diazoethane,[59] respectively. The diethyl ester of 3,6-dihydro-3,6-s-tetrazinedicarboxylic acid has been reported but it was actually the ester of the 1,2-dihydro acid. Silberrad[144] claimed to have prepared dimethyl 1,4-dihydro-3,6-s-tetrazinedicarboxylate, but the acid he used was later shown[50] to be 4-amino-1,2,4,4H-triazole-3,5-dicarboxylic acid and thus the ester must have been a derivative of this acid.

The reaction of sodium or potassium ethoxide with ethyl diazoacetate in ether or alcohol gives an ester which according to Curtius and co-workers[49] has the formula LI although in view of later knowledge the M must be on the nitrogen. Their conclusion was derived from the

$$\underset{\text{(LI)}}{C_2H_5OC\overset{\overset{\displaystyle O}{\|}}{-}C\underset{N=\!\!=\!\!N}{\overset{N-NH}{<}}\!\!\!\!>\!\!C\underset{COOC_2H_5}{\overset{M}{<}}\ \ .MOC_2H_5}$$

M = K or Na

facts that acid hydrolysis yields hydrazine and ethyl glyoxylate and treatment with 50% potassium hydroxide at 30° gives the potassium salt of 1,6-dihydro-3,6-s-tetrazinedicarboxylic acid and at 100° the potassium salt of 1,2-dihydro-3,6-s-tetrazinedicarboxylic acid. Curtius and co-workers stated that this is the same compound that Hantzsch and Lehmann[74] had believed was a salt of ethyl isodiazoacetate. These latter authors obtained a noncrystalline ester by treatment of their product with acid. This ester might be diethyl 1,6-dihydro-3,6-s-tetrazinedicarboxylate.

The diamide of 1,2-dihydro-3,6-s-tetrazinedicarboxylic acid (Table V-2) has been obtained by the reaction of alcoholic ammonia with ethyl diazoacetate at 100°, from the ethyl ester of the 1,2-dihydro-s-tetrazine acid and ammonia at room temperature and by treatment of the isomeric 1,6-dihydro amide with warm concentrated alkali solution.[43,58] It has a melting point of above 300° and is somewhat brighter yellow than the isomeric 1,6-dihydro amide. The 1,2-dihydro amide is usually referred to in the literature as *bisdiazoacetamide*.

If aqueous ammonia is allowed to react with ethyl diazoacetate in the cold, there are formed diazoacetamide and the ammonia salt of 1,6-dihydro-3,6-s-tetrazinedicarboxamide[38,43] (eq. 40). Treatment of

$$\text{N}_2\text{CHCOOC}_2\text{H}_5 \xrightarrow{\text{NH}_3} \overset{\displaystyle O}{\overset{\|}{\text{H}_2\text{NC}}}-\overset{\overset{\text{N}==\text{N}}{\diagup\qquad\diagdown}}{\underset{\diagdown\text{NH}-\text{N}\diagup}{\text{CH}}}\text{CCONH}_2\cdot\text{NH}_3 + \text{N}_2\text{CHCONH}_2 \quad (40)$$

the ammonium salt with acetic acid gives a yellow solid that is 1,6-dihydro-3,6-s-tetrazinedicarboxamide (also called pseudodiazoacetamide). This amide has been reported to melt at 170° when air dried but to explode at 133° when dried *in vacuo*. The same product can be obtained in 80–85% yield by the reaction of liquid ammonia with ethyl diazoacetate at room temperature followed by treatment of the ammonium salt with acetic acid. Silberrad[144] first prepared this amide and called it *iminoazoacetamide*. The structure proposed was LII. Careful acid

$$\begin{array}{c} \text{NH}{=}\text{C}-\text{N}{=}\text{N}-\text{C}{\equiv}\text{NH} \\ \quad|\qquad\qquad\quad| \\ \quad\text{CONH}_2\qquad\text{CONH}_2 \\ \text{(LII)} \end{array}$$

hydrolysis of 1,6-dihydro-3,6-s-tetrazinedicarboxamide gives nitrogen, hydrazine, and glyoxylamide in the ratio of one-half mole of hydrazine to one mole of each of the other products. Nitrous acid oxidizes the amide to 3,6-s-tetrazinedicarboxamide.[43] Treatment of 1,6-dihydro-3,6-s-tetrazinedicarboxamide with diazomethane gives a 1-methyl derivative LIII as well as N^3-methyl-1,2-dihydro-3,6-s-tetrazinedicarboxamide (LIV). The compound LIII is a yellow powder, m.p. 118° (dec.).[51]

$$\overset{\displaystyle O}{\overset{\|}{\text{H}_2\text{NCCH}}}\overset{\overset{\text{N}==\text{N}}{\diagup\quad\diagdown}}{\underset{\diagdown\text{NH}-\text{N}\diagup}{}}\text{CCONH}_2 \xrightarrow{\text{CH}_2\text{N}_2} \overset{\displaystyle O}{\overset{\|}{\text{H}_2\text{NCCH}}}\overset{\overset{\text{N}=\text{N}}{\diagup\quad\diagdown}}{\underset{\diagdown\underset{\displaystyle |}{\text{N}}-\text{N}\diagup}{}}\text{CCONH}_2$$

$$\qquad\qquad\qquad\qquad\qquad\qquad\qquad\qquad\qquad\text{CH}_3$$

$$\qquad\qquad\qquad\qquad\qquad\qquad\qquad\qquad\text{(LIII)} \qquad\qquad (41)$$

$$+$$

$$\overset{\displaystyle O}{\overset{\|}{\text{CH}_3\text{NHCC}}}\overset{\overset{\text{N}---\text{N}}{\diagup\qquad\diagdown}}{\underset{\diagdown\text{NH}-\text{NH}\diagup}{}}\text{CCONH}_2$$

$$\qquad\qquad\qquad\qquad\qquad\text{(LIV)}$$

The 1-ethyl-dihydro-s-tetrazine corresponding to LIII can be obtained using diazoethane. The structure of the 1-alkyl-1,6-dihydro-3,6-s-tetrazinedicarboxamides has been shown by hydrolysis of LIII to give methylhydrazine. Methylation of 1,6-dihydro-3,6-s-tetrazinedicarboxamide in the 1-position using diazomethane indicates that the acid ring hydrogen in the 1,6-dihydro-s-tetrazine series is on the nitrogen rather than on the carbon atom. This follows from the fact that diazoalkanes react at the site of more acidic hydrogen atoms.

Silberrad[144] has reported 1,4-dihydro-3,6-s-tetrazinedicarboxamide, but it is now believed that the compound he obtained was a triazole.

Ethyl diazoacetate reacts with methylamine to give the methylamine salt of N^3,N^6-dimethyl-1,6-dihydro-3,6-s-tetrazinedicarboxamide (LV), a yellow solid melting at 115° (dec.), and N^3,N^6-dimethyl-

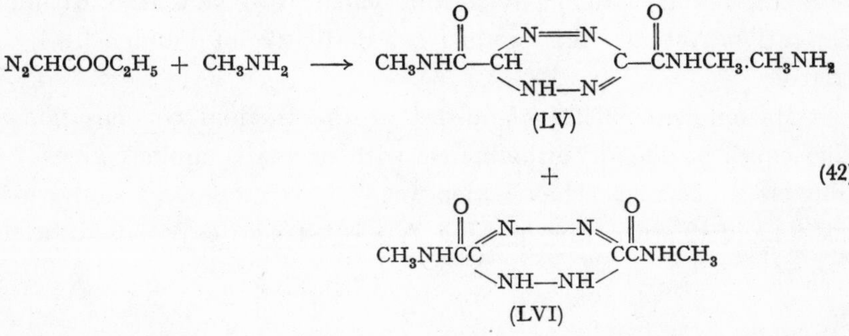

$$N_2CHCOOC_2H_5 + CH_3NH_2 \longrightarrow CH_3NHC-CH \quad C-CNHCH_3 \cdot CH_3NH_2$$

(LV)

$$+ \tag{42}$$

$$CH_3NHCC \quad CCNHCH_3$$

(LVI)

1,2-dihydro-3,6-s-tetrazinedicarboxamide (LVI).[93] Similar products are obtained with ethylamine. The reaction requires several days and gives very poor yields. n-Heptylamine, dimethylamine, and piperidine give, after several weeks, diamides of the 1,2-dihydro acid (Table V-2). Diethylamine and aniline did not give amides. Gentle warming of the 1,6-dihydro amides with the corresponding amines converted them to 1,2-dihydro amides. Acid hydrolysis of the 1,6-dihydro amides gives nitrogen, hydrazine, glyoxylic acid, and amines. The 1,2-dihydro amides with acid give hydrazine, oxalic acid, and amines.

Either dimethyl or diethyl 1,2-dihydro-3,6-s-tetrazinedicarboxylate react with hydrazine in boiling alcohol to give the dihydrazide.[59] This reacts readily with benzaldehyde to give a dibenzylidene derivative. At room temperature, hydrazine and the esters mentioned above react to form ester hydrazides (eq. 43) The ester hydrazides can be acetylated on the amino group of the hydrazide and react readily with aldehydes

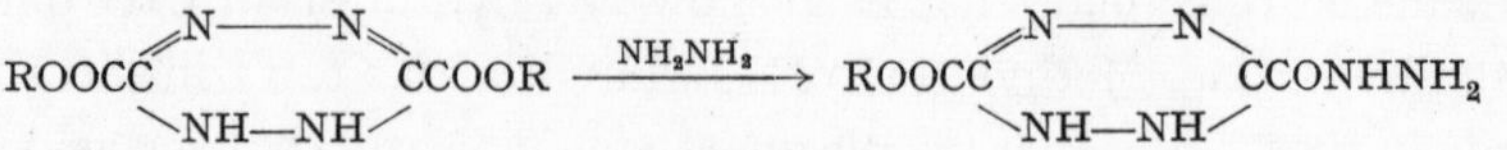

$$\text{R} = \text{CH}_3 \text{ or } \text{C}_2\text{H}_5 \qquad \text{(LVII)}$$

and ketones to give alkylidene derivatives These hydrazides and their derivatives are listed in Table V-2.

Reaction of the dihydrazide of 1,2-dihydro-3,6-s-tetrazinedicarboxylic acid with nitrous acid gives a very unstable product that is believed to be the diazide. The ester hydrazide LVII (R = C_2H_5) reacts with nitrous acid to give a very unstable ester azide.[59]

Ruhemann and Stapleton[139] have reported that 1,4-dihydro-s-tetrazine reacts with phenyl isothiocyanate to give a thiocarbamide derivative. Actually this product is a derivative of 4-amino-1,2,4,4H-triazole.

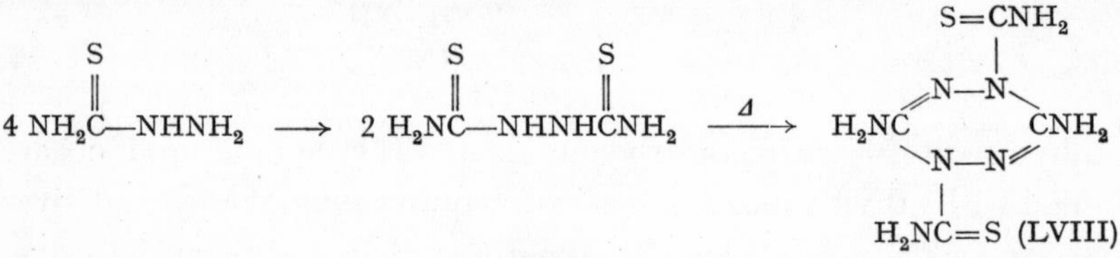

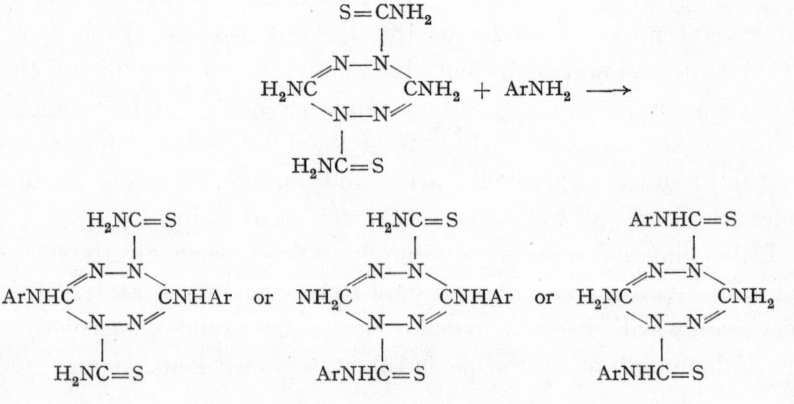

Mazourewitch[90] has claimed that the thermal condensation of thiosemicarbazide or dithiobiurea with aromatic amines gives 1,4-dihydro-s-tetrazines. The reaction was believed to proceed as shown in eqs. 44 and 45 with three possible types of structures proposed for the products. However, the author was unable to decide which was the correct one. Using aniline as the arylamine, a yellow solid, m.p. 260–261° (dec.) was obtained. The same product was obtained from 1-phenyl-dithiobiurea and aniline. o-Toluidine also gives a yellow solid, but it melts at 228–229°. The use of o-toluidine and 1-phenyldithiobiurea gives a product containing both a phenyl and an o-tolyl group. It is a white powder, m.p. 219–220°. Both thiosemicarbazide and dithio-biurea give with m-toluidine a di-m-tolyltetrazine, m.p. 259–260°. In the same reactions p-toluidine gives a colorless crystalline solid, m.p. 272–273°, containing two p-tolyl groups. In each of these reactions a high melting white solid is obtained, m.p. 297–300° (dec.), which proved to be LVIII. All of these compounds are weak dibasic acids, soluble in water but not very soluble in organic solvents. In view of the fact that these reactions were carried out at 185° the possibility that these compounds are triazoles rather than dihydro-s-tetrazines must be kept in mind.

B. Polynuclear Uncondensed s-Tetrazines

(1) Aliphatic Carbocyclic Rings Coupled Directly to s-Tetrazines

Only one example of this type of structure has been reported. Poth and Bailey[121] heated 1-cyclohexylsemicarbazide hydrochloride at 200–210° and obtained in 70% yield a product to which was assigned the structure 1,4-dicyclohexyltetrahydro-3,6-s-tetrazinedione (LIX).

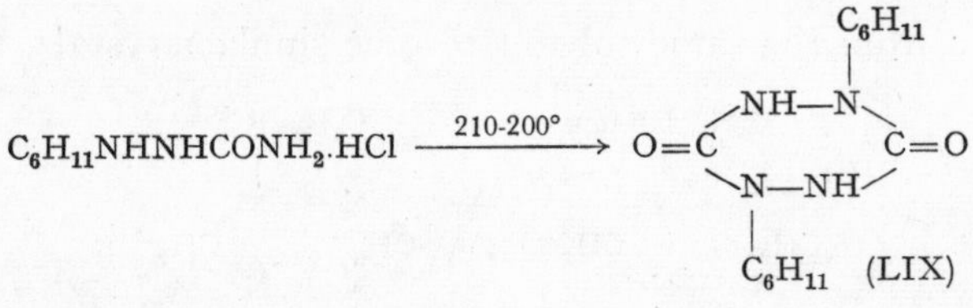

$$C_6H_{11}NHNHCONH_2 \cdot HCl \xrightarrow{210\text{-}200°} \quad (46)$$

The product is a white solid crystallizing in prisms, m.p. 197°, and soluble in water, chloroform, alcohol, and benzene. It reduces Fehling's solution readily and gives no color with ferric chloride. There was no rigorous proof of structure. Since high temperatures were used and this is known to isomerize hydro-s-tetrazines to triazoles, the proposed structure should be viewed with some doubt.

(2) Aromatic Carbocyclic Rings Coupled Directly to s-Tetrazines

Aryl and Alkyl Derivatives.   Busch, Müller, and Schwarz[30] have pre-pared ethyl 6-methyl-3-oxo-4-phenyl-1,2,3,4-tetrahydro-1-s-tetrazine-carboxylate (LXI) by rearrangement and cyclization of 1-ethylidene-2-phenyl-3,4-dicarbethoxytetrazane (LX). The product may exist as the

$$CH_3CH{=}NNHC_6H_5 + H_5C_2OOCN{=}NCOOC_2H_5 \longrightarrow$$

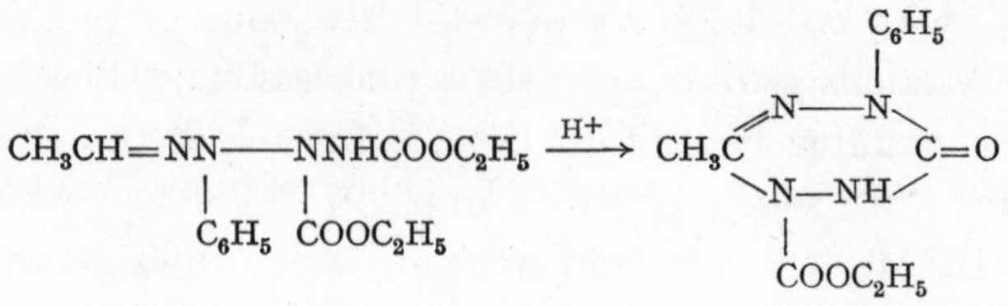

$$
CH_3CH{=}NN{-\!-\!-}NNHCOOC_2H_5 \xrightarrow{\ H^+\ }
CH_3C
\begin{array}{c}
C_6H_5 \\
|\\
{}^{N-\!-N}\diagdown \\
C{=}O \\
{}_{N-NH}\diagup \\
|\\
COOC_2H_5
\end{array}
\qquad (47)
$$

with $\underset{|}{C_6H_5}\ \underset{|}{COOC_2H_5}$ under LX

(LX)   (LXI)

enolic form since it is soluble in dilute alkali. It crystallizes from alcohol in white needles, m.p. 112°.

Hexahydro-s-tetrazines having alkyl and phenyl groups on the nitrogen atoms have been synthesized by reaction of formaldehyde with substituted hydrazines in aqueous solution at room temperature (eq. 8).[69,82] The yields of water insoluble products were almost quantitative. The structures of the products were not definitely ascertained because they could in each case be one of two isomers, since unsymmetrical hydrazines were used; for example LXII or LXIII (R = CH₃). The product LXII or LXIII (R = CH₃) crystallizes from alcohol in white leaflets, m.p. 148°. The ethyl substituted compound was recrystallized from the same solvent to give similar crystals, m.p. 123°.

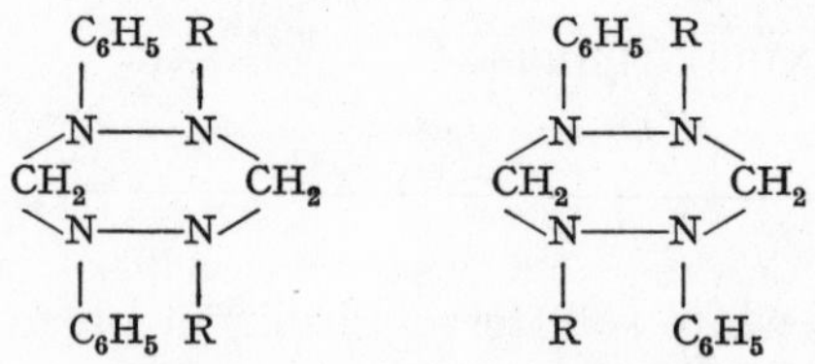

$$
\begin{array}{cc}
C_6H_5\ \ R & C_6H_5\ \ R \\
|\quad\ \ | & |\quad\ \ | \\
{}_{N-\!-N}\diagdown & {}_{N-\!-N}\diagdown \\
CH_2\qquad CH_2 & CH_2\qquad CH_2 \\
{}^{N-\!-N}\diagup & {}^{N-\!-N}\diagup \\
|\quad\ \ | & |\quad\ \ | \\
C_6H_5\ \ R & R\ \ \ C_6H_5 \\
\text{(LXII)} & \text{(LXIII)}
\end{array}
$$

$$R = CH_3,\ C_2H_5\ \text{or}\ (CH_3)_2CH$$

The product containing isopropyl groups, LXII or LXIII (R = $(CH_3)_2CH$) forms white needles. m.p. 163°.

Rassow and Baumann[126,127] have refluxed several aldehydes with hydrazobenzene in alcohol in an attempt to prepare hexahydro-s-tetrazines. Propionaldehyde gave 3,6-diethyl-1,2,4,5-tetraphenylhexa-hydro-s-tetrazine, a light yellow compound melting at 193°, and n-heptaldehyde gave the corresponding 3,6-di-n-hexyl compound forming white crystals, m.p. 133°. Chloral reacted with hydrazobenzene but did not form a hexahydro-s-tetrazine while isobutyraldehyde and valeraldehyde did not react at all. The lack of reactivity of valeraldehyde is rather difficult to explain.

Polyphenyl Derivatives with No Substituents on the Tetrazine Ring. The 3,6-diaryl-s-tetrazines in which aryl is phenyl or substituted phenyl are listed in Table V-3. These compounds have usually been prepared by oxidation of the corresponding 1,2-dihydro-s-tetrazine (eq. 1) using

TABLE V-3. Polyraryl-s-tetrazines
$$R-C \overset{N-N}{\underset{N=N}{\Big\langle}} C-R$$

R	M.p., °C.	Color and crystal form	Ref.
C_6H_5	193, 195	Bluish-red prisms	31, 77, 80, 88, 95 107, 111, 168
p-$CH_3C_6H_4$	233, 235	Bluish-red prisms	95, 111, 113, 168
m-$CH_3C_6H_4$	150	Red needles	95
p-$(CH_3)_2CHC_6H_4$	156	Red plates	36
p-ClC_6H_4			160
p-BrC_6H_4	dec. >280	Bluish-red leaflets	160
p-$NO_2C_6H_4$	215	Red needles	113
m-$NH_2C_6H_4$	266	Red needles	81
m-$CH_3CONHC_6H_4$	295	Violet needles	81
m-$HOOCC_6H_4$	270–280 (dec.)		56
Acid hydrazine salt >277		Yellow	56
Dipyridinium salt	300–310 (dec.)	Scarlet rhombs	56

a mild oxidizing agent such as ferric chloride, air, oxygen, amyl nitrite, or nitrous acid.[77,80,88,95,107,111,168] The yields are usually quite good, being 80% or better. A number of other syntheses have been reported, some of which probably proceed through a dihydro-s-tetrazine inter-mediate, which is not isolated. Lossen and Statius[88] reported that phenyltetrazole heated to 218° decomposes to give a small amount of

3,6-diphenyl-s-tetrazine (eq. 48) and other products. The reaction was
thought to proceed through 3,6-diphenyl-1,2-dihydro-s-tetrazine as an

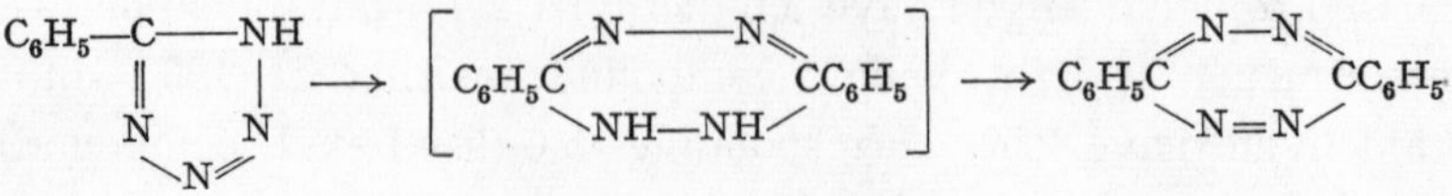

$$C_6H_5-C-NH \longrightarrow \left[C_6H_5C \underset{NH-NH}{\overset{N---N}{<}} CC_6H_5 \right] \longrightarrow C_6H_5C \underset{N=N}{\overset{N-N}{<}} CC_6H_5 \quad (48)$$

intermediate. Busch and Schneider[31] have found that N-phenyl-
benzimidyl chloride and hydrazine react in the cold to form a very
small amount of 3,6-diphenyl-s-tetrazine as well as the main product,
3,4,5-triphenyl-1,2,4,4H-triazole (eq. 49). In an attempt to prepare 3,6-
bis(α-hydroxybenzyl)-1,2-dihydro-s-tetrazine from mandelonitrile and

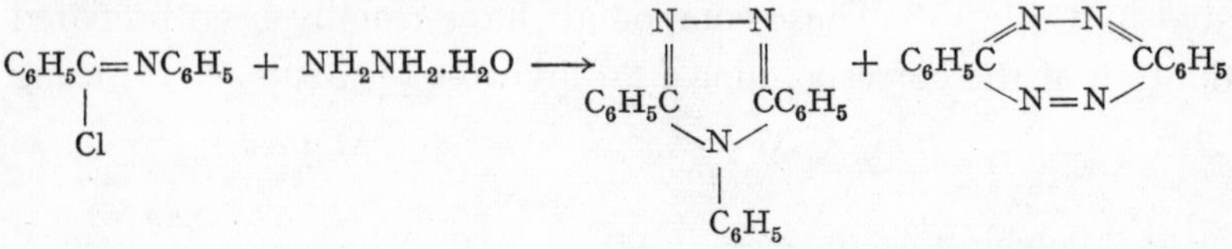

$$C_6H_5C=NC_6H_5 + NH_2NH_2.H_2O \longrightarrow \underset{C_6H_5C \quad\quad CC_6H_5}{\overset{N---N}{\underset{\underset{C_6H_5}{|}}{N}}} + C_6H_5C \underset{N=N}{\overset{N-N}{<}} CC_6H_5 \quad (49)$$
$$\underset{Cl}{|}$$

hydrazine, Darapsky and Adamczewski[60] isolated a compound of
indefinite composition that formed 3,6-diphenyl-s-tetrazine by oxidation with amyl nitrite. It was proposed that this occurred through
benzimide hydrazide (LXIV) as shown in eq. 50. Wuyts and Lacourt[168]

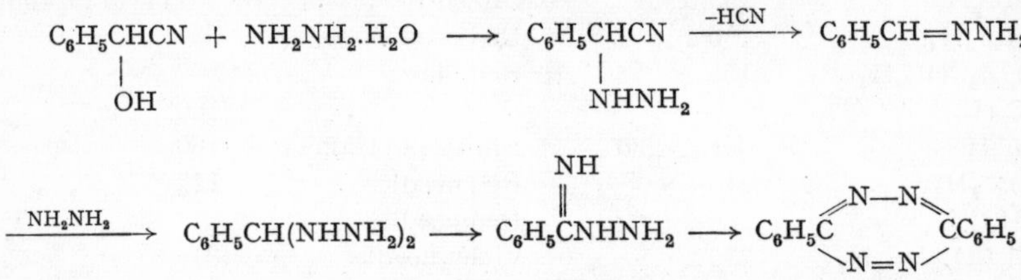

$$C_6H_5CHCN + NH_2NH_2.H_2O \longrightarrow \underset{NHNH_2}{C_6H_5CHCN} \xrightarrow{-HCN} C_6H_5CH=NNH_2$$
$$\underset{OH}{|}$$

$$\xrightarrow{NH_2NH_2} C_6H_5CH(NHNH_2)_2 \longrightarrow C_6H_5\overset{NH}{\overset{\|}{C}}NHNH_2 \longrightarrow C_6H_5C \underset{N=N}{\overset{N-N}{<}} CC_6H_5 \quad (50)$$
$$(LXIV)$$

have found that the oxidation of arylamideazines in ethanolic solution
with air gives 3,6-diaryl-s-tetrazine (eq. 51). The preparation of these

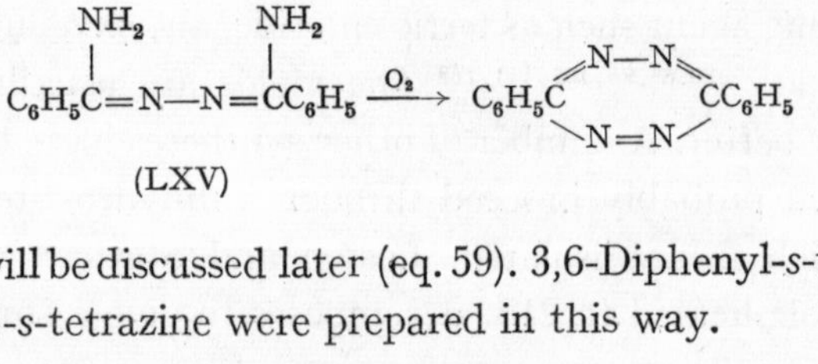

$$\underset{(LXV)}{C_6H_5C=N-N=CC_6H_5} \overset{NH_2 \quad\quad NH_2}{\underset{}{}} \xrightarrow{O_2} C_6H_5C \underset{N=N}{\overset{N-N}{<}} CC_6H_5 \quad (51)$$

amideazines will be discussed later (eq. 59). 3,6-Diphenyl-s-tetrazine and
3,6-di(p-tolyl)-s-tetrazine were prepared in this way.

Stollé and Helwerth[155] have obtained 3,6-diphenyl-s-tetrazine from benzaldehyde benzoyl chloride azine (LXVI) by allowing it to stand in the presence of ammonia, ethyl amine or phenylhydrazine. This was believed to proceed by reaction of LXVI with base to form benzoyl chloride hydrazone (LXVII) which then reacted as in equation 53.

$$C_6H_5C=N—N=CHC_6H_5 + RNH_2 \longrightarrow C_6H_5C=NNH_2 + RN=CHC_6H_5 \tag{52}$$
$$\underset{\text{Cl}}{|} \qquad\qquad\qquad\qquad \underset{\text{Cl}}{|}$$
$$\text{(LXVI)} \qquad\qquad\qquad\qquad \text{(LXVII)}$$

$$C_6H_5C=NNH_2 \longrightarrow C_6H_5C\underset{\diagdown NH—N\diagup}{\overset{\diagup N—NH\diagdown}{}}CC_6H_5 \longrightarrow C_6H_5C\underset{\diagdown N=N\diagup}{\overset{\diagup N—N\diagdown}{}}CC_6H_5 \tag{53}$$
$$\underset{\text{Cl}}{|}$$

These 3,6-diaryl-s-tetrazines are deeply colored, being red, bluish-red or violet-red. They are not basic and are therefore insoluble in dilute acid. They are unaffected by cold sulfuric acid or nitric acid. They are insoluble in water, slightly soluble in alcohol, and soluble in benzene and acetone. Hydrolysis with hot sulfuric acid forms a carboxylic acid, hydrazine, and nitrogen (eq. 54).[54,95] Treatment of 3,6-

$$ArC\underset{\diagdown N=N\diagup}{\overset{\diagup N—N\diagdown}{}}CAr \xrightarrow[\text{H}_2\text{O}]{\text{H}_2\text{SO}_4} ArCOOH + NH_2NH_2 + N_2 \tag{54}$$

diphenyl-s-tetrazine with alcoholic potassium hydroxide gives benzoyl benzaldehyde hydrazone (eq. 55).[108] Functional groups in the benzene

$$C_6H_5C\underset{\diagdown N=N\diagup}{\overset{\diagup N—N\diagdown}{}}CC_6H_5 \xrightarrow[\text{H}_2\text{O}]{\text{KOH}} C_6H_5\overset{\overset{\text{O}}{\|}}{C}NHN=CHC_6H_5 \tag{55}$$

rings react normally. 3,6-Bis(m-aminophenyl)-s-tetrazine[81] forms a dinitrate, a sulfate, a hydrochloride, and a diacetyl derivative. The acid, 3,6-bis(m-carboxyphenyl)-s-tetrazine, forms salts normally.

The 3,6-diaryl-1,2-dihydro-s-tetrazines in which the aryl groups are phenyl or substituted phenyl groups are listed in Table V-4. The first synthesis of compounds of this type was reported by Pinner,[107,108,111] who used imido ester hydrochlorides and hydrazine (eq. 5) to prepare

TABLE V-4. Polyphenyl-1,2-dihydro-s-tetrazines

$$R^1{-}C \overset{\displaystyle N{-}N}{\underset{\displaystyle \underset{R^2\ R^3}{N{-}N}}{}} C{-}R^1$$

R¹	R²	R³	M.p., °C.	Color and crystal form	Ref.
C_6H_5	H	H	160	Yellow needles	18, 33, 64, 80, 107, 108, 111, 148, 150, 159, 168
C_6H_5	CH_3CO	CH_3CO	228	White	80, 107
C_6H_5	C_6H_5CO	H	208	Lemon yellow	150
$p\text{-}CH_3C_6H_4$	H	H	223, 235	Yellow needles	95, 111, 113, 168
$m\text{-}CH_3C_6H_4$	H	H	194	Yellow needles	95
$p\text{-}ClC_6H_4$	H	H	215	Yellow	160
$p\text{-}BrC_6H_4$	H	H	235	Yellow	160
$p\text{-}BrC_6H_4$	C_6H_5CO	C_6H_5CO	248	Yellow	160
$p\text{-}NO_2C_6H_4$	H	H	215	Red needles	113
$m\text{-}NH_2C_6H_4$	H	H	179–190	Yellow needles	81
$m\text{-}HOOCC_6H_4$	H	H	>285	Yellowish-red	56
Dihydrazinium salt			dec. 203	Yellow	56
C_6H_5	C_6H_5	H	126	Orange yellow needles	150, 152, 157
Hydrochloride			180		159
C_6H_5	C_6H_5	CH_3CO	186	White	152
$p\text{-}BrC_6H_4$	C_6H_5	H	167	Yellow needles	150, 160

3,6-diphenyl- and 3,6-di(p-tolyl)-1,2-dihydro-s-tetrazine. This reaction was carried out by adding the hydrochloride of the imido ester and a hydrazine salt to aqueous alcohol containing potassium hydroxide. The desired product is formed at room temperature or on gentle warming. If the reaction is carried out with exposure to air, a considerable amount of 3,6-diaryl-s-tetrazine is formed by oxidation of the dihydro-s-tetrazine. Imide hydrazides (LXVIIIa) and amide hydrazones (LXVIIIb) are also obtained. Pinner[108,110] suggested the dihydro-s-tetrazine is formed through amide hydrazones (eqs. 56 and 57). This belief was based on the fact that benzamide hydrazone (LXVIIIb, Ar $= C_6H_5$)

$$\overset{\displaystyle NH}{\underset{\displaystyle ArCNHNH_2}{\parallel}} \qquad\qquad \overset{\displaystyle NH_2}{\underset{\displaystyle ArC{=}NNH_2}{|}}$$

(LXVIIIa)   (LXVIIIb)

reacts with hydrazine to give 3,6-diphenyl-1,2-dihydro-s-tetrazine while benzamide azine (LXV) will not. Pinner and Wuyts and Lacourt[168]

$$
\underset{\substack{\| \\ ArCOC_2H_5}}{\overset{NH}{}} \xrightarrow{NH_2NH_2} \underset{\substack{| \\ ArC=NNH_2}}{\overset{NH_2}{}} \xrightarrow{NH_2NH_2} \underset{\substack{\| \\ ArC-NHNH_2}}{\overset{NNH_2}{}} \tag{56}
$$

$$
\underset{\substack{| \\ ArC=NNH_2}}{\overset{NH_2}{}} + \underset{\substack{\| \\ ArCNHNH_2}}{\overset{NNH_2}{}} \longrightarrow \underset{\substack{\| \quad \| \\ ArC-NHNHCAr}}{\overset{NNH_2 \quad NNH_2}{}} \longrightarrow \underset{\substack{\diagdown NHNH \diagup}}{ArC \overset{\diagup N-N \diagdown}{} CAr} \tag{57}
$$

found that considerable amounts of amide azines were formed in the reaction and it was believed that they occurred by reaction of amide hydrazones with imido esters (eq. 58).

$$
\underset{\substack{\| \\ ArCOC_2H_5}}{\overset{NH}{}} + \underset{\substack{| \\ ArC=NNH_2}}{\overset{NH_2}{}} \longrightarrow \underset{\substack{| \quad | \\ ArC=NN=CAr}}{\overset{NH_2 \quad NH_2}{}} \tag{58}
$$

Hofmann and Ehrhardt,[77] Müller and Herrdegen,[95] and Curtius and Hess[56] have synthesized 3,6-diaryl-1,2-dihydro-s-tetrazines by the reaction of aromatic nitriles with hydrazine (eq. 3). Benzonitrile, p-tolunitrile, m-tolunitrile, and m-carboxybenzonitrile reacted successfully, but o-tolunitrile did not react. The only yields reported were 75% for 3,6-di(p-tolyl)-1,2-dihydro-s-tetrazine and 22% for the m-tolyl compound. Müller and Herrdegen proposed a mechanism for this reaction very similar to that proposed by Pinner for the imido esters. In the case of the nitrile the first step was believed to be reaction with hydrazine to form an imide hydrazide (LXVIIIa), which proceeds as shown in equations 56 and 57 with LXVIIIa substituted for LXVIIIb.

Junghahn[80,81] has found that aromatic thioamides react readily with hydrazine (eq. 4) in boiling aqueous alcohol to give, 3,6-diaryl-1,2-dihydro-s-tetrazines. The yield was reported as excellent using thiobenzamide. A somewhat similar method has been used by Wuyts and Lacourt.[168] These workers have treated dithio acids with hydrazine (eq. 59) to obtain 3,6-diaryl-1,2-dihydro-s-tetrazines and amide azines.

$$
\underset{\substack{\| \\ C_6H_5CSH}}{\overset{S}{}} + NH_2NH_2 \longrightarrow C_6H_5C \overset{\diagup N-N \diagdown}{\underset{\diagdown NHNH \diagup}{}} CC_6H_5 + \underset{\substack{| \quad | \\ C_6H_5C=N-N=CC_6H_5}}{\overset{NH_2 \quad NH_2}{}} \tag{59}
$$

It was believed that the first step in the reaction was the formation of thiohydrazides. In agreement with this belief is the fact that thiohydrazides react with hydrazine under the same conditions to form 1,2-dihydro-s-tetrazines and amide azines (eq. 60). Recently Chabrier and

$$C_6H_5\overset{\displaystyle S}{\overset{\displaystyle \|}{C}}-NHNHC_6H_5 + NH_2NH_2 \longrightarrow C_6H_5\overset{\displaystyle N-N}{\underset{\displaystyle NHNH}{\diagup}}CC_6H_5 + C_6H_5\overset{\displaystyle NH_2}{\underset{\displaystyle |}{C}}=NN=\overset{\displaystyle NH_2}{\underset{\displaystyle |}{C}}C_6H_5 \quad (60)$$

Renard[33] have used a variation of the reaction of thiobenzamides with hydrazine. They reported an excellent yield of dihydro-s-tetrazines by the reaction of the morpholide (LXIX) with hydrazine (eq. 61). Presumably

$$C_6H_5C(=S(CH_3)I)N\underset{\smile}{\frown}O + NH_2NH_2 \longrightarrow C_6H_5\overset{\displaystyle N-N}{\underset{\displaystyle NHNH}{\diagup}}CC_6H_5 \quad (61)$$

(LXIX)

LXIX is the S-methiodide of thiobenzmorpholide, although the published report does not make this completely clear.

Stollé[148,150,159,160] reported the synthesis of 3,6-diaryl-1,2-dihydro-s-tetrazines by the reaction of benzoyl chloride azine (LXX) and substituted aroyl chloride azines with hydrazine (6). The aroyl chloride azines were obtained by treatment of hydrazides with phosphorous pentachloride (eq. 62). Treatment of LXX with hydrazine gave a 28% yield of 3,6-diphenyl-1,2-dihydro-s-tetrazine as well as a 28% yield of 3,6-diphenyl-s-tetrazine.

$$C_6H_5CONHNHCOC_6H_5 \xrightarrow{PCl_5} \underset{\underset{\displaystyle Cl}{|}}{C_6H_5C}=N-N=\underset{\underset{\displaystyle Cl}{|}}{CC_6H_5} \quad (62)$$

(LXX)

The melting points reported for the 3,6-diaryl-1,2-dihydro-s-tetrazines are very frequently the same as those of the corresponding 3,6-diaryl-s-tetrazines. The usual melting point reported for 3,6-diphenyl-1,2-dihydro-s-tetrazine is 192°, which is the melting point of 3,6-diphenyl-s-tetrazine. It was Pinner's opinion that the dihydro-s-tetrazines were oxidized to the s-tetrazine as they were heated and the final melting point was that of the s-tetrazine. Franzen and Kraft[64] reported a melting point of 160° for 3,6-diphenyl-1,2-dihydro-s-tetrazine and this is probably the correct one. The 3,6-diaryl-1,2-dihydro-*s*-tetrazines are too weakly basic to be soluble in dilute acids. They are soluble in acetone and alcohol but insoluble in benzene and water. 1,2-Dihydro-*s*-tetrazines can frequently be separated from the corresponding *s*-tetrazine by washing away the *s*-tetrazines with benzene.

The characteristic reaction of the 3,6-diaryl-1,2-dihydro-*s*-tetrazines is their easy oxidation to *s*-tetrazines. Heating the 3,6-diaryl-1,2-dihydro-*s*-tetrazines with 25% hydrochloric acid[107,108,111] isomerizes them to what was at first believed to be the 1,4-dihydro-*s*-tetrazines but has since been shown to be 4-amino-3,5-diaryl-1,2,4,4*H*-triazoles. In some cases 3,5-diaryl-1,3,4-oxadiazoles are also obtained. Reducing agents such as zinc in acetic acid also give a triazole but in this case the 4-amino group is removed (eq. 63). 3,6-Diaryl-1,2-dihydro-*s*-tetrazines

$$
\underset{\text{NHNH}}{\overset{\text{N---N}}{C_6H_5C \diagup\diagdown CC_6H_5}} \xrightarrow{\text{Zn-H}^+} \underset{\underset{H}{N}}{\overset{\text{N----N}}{C_6H_5C \qquad CC_6H_5}} \qquad (63)
$$

are readily acylated with acetic anhydride or benzoyl chloride to form both mono and diacyl derivatives. Although 3,6-diphenyl-1,2-dihydro-*s*-tetrazine is very weakly basic, it has been reported[108] to form a dimethiodide melting with decomposition at 128°. 3,6-Di(*m*-tolyl)-1,2-dihydro-*s*-tetrazine has been heated under pressure with hydrochloric acid to give *m*-toluic acid and hydrazine.

Pinner[107] found that in addition to 3,6-diphenyl-1,2-dihydro-*s*-tetrazine several other products could be isolated from the reaction of ethyl benzimidate with hydrazine. Among these was a white crystalline solid, m.p. 258°, for which Pinner proposed the name *benzenylimino-nitrile* and the formula LXXI. Somewhat later the same product[108,111]

$$
\underset{\text{(LXXI)}}{C_6H_5C\overset{\text{NH}}{=\!\!=\!\!=}N} \qquad\qquad \underset{\text{(LXXII)}}{\overset{\text{N---NH}}{\underset{\text{NHN}}{C_6H_5C \diagup\diagdown CC_6H_5}}}
$$

was obtained by heating 3,6-diphenyl-1,2-dihydro-*s*-tetrazine with acid. It was realized that it was an isomer of the 1,2-dihydro-*s*-tetrazine; it was therefore called *diphenylisodihydrotetrazine* and the 1,4-dihydro formula LXXII was proposed for it. Curtius[41,53] obtained the same compound by the reaction of benzonitrile with hydrazine hydrate at 150°. It was first called *hydrazicarbamine* by Curtius but this name was soon dropped. Silberrad[143] heated benzhydrazide at 260° and got, in addition to numerous other products, a small amount of *diphenylisodihydrotetrazine*. Heating benzhydrazide with hydrazine at 230° gave very good yields of the same product. Stollé[148-150,159] synthesized *diphenylisodihydrotetrazine* by several methods. One of these was the reaction of benzhydrazide with hydrazine and a second was isomerization of the 1,2-dihydro-*s*-tetrazine with acid. A new method was by condensation of dibenzhydrazide with benzhydrazide to give the benzoyl derivative of *diphenylisodihydrotetrazine* from which the benzoyl group was removed by hydrolysis (eq. 64). Stollé found that 1,2-

$$C_6H_5CONHNHCOC_6H_5 + C_6H_5CONHNH_2 \xrightarrow{130°}$$

$$\xrightarrow[130°]{H^+,\ H_2O}$$ (64)

dihydro-*s*-tetrazines were readily oxidized to *s*-tetrazines, but the 1,4-dihydro-*s*-tetrazines were not. He suggested that what were believed to be 1,4-dihydro-*s*-tetrazines were 4-amino-1,2,4,4H-triazoles. This view was supported by the fact that the supposed 3,6-diphenyl-1,4-dihydro-*s*-tetrazines formed a benzaldehyde derivative in contrast to the 1,2-dihydro-*s*-tetrazines, and that the so-called 1,4-dihydro compounds were much more basic than the 1,2-dihydro ones. Pinner[110] had already considered the possibility that 1,4-dihydro-*s*-tetrazines might be triazoles but had rejected it. Stollé apparently did not take his own suggestions to heart since in a later paper[159] he still retained the 1,4-dihydro-*s*-tetrazine formulas for what he had previously proposed were triazoles. Furthermore he defended the tetrazine structure in a polemic[151] attempting to refute Bülow's arguments. However, a short time later Bülow and Weber[23] showed the compound believed to have structure LXXII actually was 3,5-diphenyl-4-amino-1,2,4,4H-triazole

(LXXIII). This was done by showing that methyl bromocumalinate (LXXIV) reacted with the supposed 3,6-diphenyl-1,4-dihydro-s-

$$N\text{——}N$$
$$C_6H_5\text{—}C \quad CC_6H_5$$
$$\diagdown N \diagup$$
$$\underset{NH_2}{|}$$

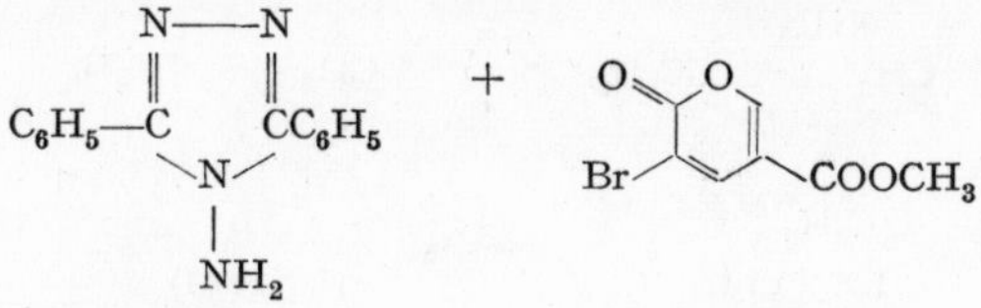

(LXXIII)   (LXXIV)

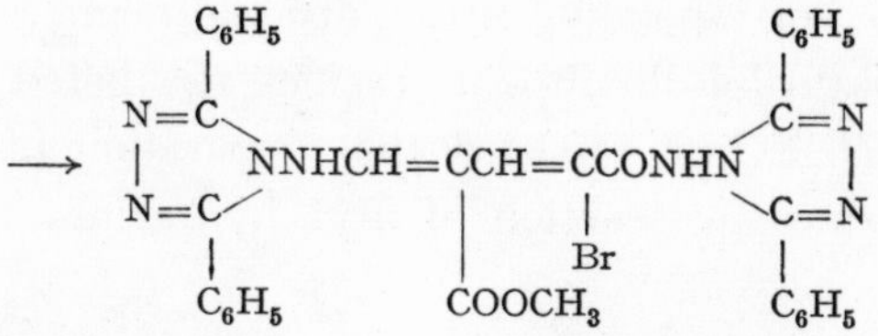

(65)

tetrazine as it had been shown to do with aminotriazoles (eq. 65). The structure LXXIII was accepted by later workers in the field.

The preparation of 3,6-di(p-tolyl)-1,4-dihydro-s-tetrazine and 3,6-bis(p-bromophenyl)-1,4-dihydro-s-tetrazine by isomerization of the corresponding 1,2-dihydro-s-tetrazines with acid has been reported.[109, 113, 150, 160] In view of the findings concerning the acid isomerization of 3,6-diphenyl-1,2-dihydro-s-tetrazine, it is very likely that these compounds also are 3,5-diaryl-4-amino-1,2,4,4H-triazoles.

Holmberg[79] has prepared what he believes to be 3,6-diphenyl-1,4-dihydro-s-tetrazine in 11% yield from thiobenzhydrazide (eq. 66).

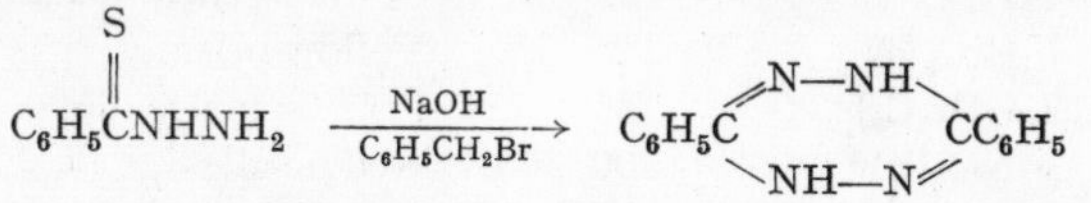

$$\overset{S}{\underset{\|}{}}$$
$$C_6H_5CNHNH_2 \xrightarrow[C_6H_5CH_2Br]{NaOH} C_6H_5C \overset{N\text{—}NH}{\underset{NH\text{—}N}{\diagdown}} CC_6H_5$$

(66)

There was no rigorous proof of structure, and the properties are very similar to those reported in most cases for the 1,2-dihydro isomer. The reaction used for preparation is very similar to that used by Chabrier and Renard (61) for the preparation of 3,6-diphenyl-1,2-dihydro-s-tetrazine. Consequently there is a strong possibility that Holmberg may have obtained the 1,2-isomer.

The synthesis of 1,3-diphenyl-1,6-dihydro-s-tetrazine (LXXVI) was carried out by Ponzio and Peroglio[120] by chromic oxide oxidation of 1,3-diphenyl-1,4,5,6-tetrahydro-s-tetrazine (LXXV). The compound LXXVI crystallizes in prisms, m.p. 238–239°. 1-Phenyl-3-(p-tolyl)1,6-

$$
\begin{array}{ccc}
\underset{\text{CH}_2}{\overset{\text{NHNH}}{\diagup}}\ \underset{}{\overset{}{\diagdown}}\text{CC}_6\text{H}_5 & \xrightarrow{\text{CrO}_3} & \underset{\text{CH}_2}{\overset{\text{N}=\text{N}}{\diagup}}\ \underset{}{\overset{}{\diagdown}}\text{CC}_6\text{H}_5 \\
\diagdown\text{N}\!-\!\text{N}\diagup & & \diagdown\text{N}\!-\!\text{N}\diagup \\
\mid & & \mid \\
\text{C}_6\text{H}_5 & & \text{C}_6\text{H}_5 \\
\text{(LXXV)} & & \text{(LXXVI)}
\end{array} \qquad (67)
$$

dihydro-s-tetrazine, m.p. 239°, has been synthesized in the same way starting with the corresponding tetrahydro-s-tetrazine.

The 1,4-diaryl-1,4-dihydro-s-tetrazines are listed in Table V-5. Ruhemann[130–132, 135] first reported the preparation of 1,4-diaryl-1,4-dihydro-s-tetrazines by reaction of aryl hydrazines with potassium

TABLE V-5. Polyphenyl-1,4-dihydro-s-tetrazines

$$
\begin{array}{c}
\text{R}^2 \\
\mid \\
\text{N}\!-\!\text{N} \\
\text{R}^1\text{C}\diagup\qquad\diagdown\text{CR}^1 \\
\diagdown\text{N}\!-\!\text{N}\diagup \\
\mid \\
\text{R}^2
\end{array}
$$

R¹	Rᵃ	M.p., °C.	Color and crystal form	Ref.
C_6H_5	H	190–192	Yellow needles	79
H	C_6H_5	189	Yellow plates	7
H	$p\text{-CH}_3\text{C}_6\text{H}_4$	102	Yellow plates	7
Hᵃ	$o\text{-CH}_3\text{C}_6\text{H}_4$	141		132
Hᵃ	$p\text{-(CH}_3)_2\text{CHC}_6\text{H}_4$	234		132
H	$p\text{-ClC}_6\text{H}_4$	185.5	Yellow plates	7
C_6H_5	C_6H_5	203	Golden yellow needles	9
C_6H_5	$p\text{-BrC}_6\text{H}_4$	265	Yellow prisms	35
C_6H_5	$2,4\text{-Br}_2\text{C}_6\text{H}_3$	255	Pale yellow leaflets	35
C_6H_5	$p\text{-NO}_2\text{C}_6\text{H}_4$	300, 305, 312	Red needles	9, 11, 114, 115
$p\text{-CH}_3\text{OC}_6\text{H}_4$	C_6H_5	173.5	Orange yellow flat prisms	10, 12
$p\text{-CH}_3\text{OC}_6\text{H}_4$	$p\text{-BrC}_6\text{H}_4$	150		162

ᵃ It is uncertain as to whether or not these compounds have the proposed structure.

hydroxide and chloroform. The compound later thought to be 1,4-diphenyl-1,4-dihydro-s-tetrazine was called *carbophenylhydrazine*.

Somewhat later Pellizzari[98] and Bamberger[8] prepared the same compound by heating formylphenylhydrazine and proposed the 1,4-dihydro-s-tetrazine formula (VI).

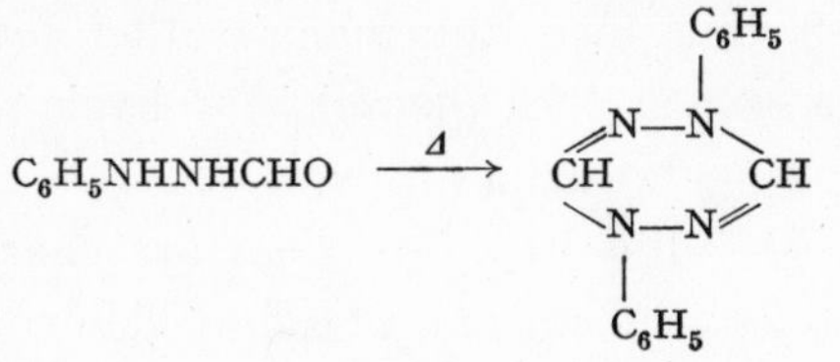

$$C_6H_5NHNHCHO \xrightarrow{\Delta}
\begin{array}{c}
C_6H_5 \\
| \\
\nearrow N—N \diagdown \\
CH \qquad CH \\
\diagdown N—N \nearrow \\
| \\
C_6H_5 \\
(VI)
\end{array}
\qquad (68)$$

Baker, Ollis, and Poole[7] have prepared 1,4-diphenyl- and 1,4-di-(p-tolyl)-1,4-dihydro-s-tetrazine and found that these compounds were different from those reported by Ruhemann and others to have these structures. Baker and colleagues first prepared 1,4-diphenyl-1,4-dihydro-s-tetrazine by treating N-phenylsydnone with phosphorous pentasulfide (eq. 69). The yield was 27%. A second method of prepara-

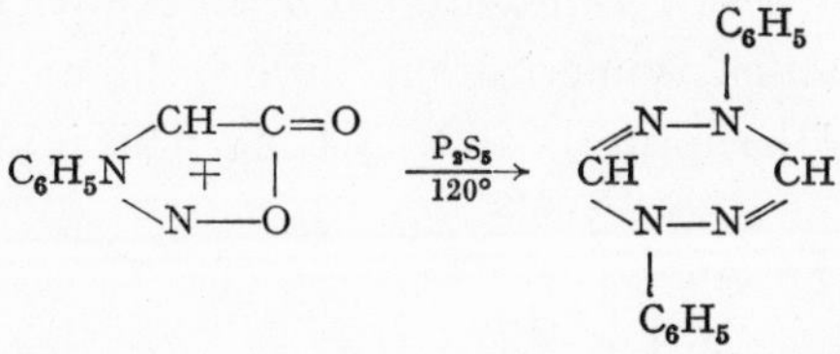

$$C_6H_5N
\begin{array}{c}
\diagup CH—C=O \\
\mp \quad | \\
\diagdown N—O
\end{array}
\xrightarrow[120°]{P_2S_5}
\begin{array}{c}
C_6H_5 \\
| \\
\nearrow N—N \diagdown \\
CH \qquad CH \\
\diagdown N—N \nearrow \\
| \\
C_6H_5
\end{array}
\qquad (69)$$

tion was the action of sodium methoxide in cold methanol on thioformylphenylhydrazine (eq. 7). This reaction gave a 43% yield. Preparation of VI by treatment of formylphenylhydrazine with phosphorous pentasulfide gave only 5% yield. 1,4-Di(p-tolyl)- and 1,4-bis(p-chlorophenyl)-1,4-dihydro-s-tetrazines were prepared by treatment of the appropriate thioformylarylhydrazine with sodium methoxide. The structures of these products were assigned on the basis of the following facts. Hydrolysis of 1,4-diphenyl-1,4-dihydro-s-tetrazine with hydrochloric acid gave two molar equivalents of phenylhydrazine and two of formic acid. The 1,4-dihydro-s-tetrazines were not basic and formed no acetyl derivatives. Their dipole moments were essentially zero.[63] There was a great similarity in physical properties between these compounds and the 1,3,4,6-tetraaryl-1,4-dihydro-s-tetrazines prepared by Bamberger and Grob[9] and Chattaway and Walker.[35]

Ruhemann[130] [131] reported, in addition to compounds also prepared by Baker and co-workers the synthesis of 1,4-di(o-tolyl)- and 1,4-bis(p-isopropylphenyl)-1,4-dihydro-s-tetrazine. These compounds are listed in Table V-5, but since Ruhemann's other compounds did not have the structure proposed for them it is probable that these are not 1,4-diaryl-1,4-dihydro-s-tetrazines.

The 1,4-diaryl-1,4-dihydro-s-tetrazines are characterized by absorption maxima at 290–300 mμ and a bright yellow color. This indicates interaction of the phenyl group with the ring as shown in LXXVII and a planar structure with no *cis-isomerism*. They are soluble in chloroform but insoluble in petroleum ether.

$$-\left\langle \bigcirc \right\rangle = \overset{+}{N} \overset{C=N}{\underset{N=C}{\diagdown}} \overset{+}{N} = \left\langle \bigcirc \right\rangle -$$

(LXXVII)

Treatment of these 1,4-dihydro-s-tetrazines with sodium ethoxide in hot alcohol causes isomerization to 1-aryl-3-arylamino-1,2,4,1H-triazoles (eq. 70) with rupture of an N–N bond. This is in contrast to the

$$
\begin{array}{ccc}
& \overset{\displaystyle Ar}{\underset{\displaystyle |}{}} & \\
& \overset{N-N}{\diagup\;\diagdown} & \\
CH & & CH \\
& \overset{N-N}{\diagdown\;\diagup} & \\
& \overset{\displaystyle |}{\underset{\displaystyle Ar}{}} &
\end{array}
\xrightarrow{\;\;NaOC_2H_5\;\;}
\begin{array}{cc}
ArN\!-\!-\!-\!N & \\
|\qquad\; \| & \\
HC \quad\; C\!-\!NHAr \\
\diagdown N \diagup &
\end{array}
\qquad (70)
$$

the 3,6-diaryl-1,2-dihydro-s-tetrazines, which isomerize to 4,-amino-3,5-diaryl-1,2,4H-triazoles with rupture of a C–N bond.

Stollé[150, 152, 159, 160] has synthesized 1,3,6-triphenyl-1,2-dihydro-s-tetrazine (LXXVIII) by two methods. In one method dibenzhydrazide and phenylhydrazine were heated together in boiling alcohol (eq. 71).

$$
C_6H_5CONHNHCOC_6H_5 + C_6H_5NHNH_2 \;\longrightarrow\; C_6H_5C\overset{\displaystyle N-N}{\underset{\displaystyle \underset{|}{\underset{C_6H_5}{N-NH}}}{\diagdown\qquad\diagup}}CC_6H_5 \qquad (71)
$$

(LXXVIII)

The second method of preparation was the reaction of benzoyl chloride azine (LXX) with phenylhydrazine (eq. 72). In this case LXXIX was

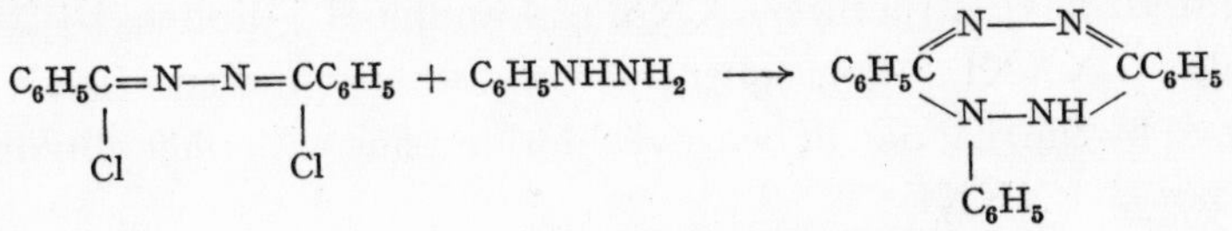

$$C_6H_5C{=}N{-}N{=}CC_6H_5 \ + \ C_6H_5NHNH_2 \ \longrightarrow \ \underset{\underset{C_6H_5}{|}}{\overset{\overset{N{-}N}{\diagup\diagdown}}{C_6H_5C}}\!\!\!\!\!\!\!\underset{N{-}NH}{\diagdown\diagup}\!\!\!\!CC_6H_5 \qquad (72)$$

(LXXIX)

obtained as its hydrochloride, and a considerable amount of an isomeric compound believed to be LXXX was obtained. 1,3,6-Triphenyl-1,2-

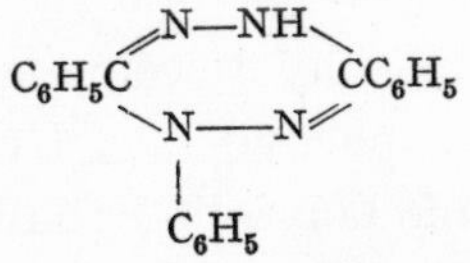

(LXXX) 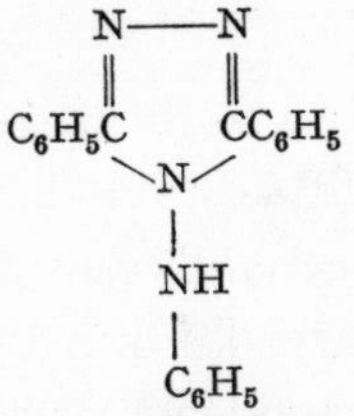   (LXXXI)

dihydro-s-tetrazine crystallizes from alcohol in golden yellow needles. Heating it with mineral acid isomerizes it to a compound identical with the one thought to have structure LXXX. Reaction of LXXIX with nitrous acid gives 2,5-diphenyl-1,3,4-oxadiazole. An acetyl derivative is obtained with acetic anhydride. 1,3,6-Triphenyl-1,2-dihydro-s-tetrazine is slightly basic forming a hydrochloride, which is decomposed by boiling water.

Stollé[152] investigated the possibility that the compound thought to have structure LXXIX might actually have a triazole structure LXXXI. He found that the acetyl derivative of LXXIX melted at 186° and the isomeric acetyl derivative of 4-anilino-3,5-diphenyl-1,2,4,4H-triazole (LXXXI) melted at 180°. It was Stollé conclusion that the two were identical. However, this is unlikely in view of the following facts. In both of the methods of preparation of 1,3,6-triphenyl-1,2-dihydro-s-tetrazine[150, 159] a second product was obtained to which was assigned the structure 1,3,6-triphenyl-1,4-dihydro-s-tetrazine (LXXX). This is a white solid melting at 263°. The 1,2-dihydro compound LXXIX is readily isomerized by acid to the same compound. Two characteristic properties of the 1,2-dihydro-s-tetrazines are that they are relatively low melting compounds and readily isomerize with acid to high melting triazoles. These considerations make it probable that the compound thought to have structure LXXX is 4-anilino-3,5-diphenyl-1,2,4,4H-triazole (LXXXI). Consequently the other product (LXXXIX) obtained by the reaction of benzoyl chloride azine with phenylhydrazine could not be LXXXI.

Stollé and Weindel[150, 160] have reported the preparation of 3,6-bis(p-bromophenyl)-1-phenyl-1,2-dihydro-s-tetrazine by both of the methods used for 1,3,6-triphenyl-1,2-dihydro-s-tetrazine but using the appropriate p-bromophenyl compounds. 3,6-Bis(p-bromophenyl)-1-phenyl-1,2-dihydro-s-tetrazine is readily isomerized by acid to what was believed to be the corresponding 1,4-dihydro compound but which is undoubtedly 4-anilino-3,5-bis(p-bromophenyl)-1,2,4,4H-triazole.

Bamberger and co-workers[9, 10, 12] and Ponzio[114, 115] have synthesized 1,3,4,6-tetraaryl-1,4-dihydro-s-tetrazines (Table V-5) by treatment of 1-(α-nitrobenzylidene)-2-phenylhydrazine or analogs (LXXXII) with sodium methoxide in methanol (eq. 73). The nitro compounds (LXXXII)

$$\begin{array}{ccc}
\text{ArC=NNHAr}^1 & \xrightarrow{\text{CH}_3\text{ONa}} & \text{ArC}\begin{array}{c}\text{Ar}^1\\|\\\diagup\text{N—N}\diagdown\\\diagdown\text{N—N}\diagup\\|\\\text{Ar}^1\end{array}\text{CAr} \qquad (73)\\
|\\
\text{NO}_2
\end{array}$$

(LXXXII)   (LXXXIII)

were prepared by nitrosation of the arylhydrazones with nitrous acid or amyl nitrite followed by oxidation with nitrogen trioxide. The only yield reported for this method of s-tetrazine formation was 10–15% for 1,4-bis(p-nitrophenyl)-3,6-diphenyl-1,4-dihydro-s-tetrazine.[11] Compounds of the type of LXXXIII have been prepared by the action of halogens on arylaldehyde arylhydrazones (eq. 74). Bamberger and Grob[9]

$$\text{C}_6\text{H}_5\text{CH=NNHC}_6\text{H}_5 \xrightarrow{\text{Br}_2} \text{C}_6\text{H}_5\text{C}\begin{array}{c}p\text{-BrC}_6\text{H}_5\\|\\\diagup\text{N—N}\diagdown\\\diagdown\text{N—N}\diagup\\|\\p\text{-BrC}_6\text{H}_5\end{array}\text{CC}_6\text{H}_5 \qquad (74)$$

(LXXXIV)

used iodine in this reaction while Chattaway and Walker[35] and Vanghelovitch[162] used bromine. Chattaway and Walker used acetic acid as solvent and obtained a 50% yield. When bromine was used, bromination frequently occurred in the para position of the aromatic ring attached to the nitrogen. With iodine this did not occur. LXXXIV can also be obtained by action of bromine on benzaldehyde p-bromophenylhydrazone or on benzoyl chloride phenylhydrazone. Starting with benzaldehyde 2,4-dibromophenylhydrazone, 1,4-bis(2,4-dibromophenyl)-3,6-diphenyl-1,4-dihydro-s-tetrazine was obtained. Vanghelovitch found that sunlight was necessary to cause cyclization in this reaction. Bamberger and Grob[9] have nitrated 1,3,4,6-tetraphenyl-1,4-dihydro-s-tetrazine to obtain a dinitro derivative of unknown structure. This dinitro compound crystallizes in red needles, m.p. 299°.

1,3,4,6-Tetraaryl-1,4-dihydro-s-tetrazines are soluble in benzene, acetone, and chloroform. Reduction of 1,3,4,6-tetraphenyl-1,4-dihydro-s-tetrazine by means of zinc dust distillation[9] gave benzonitrile and aniline. The same treatment of 1,4-bis(p-bromophenyl)-3,6-diphenyl-1,4-dihydro-s-tetrazine[35] also gave benzonitrile while reductions with zinc and hydrochloric acid[35] gave p-bromoaniline. These reductions were considered to be adequate proof of structure for compounds of this type.

Ponzio and Perolio[120] have synthesized 1,3-diphenyl-1,4,5,6-tetrahydro-s-tetrazine (LXXXVI) by reduction of 1,3-diphenyl-6-s-tetrazineone (LXXXV) with zinc and acetic acid (eq. 75). The product

$$O=C \overset{N=N}{\underset{N-N}{\diagup\diagdown}} C-C_6H_5 \quad \xrightarrow{\text{Zn-CH}_3\text{COOH}} \quad CH_2 \overset{NHNH}{\underset{N-N}{\diagup\diagdown}} C-C_6H_5 \quad (75)$$

$$\underset{C_6H_5}{|} \qquad\qquad\qquad\qquad \underset{C_6H_5}{|}$$

$$\text{(LXXXV)} \qquad\qquad\qquad\qquad \text{(LXXXVI)}$$

melts at 86°. The same type of synthesis was used to prepare 1-phenyl-3-(p-tolyl)-1,4,5,6-tetrahydro-s-tetrazine, m.p. 104°.

Staudinger and Meyer[147] have developed an interesting tetrahydro-s-tetrazine synthesis by which they have prepared 3,3,6,6-tetraphenyl-1,2,3,6-tetrahydro-s-tetrazine (LXXXVIII). Diazodiphenylmethane and triethylphosphine were allowed to react to give an intermediate

(LXXXVII) which lost triethyl phosphine upon addition of moist benzene or chloroform and formed LXXXVIII (eq. 76). The product is a

$$(C_6H_5)_2CN_2 + (C_2H_5)_3P \longrightarrow (C_6H_5)_2C=N-N=P(C_2H_5)_3$$
$$\text{(LXXXVII)}$$

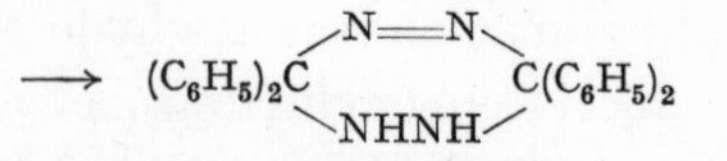

$$\longrightarrow (C_6H_5)_2C \overset{N=N}{\underset{NHNH}{\diagup\diagdown}} C(C_6H_5)_2 \qquad (76)$$
$$\text{(LXXXVIII)}$$

yellow solid soluble in benzene and chloroform, melting at 204.5–205.5°; above this temperature ammonia is evolved. The only proof of structure was analysis.

The synthesis of 1,4-diphenylhexahydro-s-tetrazine (XCI) has been claimed by Thielepape and Spreckelsen[161] by an unusual series of reactions shown in equation 77. The methochloride of 5-chloro-3-methyl-1-phenylpyrazole (LXXXIX) was treated with hydrazine hydrate to give the hydrazone of 1-phenyl-2,3-dimethyl-5-pyrazolone (XC), which then forms the hexahydro-s-tetrazine under the influence of heat and alkali. The only proof of structure was analysis. The product is a white solid, m.p. 130°. It forms a monopicrate, dec. 195°, a

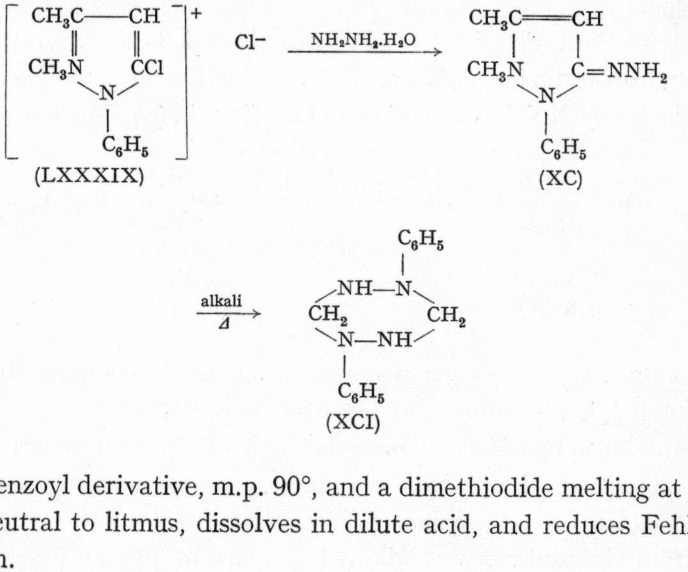

$$(77)$$

monobenzoyl derivative, m.p. 90°, and a dimethiodide melting at 188°. It is neutral to litmus, dissolves in dilute acid, and reduces Fehling's solution.

1,2,4,5-Tetraphenylhexahydro-s-tetrazine has been synthesized by reaction of formaldehyde with diphenylhydrazine[14] (equation 8, R = H, R' and R'' = C_6H_5). It crystallizes from benzene or ethanol in white plates, m.p. 200°. Reaction with nitrating mixture gives a tetranitroazobenzene.

A series of 1,2,4,5-tetraarylhexahydro-s-tetrazines was prepared by Rassow and co-workers[126, 128] by reaction of formaldehyde or acetaldehyde with hydrazobenzenes (eq. 8). The reaction of formaldehyde with p-hydrazotoluene, o-hydrazotoluene, and m-hydrazotoluene gives XCII, R = H, and Ar groups are, respectively: p-tolyl, m.p. 213°;

$$
\begin{array}{ccc}
& \text{Ar} \quad \text{Ar} & \\
& | \quad\quad | & \\
& \text{N——N} & \\
\text{RCH} & & \text{CHR} \\
& \text{N——N} & \\
& | \quad\quad | & \\
& \text{Ar} \quad \text{Ar} &
\end{array}
$$

(XCII)

o-tolyl, m.p. 187°; and m-tolyl, m.p. 166°. Formaldehyde with phenyl p-tolylhydrazine gives a compound, m.p. 191–193°, which might be either 1,4-diphenyl-2,5-di(p-tolyl)- or 1,5-diphenyl-2,4-di(p-tolyl)-hexahydro-s-tetrazine. Acetaldehyde and p-hydrazotoluene reacted to give a compound melting at 150° which has structure XCII (R = CH_3, Ar = p-tolyl). These reactions were run in alcohol. The yields reported were 30–75%. All the products obtained were white. Attempts to prepare hexahydro-s-tetrazines from p-dinitrohydrazobenzene and 2,4,6-hexanitrohydrazobenzene were unsuccessful; the hydrazines would not react with formaldehyde.

Aryl and Polyaryl Derivatives with Functional Groups Substituted on the Hydro-s-tetrazine Ring. 1,4-Diphenyltetrahydro-3,6-s-tetrazenediimine (XCVIa) or its isomer, 3,6-diamino-1,4-diphenyl-1,4-dihydro-s-tetrazine (XCVIb) has been synthesized by Pellizzari.[101] 1-Cyano-1-phenylhydrazine (XCIII) was allowed to stand at room temperature with acetic anhydride, then heated to 100° for a short time. The first product was a diacetyl derivative (XCIV), m.p. 268°. Hydrolysis of this with sodium hydroxide gave a monoacetyl compound (XCV), m.p. 228°. This was heated with dilute hydrochloric acid to form a hydrochloride, which was converted with ammonia to the free base XCVIa or XCVIb, m.p. 198°. Either XCVIa or XCVIb reacts with

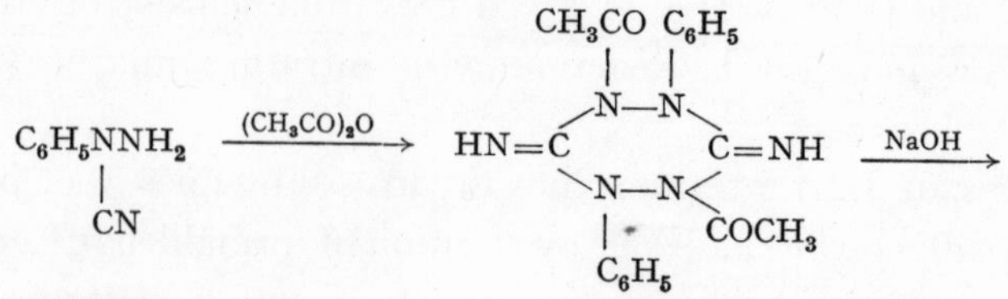

$$
C_6H_5NNH_2 \xrightarrow{(CH_3CO)_2O} \quad
$$

(XCIII)

(XCIV)

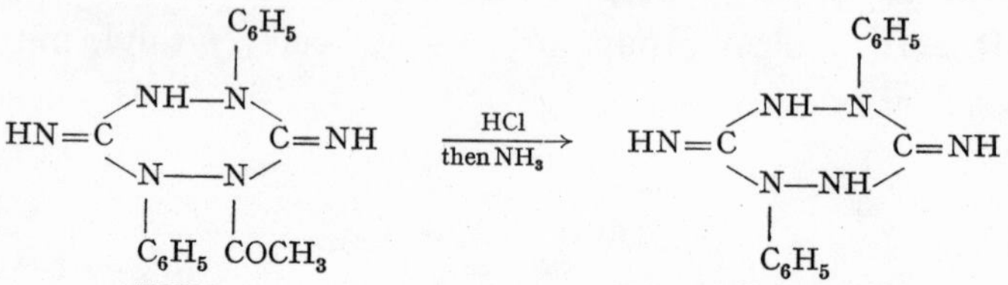

(XCV)

(XCVIa)

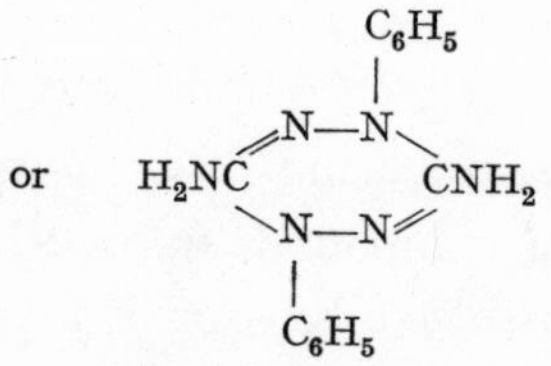

or

(78)

(XCVIb)

acetic anhydride to give the tetraacetyl derivative XCVII, which melts at 188–189°. The compound XCVIb reacts with benzaldehyde to form

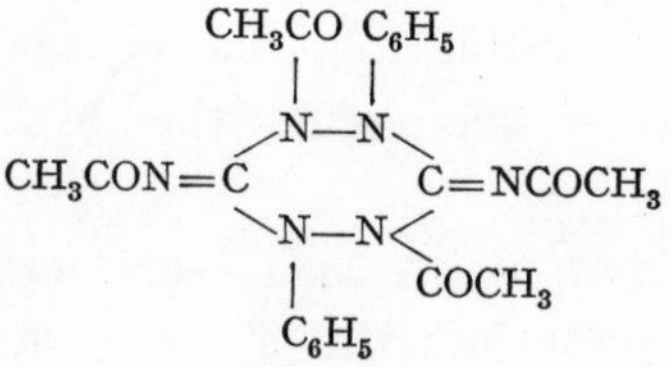

(XCVII)

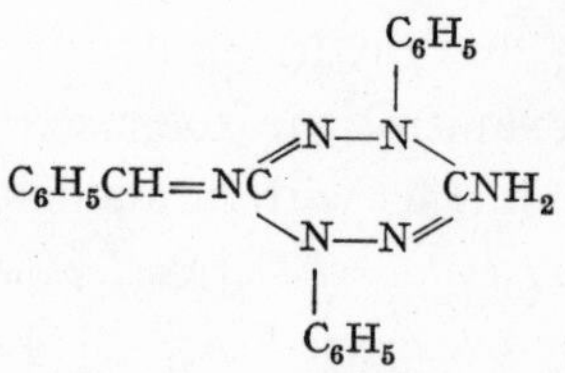

(XCVIII)

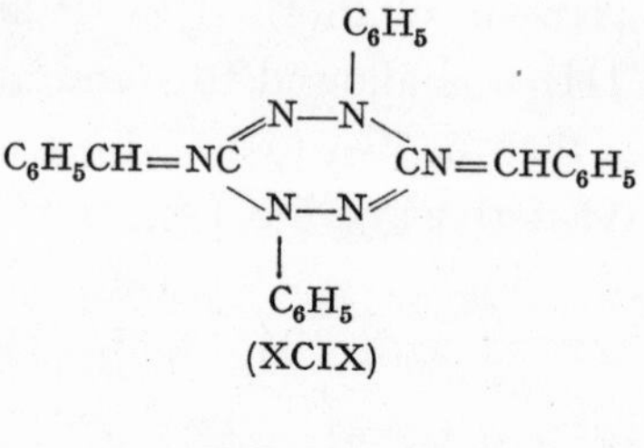

(XCIX)

the monobenzylidene derivative XCVIII, m.p. 183°, and the dibenzylidene derivative XCIX, m.p. 150°.

A series of 1,3-diaryl-6-s-tetrazinones and dihydro-6-s-tetrazinones[120] have been prepared by a rather unusual reaction starting with the dioximes of arylglyoxals (C). The reactions are shown in equation 79. When both Ar and Ar' are phenyl, the 6-s-tetrazinone CII crystallizes in white prisms and melts at 264° while the dihydro-6-s-tetrazinone

$$
\underset{\substack{\parallel \\ \text{NOH}}}{\text{ArCCH}}=\text{NOH} \xrightarrow{\text{Cl}_2} \underset{\substack{\parallel \quad \parallel \\ \text{HON} \quad \text{NOH}}}{\text{ArC--CCl}} \xrightarrow{\text{Ar'NHNH}_2} O=C\overset{\displaystyle \diagup \text{NHNH}\diagdown}{\underset{\displaystyle \diagdown \text{N--N}\diagup}{}}CAr
$$

(C)   (CI)

$$
\xrightarrow{\text{CrO}_3} O=C\overset{\displaystyle \diagup \text{N}=\text{N}\diagdown}{\underset{\displaystyle \diagdown \text{N--N}\diagup}{}}CAr \qquad\qquad (79)
$$

(CII)

CI melts at 174–175°. The dihydro-6-s-tetrazinone forms a monoacetate, m.p. 161°, and a diacetate melting at 174° The products obtained when Ar is *p*-tolyl and Ar' is phenyl are 1-phenyl-3-(*p*-tolyl)-6-s-tetrazinone, m.p. 265°, and 1-phenyl-3-(*p*-tolyl)-4,5-dihydro-6-s-tetrazinone, m.p. 190–191°. The latter compound forms a diacetyl derivative, m.p. 170°. Also obtained by this reaction was 1-(*p*-bromophenyl)-3-phenyl-4,5-dihydro-6-s-tetrazinone, m.p. 189–190°, and its diacetyl derivatives, m.p. 169–170°. Reduction of compounds of type CII with zinc and acetic acid removes the oxygen and forms tetrahydro-s-tetrazines (75).

Phenylurazine was first reported to have been synthesized by Busch and Heinrichs.[28] The structures proposed for it were CIII or

(CIII)   (CIV)

CIV. The triacetyl derivative, a benzylidene derivative and a methyl ether were prepared. Somewhat later Busch showed that phenylurazine was 4-amino-1-phenyl-1,2,4,1H-triazole-3,5-(2H,4H)-dione (CV) or its monoenolic or dienolic isomers. This was done by an unequivocal synthesis of CV (eq. 80).

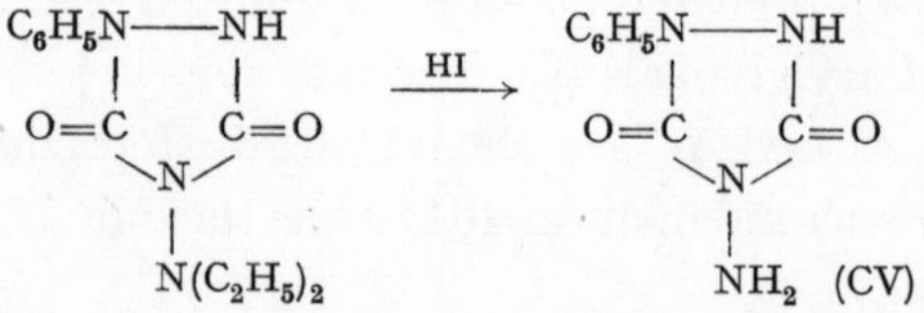

$$
\begin{array}{ccc}
\underset{\substack{| \\ O=C \\ \diagdown_N\diagup \\ | \\ N(C_2H_5)_2}}{C_6H_5N\text{---}NH} & \xrightarrow{\ \text{HI}\ } & \underset{\substack{| \\ O=C \quad C=O \\ \diagdown_N\diagup \\ | \\ NH_2 \ (CV)}}{C_6H_5N\text{---}NH}
\end{array}
\qquad (80)
$$

The synthesis of *diphenylurazine* was first reported by Pinner.[104, 106] The compound was called *phenylurazole* for a time and an incorrect molecular formula was reported. Synthesis was achieved by (a) heating 1-phenylsemicarbazide with urea, (b) heating phenylhydrazine with urea or biuret, or (c) simply heating 1-phenylsemicarbazide. The same compound and some of its derivatives were prepared by Skinner and Ruhemann,[146] Heller,[76] Rupe and Gebhardt,[140, 141] Busch and

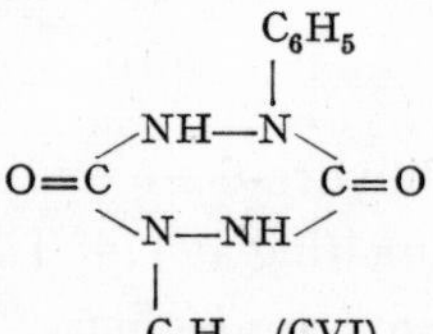

$$
\begin{array}{c}
C_6H_5 \\
| \\
N \\
O=C \overset{\diagup NH-N\diagdown}{\underset{\diagdown N-NH\diagup}{}} C=O \\
| \\
C_6H_5 \ (CVI)
\end{array}
$$

Stern,[32] and Acree.[1] After considerable controversy it was agreed that the compound was either 1,4-diphenyltetrahydro-3,6-s-tetrazinedione (CVI) or more probably its monoenolic form. However, this structure was retained for only a very short time. Busch[24] found that *diphenyl-*

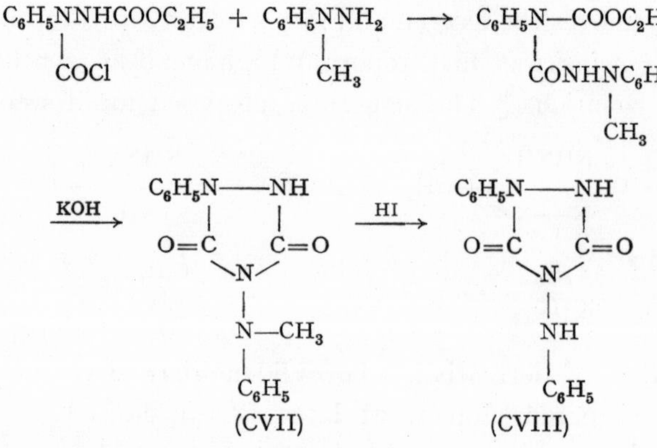

$$
\underset{\substack{| \\ COCl}}{C_6H_5NNHCOOC_2H_5} + \underset{\substack{| \\ CH_3}}{C_6H_5NNH_2} \longrightarrow \underset{\substack{| \\ CONHNC_6H_5 \\ | \\ CH_3}}{C_6H_5N\text{---}COOC_2H_5}
$$

$$
\xrightarrow{\ \text{KOH}\ } \underset{\substack{| \\ O=C \quad C=O \\ \diagdown_N\diagup \\ | \\ N\text{---}CH_3 \\ | \\ C_6H_5 \\ (CVII)}}{C_6H_5N\text{---}NH} \xrightarrow{\ \text{HI}\ } \underset{\substack{| \\ O=C \quad C=O \\ \diagdown_N\diagup \\ | \\ NH \\ | \\ C_6H_5 \\ (CVIII)}}{C_6H_5N\text{---}NH} \qquad (81)
$$

urazine could be synthesized by cleaving an N-methyl group from 4-(*N*-methylanilino)-1-phenyl-1,2,4,1*H*-triazole-3,5-(2*H*,4*H*)-dione (CVII) to give 4-anilino-1-phenyl-1,2,4,1*H*-triazole-3,5-(2*H*,4*H*)-dione (CVIII). This was identical with the compound that had been called diphenylurazine.

Peratoner and Siringo[103] have synthesized a compound that is either CVI or its 1,5-diphenyl isomer (CIX) by the action of phosgene on the sodium salt of phenylhydrazine (eq. 82). The product is a white

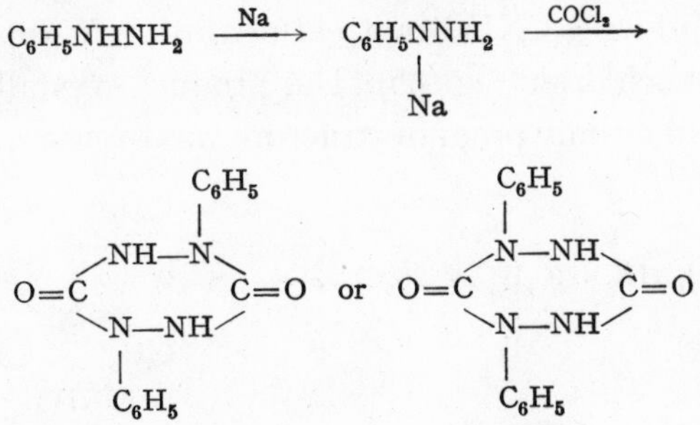

$$C_6H_5NHNH_2 \xrightarrow{\text{Na}} C_6H_5NNH_2 \xrightarrow{\text{COCl}_2}$$
$$\underset{\text{Na}}{|}$$

(82)

(CIX)

solid, m.p. 148°. This compound is soluble in alcohol and chloroform but insoluble in ether, petroleum ether, and water. It forms an amorphous acetyl derivative when it is treated with hot acetic anhydride.

Busch and co-workers[29] have synthesized 1,4-dihydro-1,6-diphenyl-3-*s*-tetrazinethiol (CXI), or more probably the isomer CXII, in

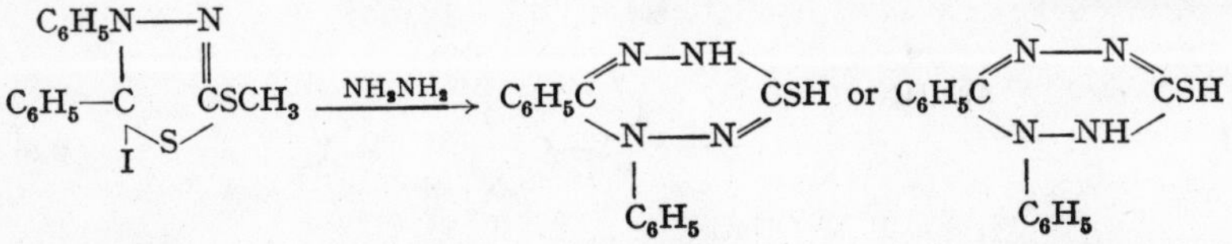

(83)

(CX)   (CXI)   (CXII)

which the double bonds are conjugated, by the reaction of hydrazine hydrate with 2,3-diphenyl-2-iodo-5-methylmercapto-1,3,4-thiodiazoline (CX). The thiol structure rather than the thione structure was assigned because the product is base soluble. It crystallizes in yellow needles, m.p. 208°. Reaction of CXI (or CXII) with methyl iodide gives a 3-methylmercapto derivative.

1-Phenylcarbohydrazide refluxed in alcohol with carbon disulfide and potassium hydroxide gives 3-oxo-1-phenyl-1,2,3,4-tetrahydro-6-s-tetrazinethiol (CXIII) melting at 206°.[72]

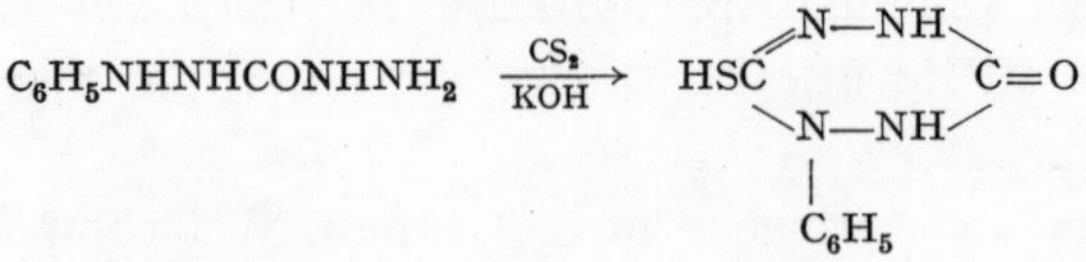

$$C_6H_5NHNHCONHNH_2 \xrightarrow[KOH]{CS_2} HSC \underset{N—NH}{\overset{N—NH}{<}} C=O \qquad (84)$$

$$\underset{(CXIII)}{\overset{|}{C_6H_5}}$$

Naik[96] has reported the synthesis of 1,2,4,5-tetraphenyltetrahydro-3,6-s-tetrazinedithione (CXIV) by treatment of N,N'-diphenylthiourea with sulfur monochloride (eq. 85) The product crystallizes in prisms melting at 160°. The only proof of structure was by the analyses. These

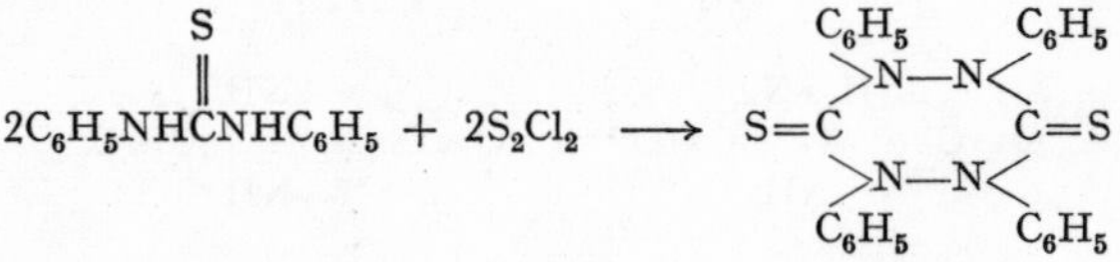

$$2C_6H_5\overset{S}{\overset{\|}{N}HCNHC_6H_5} + 2S_2Cl_2 \longrightarrow S=C \underset{\underset{C_6H_5}{>}N—N<}{\overset{\overset{C_6H_5}{>}N—N<}{}} C=S \qquad (85)$$

$$\underset{(CXIV)}{}$$

were not very good but they were close enough to the theoretical values to make the proposed structure seem likely.

Several compounds believed to be 1,4-diaryl-1,4-dihydro-s-tetrazines have been synthesized by Bowack and Lapworth,[16] Bülow and Neber,[21] [22] and Neber and Wörner[97] by treatment of haloglyoxylate and pyruvoyl chloride phenylhydrazones of the type CXV with bases.

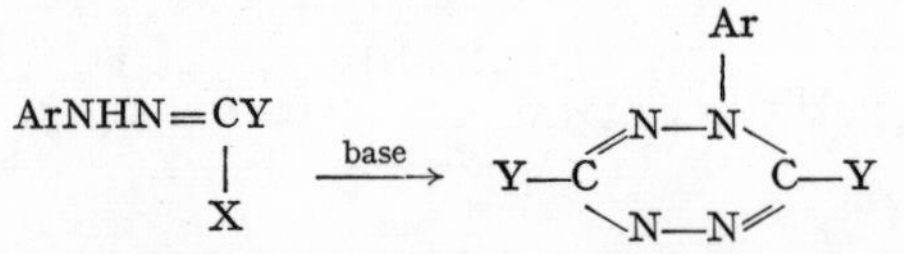

$$\underset{(CXV)}{ArNHN=CY \overset{|}{X}} \xrightarrow{base} \underset{(CXVI)}{Y—C \underset{\underset{Ar}{|}}{\overset{\overset{Ar}{|}}{\underset{N—N}{\overset{N—N}{}}}} C—Y} \qquad (86)$$

X = Cl or Br
Y = CH₃CO or COOC₂H₅

X = Cl or Br
Y = CH_3CO or $COOC_2H_5$

In the work of Bowack and Lapworth the compounds used of type CXV were those in which X = Br, Y = $COOC_2H_5$, and Ar was phenyl or p-tolyl. The bases used were hydroxides and carbonates of the alkali metals. The structures proposed for the products were diethyl 1,4-diphenyl and diethyl 1,4-di(p-tolyl)-1,4-dihydro-3,6-s-tetrazine dicarboxylate (CXVI, Ar = C_6H_5 or p-$CH_3C_6H_4$ and Y = $COOC_2H_5$).

Both compounds crystallize from ethyl acetate to form deep red crystals. The diphenyl compound melts at 145–146° while the di(*p*-tolyl) compound melts at 158–159°. Hydrolysis of the diphenyl compound in methanolic KOH gives 1,4-diphenyl-1,4-dihydro-3-*s*-tetrazinecarboxylic acid, which is yellow, m.p. 206–207° (dec.). Baker and co-workers report that the two dicarbethoxy compounds have ultraviolet absorption maxima at 375 mμ. They believe that this absorption peak is not consistent with these proposed structures. Bülow and Neber[21,22] have used this same reaction to prepare compounds of structure CXVI, Ar $= 2,4\text{-}Cl_2C_6H_3$ and Y $= COOC_2H_5$. The halogen in their starting material was chlorine. They used potassium ethoxide and potassium cyanide as bases. The product was believed to be diethyl 1,4-bis(2,4-dichlorophenyl)-1,4-dihydro-3,6-*s*-tetrazinedicarboxylate. This compound crystallizes from acetic acid in yellow needles melting at 196°. Since the method of synthesis used for this compound is essentially the same as that used by Bowack and Lapworth, it is likely that, if these latter workers' products are not 1,4-dihydro-*s*-tetrazines, neither is Bülow's product. Neber and Wörner[97] have used an organic base, pyridine, on pyruvoyl chloride phenylhydrazone (CXVII) to prepare what they believed to be 3,6-diacetyl-1,4-diphenyl-1,4-dihydro-*s*-tetrazine (CXIX). The first product obtained was believed to be the

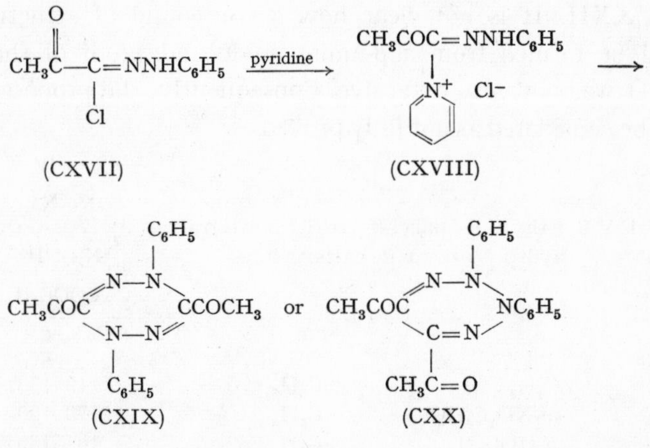

inner salt CXVIII. This, in boiling alcohol, forms CXIX and pyridine. CXIX crystallizes in deep red leaflets, m.p. 163°, from benzene and ligroin. The isomeric tetrazine CXX was also considered as a possibility but CXIX was preferred. In view of Baker's objections to the structures proposed by Bowack and Lapworth for their products and the similarity of their products to the others discussed here, it cannot be said with certainty that any of these compounds are 1,4-dihydro-s-tetrazines. It may be possible that they are all isomeric tetrazines similar to CXX. However, methods of synthesis would make the CXVI structures appear more likely.

A compound believed to be 3,6-diphenyl-1,2-dihydro-1,2-s-tetrazinedicarboxylic acid (CXXII)[129] has been isolated in 29% yield from treatment of β-benzoylaminohydrocinnamide with potassium hypobromite (eq. 88). The principal product was 4-phenyl-2-imidazolidone

$$
\begin{array}{c}
C_6H_5CHCH_2CONH_2 \xrightarrow{\ KOBr\ } C_6H_5CH-CH_2 + C_6H_5C\overset{N-N}{\underset{N-N}{\diagup \diagdown}}CC_6H_5 \\
|\qquad\qquad\qquad\qquad\qquad | \quad | \qquad\qquad\quad |\ | \\
NH \qquad\qquad\qquad\qquad NH\ NH \qquad\qquad HOOC\ COOH \\
|\qquad\qquad\qquad\qquad\qquad\ \diagdown C \diagup \\
CO \qquad\qquad\qquad\qquad\qquad \| \qquad\qquad\qquad (CXXII) \qquad (88) \\
|\qquad\qquad\qquad\qquad\qquad\ O \\
C_6H_5 \qquad\qquad\qquad\qquad (CXXI)
\end{array}
$$

(CXXI). The compound thought to have structure CXXII is acidic with a neutral equivalent of 165. It melts at 137–138°. Other acylaminohydrocinnamides also react with hypobromite to form 2-imidazolidones and CXXII. It is not clear how a compound of structure CXXII would be formed from a β-aminoamide and proof of the structure CXXII was not very extensive. Consequently, the proposed structure must be considered as not fully proved.

TABLE V-6. Ethyl 4,6-Diaryl-3-oxo-1,2,3,4-tetrahydro-1-s-tetrazinecarboxylates

$$
R-C\overset{N-N}{\underset{N-NH}{\diagup \diagdown}}C=O
$$
with R' on N and COOC$_2$H$_5$

R	R'	M.p., °C.
C_6H_5	C_6H_5	149–150
$m\text{-}NO_2C_6H_4$	C_6H_5	179–180
$p\text{-}HOC_6H_4$	C_6H_5	184–185
C_6H_5	$o\text{-}CH_3C_6H_4$	93–94
$o\text{-}HOC_6H_4$	$o\text{-}CH_3C_6H_4$	178

A series of ethyl 4,6-diaryl-3-oxo-1,2,3,4-tetrahydro-1-s-tetrazine-carboxylates (Table V-6) has been prepared by Busch and co-workers.[30] Arylhydrazones of aromatic aldehydes were allowed to react with diethyl azodicarboxylate to form tetrasubstituted tetrazanes of the type LX (eq. 47). These were then rearranged to the tetrahydro-s-tetrazines. These compounds all crystallize in white needles from alcohol. They probably exist in the enolic form as they are soluble in alkali.

Wuyts and Lacourt[169] have synthesized 2,4- or 2,5-bis(thioacyl)-1,4- or 1,5-diphenylhexahydro-s-tetrazines (CXXIII or CXXIV) by reaction of thioacyl derivatives of phenylhydrazine with paraformaldehyde (eq. 89). Equimolar amounts of the reagents were heated in alcohol. These structures were assigned on the basis of the known

$$
\underset{\text{RCNHNHC}_6\text{H}_5}{\overset{\text{S}}{\overset{\|}{}}} \xrightarrow{\text{CH}_2\text{O}}
\begin{array}{c}
\text{C}_6\text{H}_5 \quad \text{R—C=S} \\
\text{>N—N<} \\
\text{CH}_2 \qquad \text{CH}_2 \\
\text{>N—N<} \\
\text{C}_6\text{H}_5 \quad \text{RC=S} \\
\text{(CXXIII)}
\end{array}
\text{ or }
\begin{array}{c}
\text{RC=S} \quad \text{C}_6\text{H}_5 \\
\text{>N—N<} \\
\text{CH}_2 \qquad \text{CH}_2 \\
\text{>N—N<} \\
\text{C}_6\text{H}_5 \quad \text{RC=S} \\
\text{(CXXIV)}
\end{array}
\qquad (89)
$$

reaction of formaldehyde with hydrazines to give hexahydro-s-tetrazines and from a consideration of molecular weights and analytical data. Structure CXXIII was preferred on the basis that only one active hydrogen was present and the hydrogen atoms in CXXIV would be expected to be equivalent. This argument is not well founded, as the presence of active hydrogen in the product would argue against either of the proposed structures. The compounds obtained were: $R = CH_3$, m.p. 186°; $R = C_6H_5$, m.p. 187°; $R = p\text{-}CH_3C_6H_4$, m.p. 190°; $R = C_6H_5CH_2$, m.p. 172°; $R = \alpha\text{-}C_{10}H_7$, m.p. 200°. These compounds are soluble in chloroform. The bis(thiobenzoyl)diphenylhexahydro-s-tetrazine reacts with iodine in chloroform to give a blue decaiodo compound melting at 195°. Solution of this compound in acetone and precipitation with ether converted it to a hexaiodo derivative melting at 225°.

Other Carbocycles. 3,6-Di(β-naphthyl)-s-tetrazine has been synthesized by oxidation of the corresponding 1,2-dihydro-s-tetrazine (eq. 1, C_6H_5 is $\beta\text{-}C_{10}H_7$) using air, nitric acid, or nitrous acid.[81, 95, 110, 113] The product forms red needles, m.p. 246°. Wuyts and Lacourt[168] have reported the synthesis of 3,6-di(α-naphthyl)-s-tetrazine but they must have obtained the β-naphthyl compound, as 246°, the melting point given, was correct for the β-naphthyl compound. 3,6-Di(α-naphthyl)-s-tetrazine, red, m.p. 185°, was prepared by nitric acid oxidation of the product obtained from the reaction of hydrazine with thio-α-naphthamide.[81] It is presumed that the intermediate is 3,6-di(α-naphthyl)-1,2-dihydro-s-tetrazine, but this is not necessarily so. Stollé and co-workers[157] have synthesized 3,6-di(9-fluorenyl)-s-tetrazine (CXXV), crystallizing in rose-red needles, m.p. 225° (dec.), by oxidation of the corresponding 1,2-dihydro-s-tetrazine with amyl nitrite at room temperature. These tetrazines undergo the usual easy reduction to 1,2-dihydro-s-tetrazines with such reagents as zinc in acetic acid. 3,6-Di(9-fluorenyl)-s-tetrazine can be chlorinated in boiling carbon tetrachloride under ultraviolet light to give 3,6-bis(9-chloro-9-fluorenyl)-s-tetrazine (CXXVI). The dichloro compound can then be shaken with mercury to give a 75%

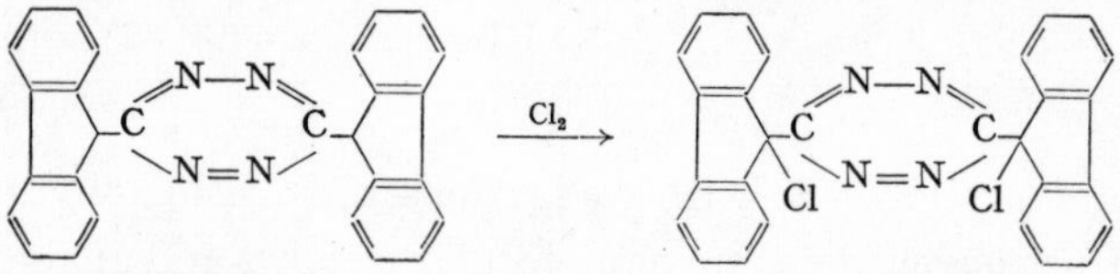

(90)

(CXXV)   (CXXVI)

yield of 3,6-bis(9-fluorenylidene)-3,6-dihydro-s-tetrazine (CXXVII), which then reacts readily with bromine to form 3,6-bis(9-bromo-9-fluorenyl)-s-tetrazine (CXXVIII). The chloro compound forms violet

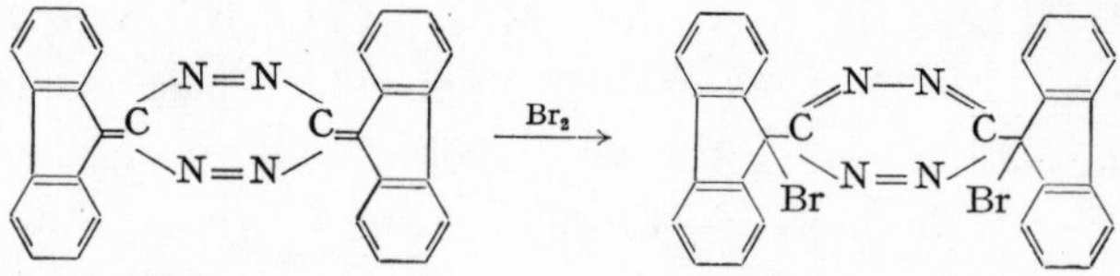

(91)

(CXXVII)   (CXXVIII)

needles, m.p. 206° (dec.). The bromo compound is a red violet powder decomposing at 260°. Attempted replacement of the bromine atoms in CXXVIII with ethoxyl groups by use of sodium ethoxide gave only bifluorene.

3,6-Di(β-naphthyl)-1,2-dihydro-s-tetrazine has been prepared by reaction of hydrazine with thio-β-naphthamide (eq. 4),[81] β-naphthonitrile (3),[95] and ethyl β-naphthimidate (5).[110, 113] The yields in all cases were very small. The compound is reported as crystallizing in yellow needles, and the usual melting point reported was 246° although one report[95] gave 239–240°. This compound was hydrolyzed with acid to β-naphthoic acid and 2,5-bis(β-naphthyl)-1,3,4-furodiazole.[95] Reaction of this dihydro-s-tetrazine with acetic anhydride gives a 1,2-diacetyl derivative melting at 210°.

3,6-Di(9-fluorenyl)-1,2-dihydro-s-tetrazine (CXXX) has been prepared in 50% yield by the action of hydrazine in boiling benzene on 9-diphenyleneacetyl chloride azine (CXXIX).[157] The same product was obtained from 1,1'-dichloro-1,1'-di-9-fluorenylideneazomethane (CXXXI) and hydrazine under the same conditions. Using CXXIX

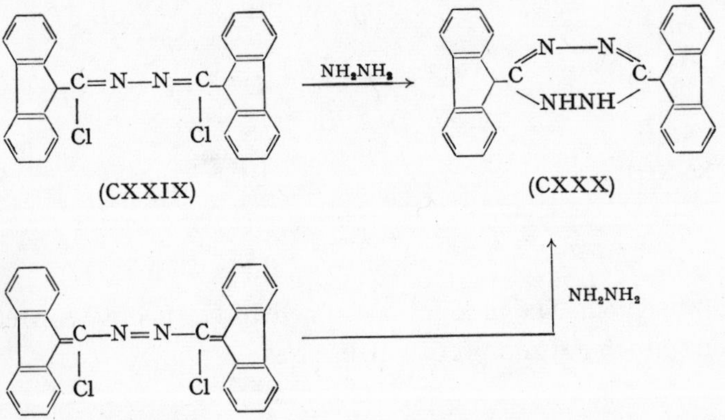

(CXXIX)   (CXXX)   (92)

(CXXXI)   (93)

there was obtained a 45% yield of 4-amino-3,5-di(9-fluorenyl)-1,2,4,4H-triazole in addition to CXXX. The compound CXXX melts at 296°. It can be oxidized with amyl nitrite at room temperature to give 3,6-di(fluorenyl)-s-tetrazine but in boiling benzene with amyl nitrite the product is 3,6-di(9-fluorenylidene-3,6-dihydro-s-tetrazine (CXXVII) obtained in 75% yield. At 240° CXXVII decomposes to α,α'-di(9-fluorenyl)succinonitrile and nitrogen.

Diazofluorene has been used by Staudinger[147] to synthesize 3,6-dibiphenylene-1,2,3,6-tetrahydro-s-tetrazine (CXXXII), as has already been discussed for 3,3,6,6-tetraphenyl-1,2,3,6-tetrahydro-s-tetrazine (eq. 76). Triethylphosphine forms an addition compound with diazo-

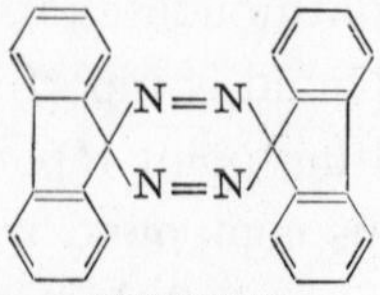

(CXXXII)

fluorene that reacts with water to give CXXXII. This product dissolves in sulfuric acid and precipitates out in fine orange needles, m.p. 325°, when water is added. It is insoluble in all organic solvents.

Friedheim has reported the synthesis of CXXXIV from formaldehyde and the hydrazine CXXXIII.[66,67] Neither proof of structure nor

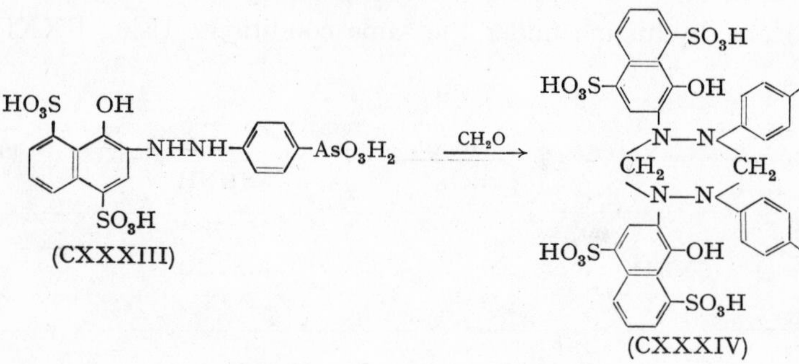

(94)

analysis was given. The product is claimed to be effective in treatment of certain spirochetal and protozoal diseases.

(3) Heterocyclic Rings Coupled Directly to s-Tetrazines

3,6-Di(5-tetrazolyl)-1,2-dihydro-s-tetrazine (CXXXV) and 3,6-di(5-tetrazolyl)-s-tetrazine (CXXXVI) have been synthesized by Lifschitz[84-86] and Curtius, Darapsky, and Müller[52] by the action of

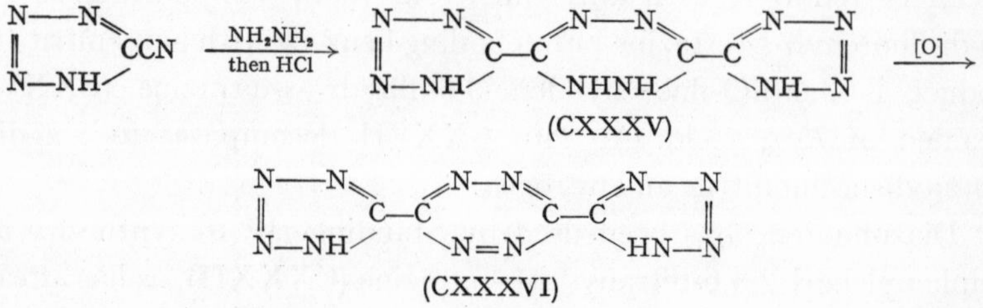

(95)

hydrazine on 5-cyanotetrazole (eq. 95). Lifschitz first reported these compounds as being pentazoleacetic acid derivatives. The *s*-tetrazine **CXXXVI** was called *isonitrosoazidoacetic acid hydrazide* (**CXXXVII**)

$$
\begin{array}{cc}
\underset{N=N}{\overset{N=N}{\big|}}\text{N—CCONHNH}_2 & \underset{N=N}{\overset{N=N}{\big|}}\text{NCH}_2\text{CONHNH}_2 \\
\qquad\quad \overset{\|}{\text{NOH}} & \\
\text{(CXXXVII)} & \text{(CXXXVIII)}
\end{array}
$$

and the 1,2-dihydro-*s*-tetrazine **CXXXV** was called *pentazidoacetic acid hydrazide* (**CXXXVIII**). Curtius and co-workers showed that these compounds were *s*-tetrazines by hydrolyzing **CXXXV** to 5-tetrazole-carboxylic acid and hydrazine. The reaction of 5-cyanotetrazole with hydrazine hydrate gave first a white dihydrazine salt of **CXXXV**, m.p. 230°, and a yellow diammonium salt melting above 280°. The total yield of both salts was 54%. These salts could be converted to the 1,2-dihydro-*s*-tetrazine **CXXXV** by treatment with hydrochloric acid. The 1,2-dihydro-*s*-tetrazine is a yellow solid that decomposes on heating. It is not very soluble in water or organic solvents. Treatment with sodium carbonate or potassium hydroxide gives metal salts believed to be of the type **CXXXIX**. The salts are neutralized by mineral acids but not

$$
\begin{array}{c}
\underset{\underset{M}{\big|}}{\underset{N=N}{\overset{N—N}{\big\|}}}\text{C—C}\overset{N—N}{\underset{\text{NHNH}}{\big\|}}\text{C—C}\underset{\underset{M}{\big|}}{\underset{N—N}{\overset{N—N}{\big\|}}} \\
\text{(CXXXIX)}
\end{array}
$$

by acetic acid. Oxidation of the 1,2-dihydro-*s*-tetrazine **CXXXV** with nitrous acid or chromic oxide gives the *s*-tetrazine **CXXXVI**. This compound crystallizes in crimson needles that decompose upon heating. The *s*-tetrazine forms an ammonium salt melting at 210° as well as two series of potassium and sodium salts. Lifschitz and Donath[86] have suggested that the two series of salts, one yellow and the other violet, are due to isomerism in the tetrazole rings. In one series the salts would be derived from the 1*H*-tetrazole rings and in the other series from the 2*H*-tetrazole rings.

It has been proposed by Lifschitz and Donath[86] that the dihydro-*s*-tetrazine has, instead of structure **CXXXV**, the structure **CXLII**, which would be 3,6-di(5-tetrazolyl)-1,4-dihydro-s-tetrazine. It was suggested that the reaction proceeds by formation of the imide hydra-

$$
\underset{(CXL)}{
\begin{array}{l}
N\text{---}N \\
\| \quad\;\; CCN \\
N\text{---}NH
\end{array}}
\xrightarrow{\;NH_2NH_2\;}
\underset{(CXL)}{
\begin{array}{l}
\qquad\qquad NH \\
N\text{---}N \quad\;\; \| \\
\| \quad\;\; C\text{---}C\text{---}NHNH_2 \\
N\text{---}NH
\end{array}}
\xrightarrow{\;H_2O\;}
\underset{(CXLI)}{
\begin{array}{l}
\qquad\qquad O \\
N\text{---}N \quad\;\; \| \\
\| \quad\;\; CCNHNH_2 \\
N\text{---}NH
\end{array}}
$$

$$
\longrightarrow
\underset{(CXLII)}{
\begin{array}{l}
N\text{---}N \qquad N\text{---}NH \qquad N\text{---}N \\
\| \quad\;\; C\text{---}C \qquad\qquad C\text{---}C \quad\;\; \| \\
N\text{---}NH \qquad NH\text{---}N \qquad HN\text{---}N
\end{array}}
\qquad (96)
$$

zide CXL, which is hydrolyzed to the hydrazide CXLI. This in turn dimerizes with loss of water to form CXLII. This view of the course of the reaction was mainly based on the fact that the imide hydrazide CXL could be isolated and heated with hydrazine in alcohol to give the dihydro-s-tetrazine. It has been found by other workers[99, 136, 143] that condensation of hydrazides in the manner proposed by Lifschitz and Donath[87] requires rather high temperatures and gives triazoles so it would appear that the proposals of Lifschitz as to structure and mechanism of reaction are incorrect.

Pinner and co-workers[112, 113] have synthesized 3,6-di(2-furyl)-1,2-dihydro-s-tetrazine by reaction of ethyl furimidate with hydrazine. The product crystallizes from alcohol in yellow needles, m.p. 208°. Reaction of this product with acetic anhydride gives a white diacetate melting at 197°. The 1,2-dihydro-s-tetrazine is easily oxidized with air or ferric chloride to 3,6-di(2-furyl)-s-tetrazine, which forms red needles, m.p. 195°. Heating the 1,2-dihydro-s-tetrazine with 25% hydrochloric acid produces an isomer for which Pinner proposed the structure 3,6-di(2-furyl)-1,4-dihydro-s-tetrazine. Later work indicates that the compound is 4-amino-3,5-di(2-furyl)-1,2,4,4H-triazole.

(4) Rings Coupled through Carbon Chains to s-Tetrazines

A variety of benzyl- and benzhydryl-s-tetrazines have been prepared (Table V-7). 3,6-Dibenzyl-s-tetrazine, 6-benzhydryl-3-phenyl-s-tetrazine, 3,6-dibenzhydryl-s-tetrazine, 6-benzhydryl-3-methyl-s- tetra-

TABLE V-7. s-Tetrazines Substituted by Arylmethyl Groups
$$R-C\overset{N-N}{\underset{N=N}{<}}C-R'$$

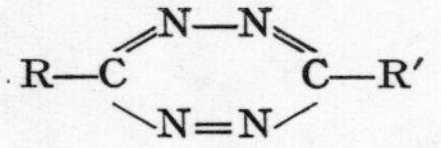

R	R'	M.p., °C.	Color and crystal form	Ref.
$C_6H_5CH_2$	$C_6H_5CH_2$	74, 76	Red needles, red prisms	80, 110, 113, 167
$(C_6H_5)_2CH$	CH_3	108		6
$(C_6H_5)_2CH$	C_6H_5	136–137	Violet-red	4, 5
$(C_6H_5)_2CH$	$(C_6H_5)_2CH$	172, 174	Violet needles	4, 6, 156
$(C_6H_5)_2C{-}OH$	C_6H_5	137		5
$(C_6H_5)_2C{-}OC_2H_5$	C_6H_5	161		5
$(C_6H_5)_2C{-}Br$	C_6H_5	126		5
$(C_6H_5)_2C{-}Cl$	$(C_6H_5)_2C{-}Cl$	162 (dec.)	Violet-red	158
$(C_6H_5)_2C{-}Br$	$(C_6H_5)_2C{-}Br$	162		158
$p\text{-}NH_2C_6H_4CH_2$	$p\text{-}NH_2C_6H_4CH_2$	166	Red platelets	81
$p\text{-}CH_3CONHC_6H_4CH_2$	$p\text{-}CH_3CONHC_6H_4CH_2$	205	Violet needles	81
$p\text{-}(\beta\text{-}HOC_{10}H_7N{=}N)C_6H_4CH_2$	$p\text{-}(\beta\text{-}HOC_{10}H_7N{=}N)C_6H_4CH_2$	200 (dec.)	Red amorphous	81

zine and 3,6-bis(p-aminobenzyl)-s-tetrazine have been prepared by oxidation of the corresponding 1,2-dihydro-s-tetrazine (eq. 1). The yields reported ranged from 10 to 35%.

Aspelund[4-6] and Stollé and Laux[156] have used nitrite in this oxidation. The yields were usually poor and considerable amounts of triazoles isomeric to the desired s-tetrazines were obtained. They found that the presence of calcined soda reduced the side reaction. 3,6-Bis(p-aminobenzyl)-s-tetrazine forms a diacetate and can be diazotized and coupled with β-naphthol to give an azo-s-tetrazine CXLIII.[81] Aspelund[5] has reported the synthesis of 3-(α-bromobenzhydryl)-6-phenyl-s-tetrazine (CXLV) by bromination of 3-benzhydryl-6-phenyl-s-tetrazine

$$p\text{-}NH_2C_6H_4CH_2C \overset{N-N}{\underset{N=N}{\diagdown\diagup}} CCH_2C_6H_4NH_2\text{-}p \quad \xrightarrow[HNO_2]{H^+} \quad \xrightarrow{\beta\text{-naphthol}}$$

$$\text{(97)}$$

(CXLIII)

(CXLIV). The bromo-s-tetrazine can be hydrolyzed to 3-(α-hydroxybenzhydryl)-6-phenyl-s-tetrazine (eq. 101), treated with alcohol and ammonia to give 3-(α-ethoxybenzhydryl)-6-phenyl-s-tetrazine (CXLVII), or heated with mercury and oxygen to give the peroxide CXLVIII (eq. 103). The hydroxy-s-tetrazine CXLVI can also be synthesized by direct oxidation of CXLIV with potassium dichromate (eq. 99) and by reduction of the peroxide CXLVIII with hydroquinone or benzidine (eq. 103). Aspelund has also synthesized CXLVI by chlorination of diphenylacetyl chloride benzoyl chloride azine (CXLIX) to give CL followed by treatment with mercury to form the peroxide CLI, which was converted to 3-(α-hydroxybenzhydryl)-6-phenyl-s-tetrazine (CXLVI) with hydrazine.

3,6-Bis(α-halobenzhydryl)-s-tetrazines have been synthesized by direct halogenation of 3,6-dibenzhydryl-s-tetrazine (CLII) and by addition of halogen to 3,6-bis(diphenylmethylene)-3,6-dihydro-s-tetrazine (CLIII).

This class of s-tetrazines is soluble in acetic acid and benzene but is

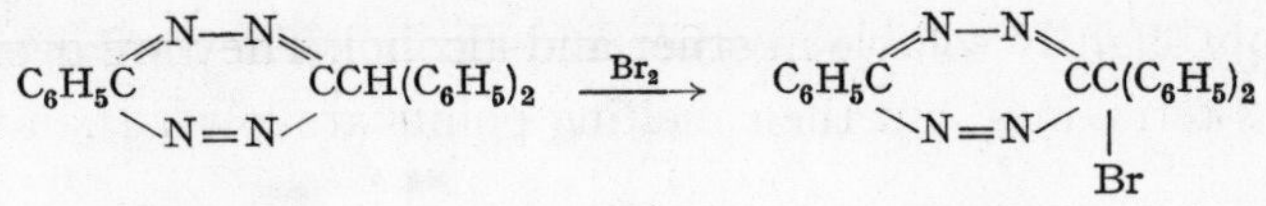

$$C_6H_5C \underset{N=N}{\overset{N-N}{\diagdown\diagup}} CCH(C_6H_5)_2 \xrightarrow{Br_2} C_6H_5C \underset{N=N}{\overset{N-N}{\diagdown\diagup}} CC(C_6H_5)_2 \quad (98)$$
$$\underset{Br}{|}$$

(CXLIV)   (CXLV)

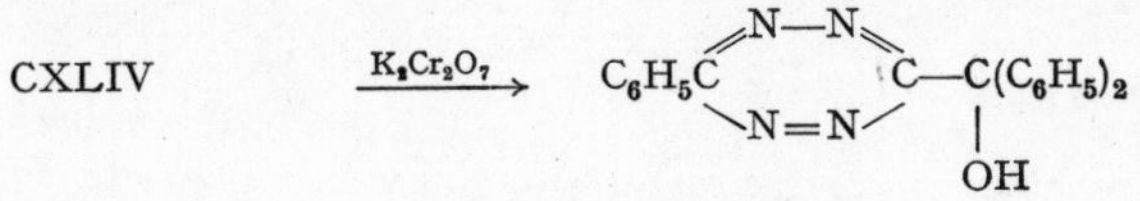

$$\text{CXLIV} \xrightarrow{K_2Cr_2O_7} C_6H_5C \underset{N=N}{\overset{N-N}{\diagdown\diagup}} C-C(C_6H_5)_2 \quad (99)$$
$$\underset{OH}{|}$$

(CXLVI)

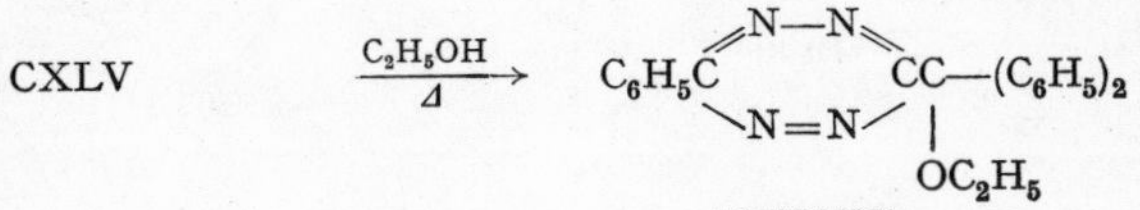

$$\text{CXLV} \xrightarrow[\Delta]{C_2H_5OH} C_6H_5C \underset{N=N}{\overset{N-N}{\diagdown\diagup}} CC-(C_6H_5)_2 \quad (100)$$
$$\underset{OC_2H_5}{|}$$

(CXLVII)

$$\text{CXLV} \xrightarrow[\Delta]{H_2O} \text{CXLVI} \quad (101)$$

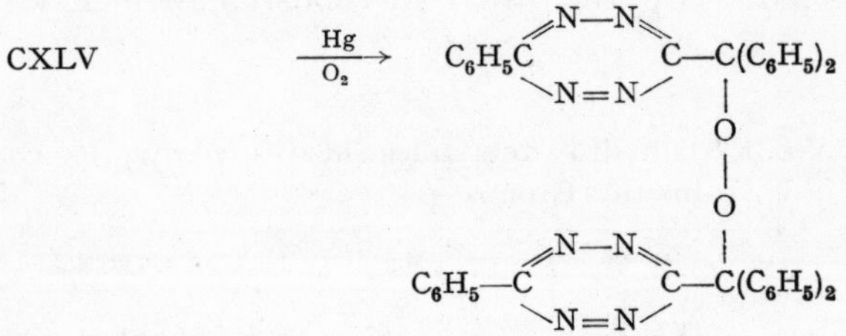

$$\text{CXLV} \xrightarrow[O_2]{Hg} C_6H_5C \underset{N=N}{\overset{N-N}{\diagdown\diagup}} C-C(C_6H_5)_2$$
$$\underset{O}{|}$$
$$\underset{O}{|}$$
$$C_6H_5-C \underset{N=N}{\overset{N-N}{\diagdown\diagup}} C-C(C_6H_5)_2 \quad (102)$$

(CXLVIII)

$$\text{CXLVIII} \xrightarrow[\text{or benzidine}]{\text{hydroqunone}} \text{CXLVI} \quad (103)$$

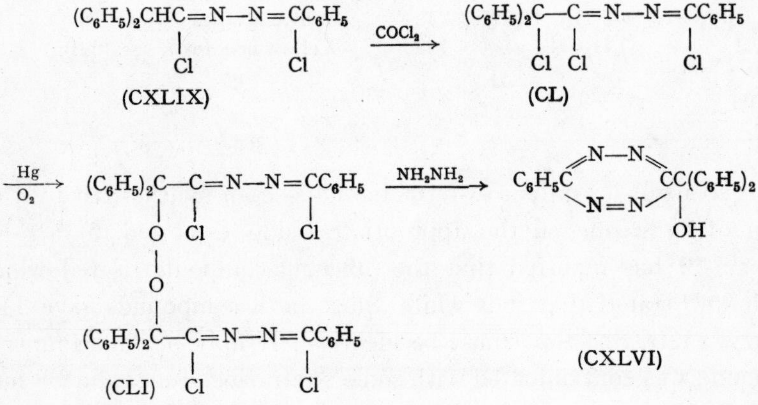

$$(C_6H_5)_2CHC=N-N=CC_6H_5 \xrightarrow{COCl_2} (C_6H_5)_2C-C=N-N=CC_6H_5$$
$$\underset{Cl}{|} \quad \underset{Cl}{|} \qquad\qquad \underset{Cl}{|}\,\underset{Cl}{|} \qquad \underset{Cl}{|}$$

(CXLIX)   (CL)

$$\xrightarrow[O_2]{Hg} (C_6H_5)_2C-C=N-N=CC_6H_5 \xrightarrow{NH_2NH_2} C_6H_5C \underset{N=N}{\overset{N-N}{\diagdown\diagup}} CC(C_6H_5)_2 \quad (104)$$
$$\underset{O}{|}\ \underset{Cl}{|} \qquad \underset{Cl}{|} \qquad\qquad\qquad \underset{OH}{|}$$
$$\underset{O}{|}$$
$$(C_6H_5)_2C-C=N-N=CC_6H_5$$
$$\underset{Cl}{|} \qquad \underset{Cl}{|}$$

(CLI)   (CXLVI)

usually only slightly soluble in ether and alcohol. They are deep red as
are other s-tetrazines, but their melting points are lower than those of

$$(C_6H_5)_2CHC \underset{\underset{\searrow N=N \nearrow}{}}{\overset{N-N}{\diagup \diagdown}} C-CH(C_6H_5)_2 \xrightarrow{\ Cl_2\ } (C_6H_5)_2C \underset{\underset{Cl}{|}}{\overset{N-N}{\diagup \diagdown}} \overset{|}{\underset{\searrow N=N \nearrow}{C}} C-C(C_6H_5)_2 \underset{Cl}{|} \quad (105)$$

(CLII)

$$Cl_2 \Big\updownarrow Hg$$

$$(C_6H_5)_2C \underset{\underset{Br}{|}}{\overset{N-N}{\diagup \diagdown}} \overset{|}{\underset{\searrow N=N \nearrow}{C}} C-C(C_6H_5)_2 \xleftarrow{\ Br_2\ } (C_6H_5)_2C \underset{\searrow N=N \nearrow}{\overset{N-N}{\diagup \diagdown}} C=C(C_6H_5)_2$$

Br   Br

(CLIII)

most s-tetrazines. As is usual, they are very easily reduced to the 1,2-
dihydro-s-tetrazines.

Benzyl- and benzhydryl-1,2-dihydro-s-tetrazines (Table V-8) have
been prepared by the usual methods. 3,6-Dibenzyl- and 3,6-bis(α-

TABLE V-8. 1,2-Dihydro-s-tetrazines Substituted by $R-C \underset{\searrow NHNH \nearrow}{\overset{N-N}{\diagup \diagdown}} C-R'$ Arylmethyl Groups

R	R'	M.p., °C.	Color and crystal form	Ref.
$C_6H_5CH_2$	$C_6H_5CH_2$	158	Red needles, white needles	83, 110,113
$(C_6H_5)_2CH$	CH_3	161–162		6
$(C_6H_5)_2CH$	C_6H_5	216	Yellow needles	4, 5, 6
$(C_6H_5)_2CH$	$(C_6H_5)_2CH$	190	Flocculent	4, 6, 156, 158
$p\text{-}NH_2C_6H_4CH_2$	$p\text{-}NH_2C_6H_4CH_2$	212	White needles	81
C_6H_5CH | OH	C_6H_5CH | OH	193	Yellow needles	110, 113

hydroxybenzyl)-1,2-dihydro-s-tetrazine have been synthesized by the
action of hydrazine on the appropriate imido ester (eq. 5).[80, 110, 113]
Pinner[110, 113] has reported that the dibenzyl compound is red while
Junghahn[80] stated that it is white. Since both compounds gave 3,6-
dibenzyl-s-tetrazine they must be identical. It may be that Pinner's
compound was contaminated with some s-tetrazine. Junghahn[80, 81] has

used thio-*p*-aminophenylacetamide and hydrazine to prepare 3,6-bis(*p*-aminobenzyl)-1,2-dihydro-*s*-tetrazine in 45% yield (eq. 4). 3,6-Di(benzhydryl)-1,2-dihydro-*s*-tetrazine was prepared by the condensation of diphenylacetyl chloride azine with hydrazine (eq. 6, $(C_6H_5)_2CH$).[156] Aspelund[5,6] has synthesized 3-benzhydryl-6-phenyl- and 3-benzhydryl-6-methyl-1,2-dihydro-*s*-tetrazine using the same method, the former compound being obtained in 20% yield. Oxadiazoles and triazoles were obtained as side products. 3,6-Bis(α-hydroxybenzhydryl)-1,2-dihydro-*s*-tetrazine forms a tetraacetate, m.p. 203°, with acetic anhydride and hydrolyses with acid to benzaldehyde, formic acid, and hydrazine.[113] 3,6-Dibenzhydryl-1,2-dihydro-*s*-tetrazine reacts with diphenylacetyl chloride in pyridine to form 3,6-dibenzhydryl-1-diphenylacetyl-1,2-dihydro-*s*-tetrazine, m.p. 185°.[158] These 1,2-dihydro-*s*-tetrazines are benzene soluble but are not very soluble in alcohol or ether.

It has been reported that 3,6-dibenzyl-1,2-dihydro-*s*-tetrazine isomerizes upon acid treatment to 3,6-dibenzyl-1,4-dihydro-*s*-tetrazine.[110, 113] Since Bülow and Weber[23] have shown that such acid treatment of 1,2-dihydro-*s*-tetrazines gives 1,2,4,4*H*-triazoles, it seems likely that the supposed 3,6-dibenzyl-1,4-dihydro-*s*-tetrazine is rather 4-amino-3,5-dibenzyl-1,2,4,4*H*-triazole.

The synthesis and some of the reactions of 3,6-bis(diphenylmethylene)-3,6-dihydro-*s*-tetrazine (CLIII) have already been mentioned (105).[158] This compound forms black prisms that deflagrate at 170°. The products of the decomposition are tetraphenylsuccinonitrile and nitrogen.

Datta and Gupta[61] have found that addition of *N,N*'-dichlorourea to a large excess of a cold solution of benzylamine gives two products (eq. 106). One of these is *p*-urazine, and the structure proposed for the other was 1,5-dibenzyl-6-phenyl-3-oxohexahydro-6-*s*-tetrazinol (CLIV).

$$ClNHCONHCl + C_6H_5CH_2NH_2 \longrightarrow$$

$$
\begin{array}{c}
C_6H_5CH_2 \\
| \\
HO{\diagdown}N{-}NH{\diagdown} \\
C \qquad\qquad C{=}O \qquad (106) \\
C_6H{\diagup}N{\diagup}{\diagdown}N{-}NH{\diagup} \\
| \\
C_6H_5CH_2 \\
(CLIV)
\end{array}
$$

This is a white crystalline compound, m.p. 146°. It was thought that a part of the benzylamine was chlorinated by the N,N'-dichlorourea. This was followed by condensation of one molecule of N,N'-dichlorourea, one molecule of benzylamine, one molecule of water, and two molecules of benzylchloramine to give CLIV, ammonium chloride, and hydrochloric acid. The structure of the product was not proved, and analysis was the only indication that it had the structure proposed. In view of this and of the great likelihood that a condensation such as the one suggested would not occur, it is probable that the proposed structure is incorrect.

While showing that phenylurazine and diphenylurazine were triazoles, Busch[24] synthesized a tetrahydro-3,6-s-tetrazinedione by unequivocal methods. The compound synthesized was 1,2-dibenzyl-5-phenyltetrahydro-3,6-tetrazinedione (CLVI). It was obtained by cyclization of 1,2-dibenzyl-4-phenyl-5-carbethoxycarbohydrazide (CLV)

$$
\begin{array}{ccc}
\text{C}_6\text{H}_5\text{N—NHCOOC}_2\text{H}_5 & & \underset{}{\overset{C_6H_5}{\underset{N——N}{\overset{N—NH}{O=C\qquad C=O}}}} \\[2mm]
\mid & \xrightarrow{\text{KOH}} & \\
\text{O}=\text{C—N—NHCH}_2\text{C}_6\text{H}_5 & & \\
\mid & & \mid\quad\mid \\
\text{C}_6\text{H}_5\text{CH}_2 & & \text{C}_6\text{H}_5\text{CH}_2\text{CH}_2\text{C}_6\text{H}_5 \\
\text{(CLV)} & & \text{(CLVI)}
\end{array}
\qquad (107)
$$

with potassium hydroxide in boiling alcohol. The yield was 50%. The product crystallizes in white leaflets, m.p. 180°. It is neutral in contrast to diphenylurazine, which is a monobasic acid. This is further support for the belief that diphenylurazine is not tetrahydro-3,6-s-tetrazinedione.

2. CONDENSED s-TETRAZINES

The reported instances of s-tetrazines having condensed ring systems are very few with the exception of aldehyde and ketone derivatives of p-urazines. Since it is believed that these compounds are derivatives of 4-amino-1,2,4,1H-triazole-3,5-(2H,4H)-diones, they will not be considered in this section.

The thermal condensation of formhydrazide with itself at 180°

gives 4-amino-1,2,4,4H-triazole, formic acid, water, and a compound crystallizing from ethanol in white plates,[100] m.p. 263°. Pellizzari called this compound *diazodimethinetetrazoline* and proposed either CLVII or CLVIII as its structure. Hydrolysis of the compound with hydrochloric

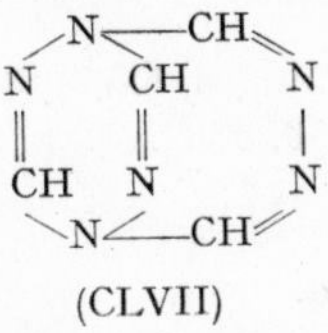

$$
\begin{array}{cc}
\text{(CLVII)} & \text{(CLVIII)}
\end{array}
$$

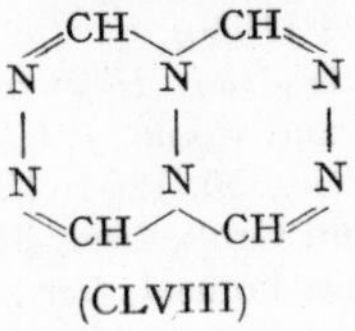

acid gives 4-amino-1,2,4,4H-triazole, formic acid, and hydrazine. The structure CLVIII is the more probable one in view of its two fused six-membered rings. If such a structure is present, it could be demonstrated by reduction to CLIX.

Hofmann and Storm[78] prepared the fused ring system CLIX, which they called *tetraformaltrisazine*, by the reaction of formalin with

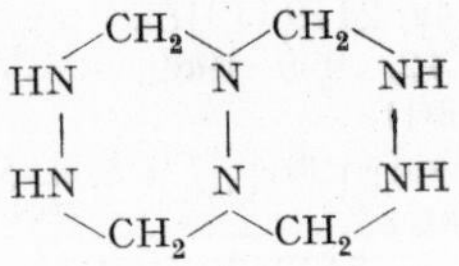

$$
\text{(CLIX)}
$$

hydrazine hydrate. In contrast to the polymer that had been reported previously from this reaction, CLIX crystallizes from water in flat needles as a dihydrate. It has no definite melting point. At about 225° the dihydrate loses water and volatilizes. CLIX is unstable to acids and stable to alkali, and forms precipitates with mercuric chloride and silver nitrate and reduces alkaline solutions of silver, mercuric, and cupric salts.

The preparation of the fused ring compound XI by Müller[294] has already been discussed (eq. 10). In this synthesis s-tetrazine reacts with diazomethane in ether to eliminate three equivalents of nitrogen and give a brown precipitate. The proposed structure for the product is shown in formula XI. It was called *trimethylenetetrazine* by Müller. The only products isolated from sulfuric acid hydrolysis were formaldehyde and hydrazine.

Bibliography

1. Acree, *Ber.*, **35**, 553 (1902).
2. Arndt and Bielich, *Ber.*, **56**, 809 (1923).
3. Aspelund, *Ber.*, **63**, 1191 (1930).
4. Aspelund, *Ber.*, **63**, 1197 (1930).
5. Aspelund, *Acta Acad. Aboensis Math. et Phys.*, **5**, No. 1, 1; through *Chem. Abstr.*, **24**, 4031 (1930).
6. Aspelund, *Acta Acad. Aboensis Math. et Phys.*, **6**, No. 4, 14 pp. (1932).
7. Baker, Ollis, and Poole, *J. Chem. Soc.*, **1950**, 3389.
8. Bamberger, *Ber.*, **30**, 1263 (1897).
9. Bamberger and Grob, *Ber.*, **34**, 523 (1901).
10. Bamberger and Pemsel, *Ber.*, **36**, 57 (1903).
11. Bamberger and Pemsel, *Ber.*, **36**, 347 (1903).
12. Bamberger and Pemsel, *Ber.*, **36**, 372 (1903).
13. Beckett and Dyson, *J. Chem. Soc.*, **1937**, 1358.
14. Bischoff, *Ber.*, **31**, 3250 (1898).
15. Bowack and Lapworth, *Pr. Chem. Soc.*, **21**, 257 (1905).
16. Bowack and Lapworth, *J. Chem. Soc.*, **87**, 1854 (1905).
17. Buckley and Ray, Brit. Pat. 622, 955, May 10, 1949.
18. Bülow, *Ber.*, **39**, 2618 (1906).
19. Bülow, *Ber.*, **39**, 4106 (1906).
20. Bülow, *Ber.*, **39**, 4109 (1906).
21. Bülow and Neber, *Ber.*, **45**, 3732 (1912).
22. Bülow and Neber, *Ber.*, **49**, 2179 (1916).
23. Bülow and Weber, *Ber.*, **42**, 1990 (1909).
24. Busch, *Ber.*, **34**, 2311 (1901).
25. Busch, *Festschrift*, Erlangen (1901); *J. Chem. Soc.*, **80**, 488 (1901).
26. Busch, *Ber.*, **40**, 2093 (1907).
27. Busch and Grohmann, *Ber.*, **34**, 2320 (1901).
28. Busch and Heinrichs, *Ber.*, **33**, 455 (1900).
29. Busch, Kamphausen, and Schneider, *J. prakt. Chem.*, **67**, 201 (1903).
30. Busch, Müller, and Schwarz, *Ber.*, **56**, 1600 (1923).
31. Busch and Schneider, *J. prakt. Chem.*, **89**, 319 (1914).
32. Busch and Stern, *J. prakt. Chem.*, [2], **60**, 235 (1899).
33. Chabrier and Renard, *Compt. rend.*, **230**, 1673 (1950).
34. Chattaway, *J. Chem. Soc.*, **95**, 235 (1909).
35. Chattaway and Walker, *J. Chem. Soc.*, **127**, 975 (1925).
36. Colman, *Ber.*, **30**, 2010 (1897).
37. Curtius, *Ber.*, **17**, 953 (1884).
38. Curtius, *Ber.*, **18**, 1284 (1885).
39. Curtius, *Ber.*, **20**, 1632 (1887).
40. Curtius, *J. prakt. Chem.*, **39**, 107 (1889).
41. Curtius, *J. prakt. Chem.*, **52**, 272 (1895).
42. Curtius, *Z. angew. Chem.*, **24**, 2 (1911).
43. Curtius, Darapsky, and Müller, *Ber.*, **39**, 3410 (1906).
44. Curtius, Darapsky, and Müller, *Ber.*, **39**, 3776 (1906).
45. Curtius, Darapsky, and Müller, *Ber.*, **40**, 84 (1907).
46. Curtius, Darapsky, and Müller, *Ber.*, **40**, 815 (1907).
47. Curtius, Darapsky, and Müller, *Ber.*, **40**, 1176 (1907).
48. Curtius, Darapsky, and Müller, *Ber.*, **40**, 1470 (1907).
49. Curtius, Darapsky, and Müller, *Ber.*, **41**, 3140 (1908).

50. Curtius, Darapsky, and Müller, *Ber.*, **41**, 3161 (1908).
51. Curtius, Darapsky, and Müller, *Ber.*, **42**, 3284 (1909).
52. Curtius, Darapsky, and Müller, *Ber.*, **48**, 1614 (1915).
53. Curtius and Dedichen, *J. prakt. Chem.*, **50**, 241 (1894).
54. Curtius and Heidenreich, *Ber.*, **27**, 2684 (1894).
55. Curtius and Heidenreich, *J. prakt. Chem.*, **52**, 454 (1895).
56. Curtius and Hess, *J. prakt. Chem.*, **125**, 40 (1930).
57. Curtius and Jay, *J. prakt. Chem.*, **39**, 27 (1889).
58. Curtius and Lang, *J. prakt. Chem.*, **38**, 531 (1888).
59. Curtius and Rimele, *Ber.*, **41**, 3108 (1908).
60. Darapsky and Adamczewski, *J. prakt. Chem.*, **97**, 182 (1918).
61. Datta and Gupta, *J. Am. Chem. Soc.*, **35**, 1183 (1913).
62. Diels, *Ber.*, **47**, 2183 (1914).
63. Edgerley and Sutton, *J. Chem. Soc.*, **1950**, 3394.
64. Franzen and Kraft, *J. prakt. Chem.*, **84**, 122 (1911).
65. French Patent 866,741, August 30, 1941.
66. Friedheim, Brit. Patent 582,043, November 4, 1946.
67. Friedheim, U.S. Patent 2,419,348, April 22, 1947.
68. Fromm, Layer, and Nerz, *Ann.*, **433**, 1 (1923).
69. Goodwin and Bailey, *J. Am. Chem. Soc.*, **47**, 167 (1925).
70. Guha and De, *J. Chem. Soc.*, **125**, 1215 (1924).
71. Guha and De, *Quart J. Indian Chem. Soc.*, **1**, 141 (1924).
72. Guha and Hye, *J. Indian Chem. Soc.*, **7**, 933 (1930).
73. Hantzsch and Lehmann, *Ber.*, **33**, 3668 (1900).
74. Hantzsch and Lehmann, *Ber.*, **34**, 2506 (1901).
75. Hantzsch and Silberrad, *Ber.*, **33**, 58 (1900).
76. Heller, *Ann.*, **263**, 269 (1891).
77. Hofmann and Ehrhart, *Ber.*, **45**, 2731 (1912).
78. Hofmann and Storm, *Ber.*, **45**, 1725 (1912).
79. Holmberg, *Arkiv Kemi Mineral. Geol.*, **A25**, No. 18, 18 pp. (1947).
80. Junghahn, *Ber.*, **31**, 312 (1898).
81. Junghahn and Bunimowicz, *Ber.*, **35**, 3932 (1902).
82. Knorr and Weidel, *Ber.*, **42**, 3523 (1909).
83. Koenigsberger and Vogt, *Physik. Z.*, **14**, 1269 (1913).
84. Lifschitz, *Ber.*, **48**, 410 (1915).
85. Lifschitz, *Ber.*, **49**, 489 (1916).
86. Lifschitz and Donath, *Rec. trav. chim.*, **37**, 270 (1918).
87. Linch, *J. Chem. Soc.*, **101**, 1755 (1912).
88. Lossen and Statius, *Ann.*, **298**, 91 (1897).
89. Maccoll, *J. Chem. Soc.*, **1946**, 670.
90. Mazourewitch, *Bull. soc. chim.*, **41**, 637 (1927).
91. Mester, *Magyar Chem. Folyóirat*, **51/53**, 32 (1945–47); through *Chem. Abstr.*, **43**, 8979 (1949).
92. Müller, *Ber.*, **41**, 3116 (1908).
93. Müller, *Ber.*, **42**, 3270 (1909).
94. Müller, *Ber.*, **47**, 3001 (1914).
95. Müller and Herrdegen, *J. prakt. Chem.*, **102**, 113 (1921).
96. Naik, *J. Chem. Soc.*, **119**, 1166 (1921).
97. Neber and Wörner, *Ann.*, **526**, 173 (1936).
98. Pellizzari, *Gazz. chim. ital.*, **26**, *II*, 430 (1896).
99. Pellizzari, *Atti accad. Lincei*, [5], **8**, 327 (1899).
100. Pellizzari, *Gazz. chim. ital.*, **39**, *I*, 520 (1909).

101. Pellizzari, *Gazz. chim. ital.*, **53**, 661 (1923).
102. Pellizzari and Roncoglio, *Gazz. chim. ital.*, **37**, *I*, 434 (1907).
103. Peratoner and Siringo, *Gazz. chim. ital.*, **22**, *II*, 99 (1892).
104. Pinner, *Ber.*, **20**, 2358 (1887).
105. Pinner, *Ber.*, **21**, 1219 (1888).
106. Pinner, *Ber.*, **21**, 2329 (1888).
107. Pinner, *Ber.*, **26**, 2126 (1893).
108. Pinner, *Ber.*, **27**, 984 (1894).
109. Pinner, *Ann.*, **297**, 221 (1897).
110. Pinner, *Ber.*, **30**, 1871. (1897).
111. Pinner and Caro, *Ber.*, **27**, 3273 (1894).
112. Pinner and Caro, *Ber*, **28**, 465 (1895).
113. Pinner, Göbel, Colman, Salomon, and Gradenwitz, *Ann.*, **298**, 1 (1897).
114. Ponzio, *Gazz. chim. ital.*, **39**, *II*, 535 (1909).
115. Ponzio, *Gazz. chim. ital.*, **40**, *I*, 77 (1910).
116. Ponzio and Gastaldi, *Gazz. chim. ital.*, **43**, *II*, 129 (1913).
117. Ponzio and Gastaldi, *Gazz. chim. ital.*, **44**, *I*, 257 (1914).
118. Ponzio and Gastaldi, *Gazz. chim. ital.*, **44**, *I*, 277 (1914).
119. Ponzio and Gastaldi, *Gazz. chim. ital.*, **45**, *I*, 181 (1915).
120. Ponzio and Perolio, *Gazz. chim. ital.*, **55**, 688 (1925).
121. Poth and Bailey, *J. Am. Chem. Soc.*, **45**, 3008 (1923).
122. Purgotti, *Chem. Zentr.*, **1897**, *II*, 569.
123. Purgotti, *Atti accad. Lincei*, [5], **6**, 415 (1897).
124. Purgotti, *Gazz. chim. ital.*, **27**, *II*, 60 (1897).
125. Purgotti and Vigano, *Gazz. chim. ital.*, **31**, *II*, 550 (1901).
126. Rassow, *J. prakt. Chem.*, **64**, 129 (1901).
127. Rassow and Baumann, *J. prakt. Chem.*, **80**, 511 (1909).
128. Rassow and Rülke, *J. prakt. Chem.*, **65**, 97 (1902).
129. Rodinov and Kiseleva, *Zhur. Obschechei Khim.* (*J. Gen. Chem.*), **18**, 1905 (1948); through *Chem. Abstr.*, **43**, 3821 (1949).
130. Ruhemann, *J. Chem. Soc.*, **55**, 242 (1889).
131. Ruhemann, *J. Chem. Soc.*, **57**, 50 (1890).
132. Ruhemann, *Ber.*, **30**, 2869 (1897).
133. Ruhemann, *J. Chem. Soc.*, **89**, 1268 (1906).
134. Ruhemann, *Pr. Chem. Soc.*, **22**, 238 (1906).
135. Ruhemann and Elliott, *J. Chem. Soc.*, **53**, 850 (1888).
136. Ruhemann and Merriman, *J. Chem. Soc.*, **87**, 1768 (1905).
137. Ruhemann and Merriman, *Pr. Chem. Soc.*, **21**, 258 (1905).
138. Ruhemann and Stapleton, *J. Chem. Soc.*, **75**, 1131 (1899).
139. Ruhemann and Stapleton, *J. Chem. Soc.*, **81**, 261 (1902).
140. Rupe, *Ber.*, **29**, 829 (1896).
141. Rupe and Gebhardt, *Ber.*, **32**, 10 (1899).
142. Seiberlich, U.S. Patent 2,369,371, February 13, 1945.
143. Silberrad, *J. Chem. Soc.*, **77**, 1185 (1900).
144. Silberrad, *J. Chem. Soc.*, **81**, 598 (1902).
145. Silberrad, *Pr. Chem. Soc.*, **18**, 44 (1902).
146. Skinner and Ruhemann, *Ber.*, **20**, 3372 (1887).
147. Staudinger and Meyer, *Helv. Chim. Acta*, **2**, 619 (1919).
148. Stollé, *J. prakt. Chem.*, **68**, 464 (1903).
149. Stollé, *J. prakt. Chem.*, **71**, 30 (1905).
150. Stollé, *J. prakt. Chem.*, **73**, 277 (1906).
151. Stollé, *J. prakt. Chem.*, **75**, 94 (1907).

152. Stollé, *J. prakt. Chem.*, **75**, 416 (1907).
153. Stollé, *Ber.*, **46**, 260 (1913).
154. Stollé and Gaertner, *J. prakt. Chem.*, **132**, 209 (1931).
155. Stollé and Helwerth, *Ber.*, **47**, 1132 (1914).
156. Stollé and Laux, *Ber.*, **44**, 1127 (1911).
157. Stollé, Münzel and Wolf, *Ber.*, **46**, 2339 (1913).
158. Stollé and Schmidt, *Ber.*, **45**, 3116 (1912).
159. Stollé and Thomä, *J. prakt. Chem.*, **73**, 288 (1906).
160. Stollé and Weindel, *J. prakt. Chem.*, **74**, 3, 550 (1906).
161. Thielepape and Spreckelsen, *Ber.*, **55**, 2929 (1922).
162. Vanghelovitch, *Bull. soc. chim. Romania*, **8**, 20 (1926); through *Chem. Abstr.*, **22**, 1341 (1928).
163. Walter, U.S. Patent 2,475,440, July 5, 1949.
164. Wieland, *Ber.*, **38**, 1445 (1905).
165. Wieland and Bauer, *Ber.*, **40**, 1686 (1907).
166. Wiley, *J. Am. Chem. Soc.*, **76**, 1576 (1954).
167. Wood and Bergstrom, *J. Am. Chem. Soc.*, **55**, 3648 (1933).
168. Wuyts and Lacourt, *Bull. soc. chim. Belg.*, **45**, 685 (1936).
169. Wuyts and Lacourt, *Bull. soc. chim. Belg.*, **48**, 165 (1939).
170. Lin, Lieber, and Horowitz, *J. Am. Chem., Soc.*, **76**, 427 (1954).

CHAPTER VI

The Pentazines

Only one compound (I) containing the pentazine ring (*R.I.* 123) has been described. Chattaway and Parkes[1] claimed to have prepared it by the reaction of nitrous acid with the 2,4-dibromophenylhydrazone of benzhydrazide (eq. 1). This reaction might conceivably have yielded an

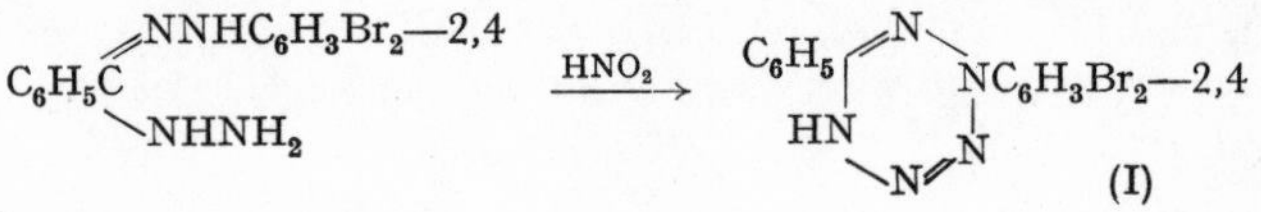

$$C_6H_5C \underset{\diagdown NHNH_2}{\overset{\diagup NNHC_6H_3Br_2-2,4}{}} \quad \xrightarrow{\text{HNO}_2} \quad C_6H_5 \underset{HN \diagdown N \diagup N}{\overset{N \diagdown NC_6H_3Br_2-2,4}{}} \quad \text{(I)}$$

$$\text{(I)}$$

$$C_6H_5C \underset{\diagdown N_3}{\overset{\diagup NNHC_6H_3Br_2-2,4}{}} \quad \text{(II)}$$

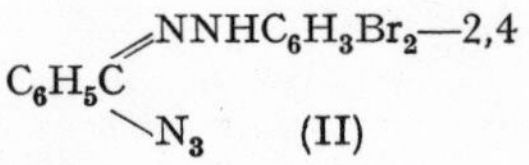

isomeric azide (II), produced by the action of nitrous acid upon the hydrazide grouping alone. Chattaway and Parkes thought that this possibility could be definitely excluded; they recovered their product unchanged after it had been heated for sixty hours at 100° with a saturated solution of acetylene in acetone. If their material were an azide, it would presumably be converted to a triazole under these conditions.[2] Considering the stability and the good nitrogen and bromine analyses of their compound, they concluded that it actually is 2-(2,4-dibromophenyl)-6-phenyl-2,5-dihydropentazine (I). It was obtained as colorless, odorless, and weakly basic crystals, m.p. 172°, easily soluble in the usual organic solvents. When strongly heated, it decomposes with a puff of black smoke and benzonitrile is formed.

The pentazine structure has been challenged on the basis of work done by Stollé and Helwerth,[4] who carried out reactions (eq. 2) similar to that of Chattaway and Parkes. The course taken by these reactions is shown by the isolation of 5-phenyltetrazole. The structure of this compound had previously been established. Stollé felt that these reactions were quite similar to the Chattaway-Parkes reaction-so similar, in fact, as to make it likely that the product of Chattaway and

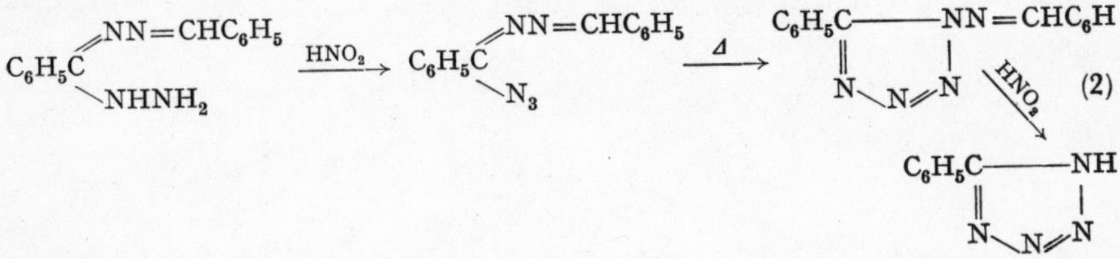

$$
\underset{\substack{\text{C}_6\text{H}_5\text{C}}}{\overset{\text{NN}=\text{CHC}_6\text{H}_5}{\diagdown}}_{\text{NHNH}_2} \xrightarrow{\text{HNO}_2} \underset{\substack{\text{C}_6\text{H}_5\text{C}}}{\overset{\text{NN}=\text{CHC}_6\text{H}_5}{\diagdown}}_{\text{N}_3} \xrightarrow{\Delta} \quad (2)
$$

Parkes is really a tetrazole derivative **(III)**. We can recognize this possibility by rewriting equation 1, using the tautomeric structure of the starting material (eq. 3).

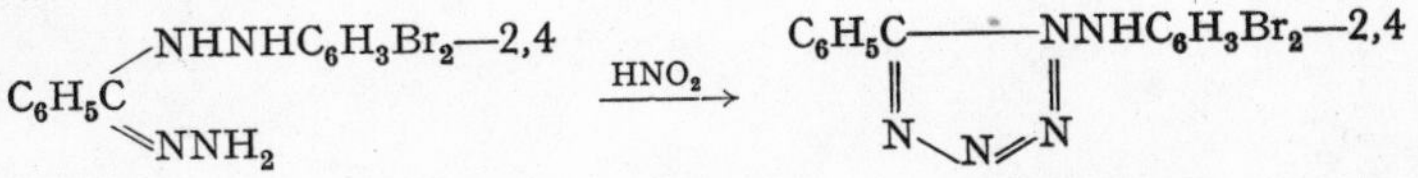

$$
\underset{\substack{\text{C}_6\text{H}_5\text{C}}}{\overset{\text{NHNHC}_6\text{H}_3\text{Br}_2-2,4}{\diagdown}}_{\text{NNH}_2} \xrightarrow{\text{HNO}_2} \quad (3)
$$

(III)

Apparently, we cannot yet say definitely that any pentazines have been synthesized.

Bibliography

1. Chattaway and Parkes, *J. Chem. Soc.*, **1926**, 113.
2. Dimroth and Fester, *Ber.*, **43**, 2222 (1910).
3. Stollé, *J. prakt. Chem.*, **114**, 348 (1926).
4. Stollé and Helwerth, *Ber.*, **47**, 1132 (1914).

SUBJECT INDEX

A

Acenaphtho[1,2]-*as*-triazine,
  derivatives, 120
Acetanilide, α-1-phenylhydrazino-,
  reaction with phosgene, 76
Acetophenone, α-carbamylazo-,
  cyclization, 57
—, α-cyanoazo-, cyclization, 49
Acetophenone oxime, *o*-amino-,
  reaction with nitrous acid, 7
Acetophenone semicarbazone,
  cyclization, 49
Acetylene bis(magnesium bromide),
  reaction with phenylazides, 159,
  161
o-Aminoazo compounds, reaction
  with aldehydes, 100
Aminoguanidine, reaction with di-
  carbonyl compounds, 51, 121,
  125, 126
Anthranilamides, reaction with
  nitrous acid, 14
Anthranilhydrazide, reaction with
  nitrous acid, 14, 24
Arylhydrazines, 1-(*o*-aminobenzyl)-,
  reaction with nitrous acid, 11
Azipyrazoles, 86

B

Benzaldehydes, *o*-azido-, 8
Benzaldoximes, *o*-amino-, reaction
  with nitrous acid, 7
Benzamidoxime, *o*-amino-, reaction
  with nitrous acid, 13
Benzazimides, preparation, 8, 14
  reactions, 17
  tautomerism, 13
Benzil bis(benzoylhydrazone),
  oxidation of, 155–156
— bis(*o*-nitrophenylhydrazone),
  oxidation of, 146
—, 2,2′-dimethoxy-, dihydrazone,
  oxidation of, 158

Benzimidazo[1,2-*c*][1,2,3]-benzo-
  triazine, 39
  derivatives, 40
Benzo[1,2-*e*, 4,3-*e*′]bis[1,2,4]-
  triazine, ring system, 112
Benzo[1,2-*e*, 5,4-*e*′]bis[1,2,4]-
  triazine, ring system, 112
Benzophenone oxime, *o*-amino-,
  reaction with nitrous acid, 7
Benzophenones, *o*-azido-, 8
Benzo-*v*-tetrazine. *See* Benzotetrazine
Benzotetrazine, derivatives, 165–169
—, 2-aryl-1,2-dihydro, derivatives,
  166–168
—, 5,7-dimethyl-2-(2,4-dimethyl-
  phenyl)-1,2-dihydro-, 167
—, 1-methyl-1,4-dihydro-, 165–166
—, 7-methyl-2-(4-methylphenyl)-1,2-
  dihydro-, 166–167
—, 5,7,8-trimethyl-2-(2,4,5-trimethyl-
  phenyl)-1,2-dihydro-, 168
1,2,3-Benzotriazine, 5
  table of derivatives, 6
1,2,4-Benzotriazine, preparation, 93
  tables of derivatives, 94, 97
—, 3-acetyl-, 111
1,2,3-Benzotriazine, 3-acetyl-3,4-
  dihydro-, 11
—, 3-acyl-3,4-dihydro-, derivatives, 11
—, 3-acylamino-4-oxo-3,4-dihydro-,
  25–26
—, 3-alkyl-4-oxo-3,4-dihydro, 18, 20
1,2,4-Benzotriazine, 3-amino-, 102–103
—, 3-amino-2-oxide, 101–102
1,2,3-Benzotriazine, 3-amino-4-oxo-
  3,4-dihydro-, 24–25
—, 3-anilino-4-oxo-3,4-dihydro, 26
—, 3-*p*-anisyl-4-*p*-anisylimino-3,4-
  dihydro-, 23
1,2,4-Benzotriazine, 2-aryl-3-aryl-
  imino-2,3-dihydro-, 104
1,2,3-Benzotriazine, 3-aryl-3,4-
  dihydro-, 11
—, 3-aryl-4-oxo-3,4-dihydro-, 20